KU-511-219

INSTITUTE OF ECONOMICS
AND STATISTICS
OXFORD QA76.5
ARD

WITHDRAWN

AN INTRODUCTION TO

DIGITAL
COMPUTING

This book is in the

ADDISON-WESLEY SERIES IN
COMPUTER SCIENCE AND INFORMATION PROCESSING

———————

Consulting Editors

DEAN ARDEN AND RICHARD S. VARGA

AN INTRODUCTION TO

DIGITAL
COMPUTING

by
BRUCE W. ARDEN
Computing Center
University of Michigan

ADDISON-WESLEY PUBLISHING COMPANY, INC.
READING, MASSACHUSETTS · PALO ALTO · LONDON

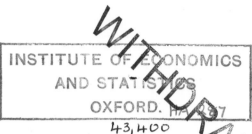

INSTITUTE OF ECONOMICS
AND STATISTICS
OXFORD.

43,400

Copyright © 1963

ADDISON-WESLEY PUBLISHING COMPANY, INC.

Printed in the United States of America

ALL RIGHTS RESERVED. THIS BOOK, OR PARTS THERE-
OF, MAY NOT BE REPRODUCED IN ANY FORM WITH-
OUT WRITTEN PERMISSION OF THE PUBLISHERS.

Library of Congress Catalog Card No. 63–10960

Preface

This text is based on an undergraduate course, "Introduction to Computing Techniques," which has been taught at The University of Michigan for several years. The course requires integral calculus as a prerequisite, and consists of one hour of lecture and one hour of recitation each week. The students are expected, in the course of a semester, to program and successfully run three or four problems of the order of difficulty of the intermediate examples in this text. The recitation sections are devoted to programming questions and the detailed consideration of example programs; the lectures present the material included here without the program examples. Quite obviously, not all of this material is covered in a single semester of a one credit-hour course. For a limited course the material in Chapters 1 through 9 can be covered and one or two of the remaining topics as time permits.

Each topic is treated on an introductory level. However, there is a repeated emphasis on the systematic statement of algorithms in terms of array elements and subscript variables, and several quite complicated procedures are developed. The production of such algorithm descriptions is the challenging part of programming; the subsequent restatement in a particular programming language is readily learned.

The reasoning which has led to the order and inclusion of certain topics is implicit in the following remarks.

1. As a practical matter, a programming language should be introduced early in a course so that the student will be able to start on assigned problems.

2. The vast majority of computer users today, even "professional" programmers, use exclusively a statement-type language, and hence this type of programming is emphasized. Moreover, this approach permits the consideration of algorithms more complicated than a machine-language approach would allow.

3. It is nonetheless important that a programmer know how a machine works—if for no other eason than to understand the details of the arithmetic operations. The logic and storage of simple Turing machines provide a natural point of departure for the description of an actual machine. This approach, which provides a link with the theoretical consideration of computability, is particularly useful for binary machines, but the fundamental binary representation of decimal machines also makes it applicable in the decimal case.

4. The initial enthusiasm of computer users is often dampened by the later experience that accumulated error causes the "right" algorithm to

produce the wrong answers. It is important at the outset, even if the subject is not pursued, to make clear what types of errors are possible.

5. Numerical analysis is often confused with numerical methods. Several analytic topics and simple proofs are included to illustrate the analytic basis of numerical methods. These subjects do not constitute a course in numerical analysis, but they should serve to accelerate the discussion of elementary topics in a subsequent course.

The programming language developed here and used in the examples may be regarded as a hypothetical language, typical of the many that have evolved. As a matter of fact, it is a working language, directly acceptable to a computer, and has been used by many hundreds of the students and staff of the University of Michigan. As a further comment along these lines, the knowledge of one statement-type language seems to be readily transferable to another. Curiously, and in opposition to some educators' views, knowledge of algorithm structure does not seem to be easily transferable from one problem to another; that is, a student who is capable of writing a program to solve a puzzle requiring nested iterations rarely seems to recognize that the same structure applies to the solution of linear equations. In this text, numerical methods have been used as the primary vehicle for illustrating the statement of algorithms. This approach seems to be preferred by the students over problems unrelated to physical phenomena. Whether this preference is due to the natural pragmatism of applied-science students, or whether posing problems in terms of equations, functions, etc., provides a familiar point of departure, will not be argued here. Certainly, when students are from various areas of applied science and the course is a terminal course in computing for most of them, there is a strong argument for including an introduction to numerical methods for their own value without regard for the pedagogical strength or weakness of such material.

The assistance of the Ford Foundation Project on the Use of Computers in Engineering Education at the University of Michigan in the preparation of this material is gratefully acknowledged.

Ann Arbor, Mich.   B.W.A.
November 1962

Contents

Language and Notation

This book is concerned not so much with the solution of problems, although that will at times be an incidental result, but rather with the production of descriptions of *how* to solve problems. This goal immediately raises two questions:

(1) What types of problems are to be considered?
(2) What mode of expression, or *language*, is to be used for description?

The answer to the first question is that the problems of interest are those which can be solved by a digital computer. More explicitly, these *computable* problems are those for which the execution of an explicit, unambiguous, terminating sequence of instructions produces a solution. Such a sequence of instructions is called an *algorithm*, and therefore a somewhat trivial answer to the second question is that the language must be capable of expressing algorithms. This is not a satisfactory answer, but attempts to refine the requirements lead to difficulties arising from the fact that the definition of *computable* given above is not itself very explicit. In the theoretical treatment of this matter the opposite approach is taken. A language is formally described and, if the problems whose solutions are *intuitively* regarded as computable can be described by it, then all the problems that can be so described are said to be computable. In other words, the language provides a definition for *computable*. The question then becomes one of whether such all-encompassing languages exist and, if more than one exists, which variant is best for communicating the desired descriptions. Questions of existence are often treated mathematically, and the answers have the happy two-state property: the entity either exists or it does not. On the other hand, once existence has been established, the choice of a best form does not have such a clear result since "best" depends upon which of many possible criteria have been chosen for selection. This is precisely the case with computable problems. The existence of a language was established early; the selection of a particular form depends upon goals, point of view, constraints, etc. As a prelude to such a selection, it is worthwhile to consider briefly some aspects of *natural languages*, such as English, which have evolved over long periods of time.

ECONOMICS LIBRARY AND STA...

Two aspects of language which are desirable and yet are antithetical are simplicity of structure and capacity for concise expression. For example, the noun "woman" is expressed concisely by a single character in Chinese (女 ≡ woman) and yet it requires five characters for expression in English. On the other hand, the recognition of about 400 characters is required to read elementary Chinese, while only the 26 characters of the Roman alphabet need be recognized for English. One can imagine the notion of conciseness extended to the point where all the sentences expressible in a language would be enumerated, but outside of very specialized cases (e.g., the 25 or so possible birthday greetings that the telegraph company will transmit), the task of learning such a language is so great that it becomes unusable. At the other extreme, languages that are simple in structure and hence readily learned are cumbersome in the expression of complex ideas. The simple 500-word Basic English can provide a host of examples of this deficiency. For instance, the term "executive suite" might be rendered as "the rooms where well-paid workers work." Imagine the expression of such common technical terms as "molecule" or "atom" in Basic English. It is not hard to see that this lack of conciseness—the fact that a single notion requires the comprehension of a long string of words— could itself prevent the expression of new complicated ideas. There are many examples in primitive languages of common ideas which "could not be said." It seems, then, that languages are a compromise between the extremes of concise expression and simple structure and that even in natural languages appreciably different results have evolved. In selecting an *artificial language* (i.e., a language that is designed rather than evolved) for the expression of algorithms, the same spectrum of choice is possible, and it seems reasonable to be guided by what has evolved thus far for the purpose of stating algorithms.

The solution of a computational problem is usually described by presenting a sequence of additions, subtractions, multiplications, and divisions, along with explicit information as to what numbers are to be used as operands in these arithmetic operations. This kind of description presupposes that there are (1) a *machine* to carry out the operations (e.g., a desk calculator or a slide rule); (2) some *storage* device, such as a piece of paper, where the operands can be recorded as needed; and (3) a sequence of operations which make up a *program* for the solution of the problem.

This description already differs from the theoretical approach to problem solving where the three elements mentioned above are respectively called the *logic*, *storage*, and *program* and the combination is designated as a machine. However, for the purposes of this book, the storage and the device which carries out specified operations, such as arithmetic operations, will be grouped together and called a machine, while the set of instructions, or program, will be considered separately. With this nomenclature it is apparent that if one is given a description of a machine, the program is an algorithm, that is, the machine instructions are a language suitable for describing computational procedures. One can even go so far as to say that sequences of these instructions are sentences in the language and are called programs.

For a machine capable of performing the arithmetic operations, the natural symbols to use for instructions would be $+$, $-$, $\times$, $\div$. A very simple program might be written

Instruction No.	Operand	Operator	Operand	Next instruction No.
1	3	$+$	4	2
2	5	$+$	6	

where the integers 3, 4, 5, and 6 are the designated operands. However, to know where in the storage the results will appear, a better description of the machine is required. Instead of considering a machine which has the rather complicated arithmetic rules built in, we shall describe a machine with the ability to perform three very simple operations on symbols. The machine's storage can be regarded as simply a sequence of symbols written on a long tape in no particular order. The tape moves past the operational portion of the machine so that at any time one symbol on the tape, called the current symbol, is involved in an operation. All three operations are conditional and involve two operands. One operand is the current symbol, and the other operand is a given symbol S_i.

(1) If S_i, $\rightarrow$ means: If the current symbol is S_i, move the tape right one symbol.

(2) If S_i, $\leftarrow$ means: If the current symbol is S_i, move the tape left one symbol.

(3) If S_i, S_j means: If the current symbol is S_i, replace it on the tape with S_j.

A complete instruction is numbered and designates a successor as well. The designated instruction is carried out only if the given symbol matches the current symbol; otherwise the next instruction in sequence is executed. For example,

$$2 \quad \text{If } 3, \leftarrow 8$$

can be read:

Instruction 2 is: if the current symbol is 3, move the storage tape left one symbol and then carry out instruction 8; if the current symbol is not 3, the tape does not move and the next instruction in sequence is executed.

The sequence of instructions can also be regarded as being written one instruction per cell on a long tape. A simple problem in symbol recognition

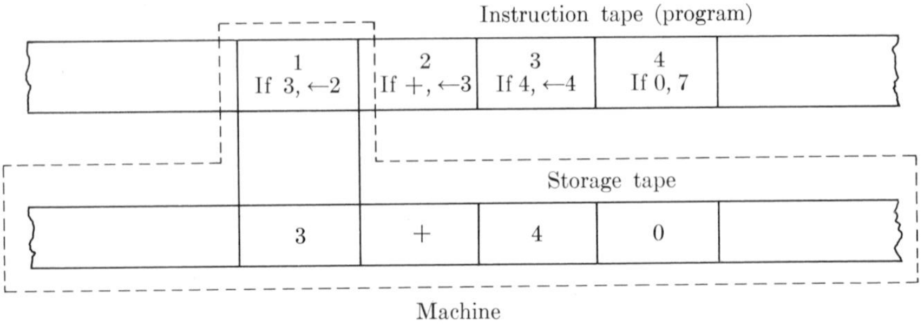

Instruction tape (program)

| | 1
If 3, ←2 | 2
If +, ←3 | 3
If 4, ←4 | 4
If 0, 7 | |

Storage tape

| | 3 | + | 4 | 0 | |

Machine

FIGURE 1–1

(or addition) is to replace the symbol 0 with the symbol 7 if the string of symbols 3 + 4 0 is encountered on the storage tape (Fig. 1–1). In columnar form the program illustrated in Fig. 1–1 is

(1) If 3, ← 2
(2) If +, ← 3
(3) If 4, ← 4
(4) If 0, 7 5

If the initial symbol were some digit other than 3, 4, or 0, none of these instructions would be executed since matching symbols would not be encountered. This absence of executions is described by saying that the *state* of the machine is unchanged. If the initial digit were 4 or 0, the state would change, but the resulting actions would not be very meaningful in terms of the original addition problem. This process of addition by symbol identification can be enlarged to produce the proper sums for all pairs of single-digit operands. For the sake of brevity, let us suppose that only the sums that can be formed from pairs of the integers 0, 1, 2 are of interest (rather than the sums obtainable for the ten decimal integers 0, 1, 2, . . . 9). That is, it must be possible for a program to generate the sums appearing in the following addition table.

+	0	1	2
0	0	1	2
1	1	2	3
2	2	3	4

A program capable of performing this task is presented in Table 1–1.

TABLE 1-1

State 1	1	If 0, ← 4	State 6	12	If +, ← 13	
	2	If 1, ← 8	State 7	13	If 0, ← 18	
	3	If 2, ← 12		14	If 1, ← 19	
State 2	4	If +, ← 5		15	If 2, ← 20	
State 3	5	If 0, ← 16	State 8	16	If 0, 0 21	
	6	If 1, ← 17	State 7	17	If 0, 1 21	
	7	If 2, ← 18	State 10	18	If 0, 2 21	
State 4	8	If +, ← 9	State 11	19	If 0, 3 21	
State 5	9	If 0, ← 17	State 12	20	If 0, 4 21	
	10	If 1, ← 18	State 13	21	...	
	11	If 2, ← 19				

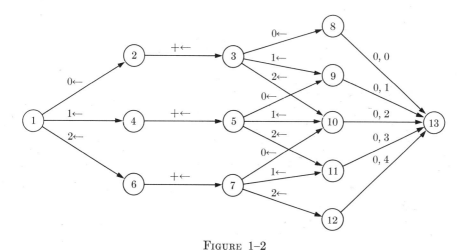

FIGURE 1-2

Assuming that the symbol tape is of the form

a	+	b	0

where a and b are either 0, 1, or 2, we find that this program simply recognizes the nine possible combinations. This is perhaps more apparent from a *state diagram* (Fig. 1-2).

The instructions which cause the state changes are written along the lines. As has already been observed, the states, which correspond to the numbered nodes in this diagram, do not correspond to instructions. A state may remain unchanged while executing a number of instructions if no symbol match is encountered. Even if a match exists, the state may not change. For instance, if the current symbol is + and the instruction

$$1 \qquad \text{If } +, + \ 1$$

is executed, the state does not change. In fact, there is no way to leave this state, and such an instruction might be used to terminate a program. The state diagram for this case is

+, +

With this illustration it is perhaps now plausible that programs could be written to form the sums of the single-digit decimal numbers. Furthermore, since the sums of multidigit numbers are obtained by repeating the single-digit summation process many times, with the carry digits added as well, programs to handle multidigit problems could also be written. Moreover, since multiplication is in fact repeated multidigit additions, this arithmetic operation could also be treated symbolically.

To be sure, the programs for the more complicated arithmetic operations become very lengthy, but nonetheless they intuitively seem possible. In 1936 a logician named Turing did, in fact, prove that such programs were possible. He proved by using a simple abstract model of a symbol-manipulating machine, such as the one described, that the programs were suitable for describing all computable procedures. Such hypothetical machines, which Turing simply called "automatic machines," have come to be known as Turing machines.

Considering the three symbol-manipulating operations as the basic elements of a language, it seems that this language must come close to being the simplest in structure of all languages that are adequate for the statement of algorithms. However, there is a further simplification which can be made that makes such a hypothetical machine correspond much more closely to the detailed, inner operation of electronic digital computers. In the operations of moving the tape right and left and replacing a symbol, reference is made to the symbols from some specified set. For the addition example the set is +, 0, 1, 2, 3, 4. It is possible, without any loss of descriptive ability, to reduce this set to two symbols. This reduction can be accomplished by simply representing the desired symbols by several of the elementary symbols. For instance, if the basic symbols are taken to be 0 and *, each of the integers 0, 1, 2, 3 can be represented by three of the basic symbols.

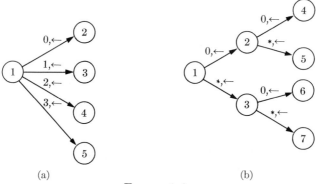

FIGURE 1–3

Original symbol	Representation in two symbols
0	00
1	0*
2	*0
3	**

The sequence,

$$\begin{cases} 1 & \text{If } 0, \leftarrow 7 \\ 2 & \text{If } 1, \leftarrow 8 \\ 3 & \text{If } 2, \leftarrow 9 \\ 4 & \text{If } 3, \leftarrow 10 \end{cases}$$

can be written by means of the two-symbol alphabet as

$$\begin{cases} 1 & \text{If } 0, \leftarrow 3 \\ 2 & \text{If } *, \leftarrow 5 \end{cases}$$
$$\begin{cases} 3 & \text{If } 0, \leftarrow 7 \\ 4 & \text{If } *, \leftarrow 8 \end{cases}$$
$$\begin{cases} 5 & \text{If } 0, \leftarrow 9 \\ 6 & \text{If } *, \leftarrow 10 \end{cases}$$

The state diagrams (Fig. 1–3) for the two cases further illustrate the equivalence.

By formally pursuing this equivalence, as Wang has done, one is able to exhibit a very simple hypothetical machine which requires only the two-character alphabet and yet is as general in its descriptive abilities as the Turing machine. As before, the symbols are considered to be written on a long (in fact, doubly infinite!) storage tape. The operational section of the machine can carry out the following operations:

(1)	←	means:	Move the storage tape left one symbol.
(2)	→	means:	Move the storage tape right one symbol.
(3)	*	means:	Write the symbol * in the current symbol space.
(4)	n	means:	Execute the nth instruction next *if* the current symbol is *; otherwise execute the next instruction in sequence.

This machine will be considered again when the details of a practical computer are introduced. For the moment its operations can be considered as the elements of the simplest language that is still adequate for the statement of algorithms. Quite obviously, even simple programs will require hundreds of such elementary instructions, and therefore the machine does not provide a practical solution to the problem of language selection. The other extreme, that of enumerating all possible algorithms, while theoretically possible, is equally unattractive since the designating numbers would be large beyond comprehension. Imagine again the enumeration of all possible sentences that could be formed in a natural language, English, for example.

It is apparent that some artificial language, intermediate between the extremes of simplest structure and most concise expression, is needed for the expression of algorithms. That such a language exists has been established by the theoretical consideration of the simple languages. Over the years, mathematicians and scientists have evolved an almost universally understood artificial language which may be best described as "mathematical notation." For lack of a better criterion, it seems wise to select this language as a point of departure for algorithm description because of its universality and also because, long before the advent of high-speed digital computers, such notation was used for the description of algorithms.

REVIEW OF NOTATION

This algebraic language is composed of variables, constants, operations, relations, and grouping marks. Before discussing variables, we think it worthwhile to review in a cursory fashion the notion of a function since a variable may be regarded as a special kind of function. A function, such as $y = f(a, x) = ax^2 + 2$, is regarded as a mapping or transformation. There are a great many possible values which the symbols a and x refer to. Indeed, in the absence of any other information, it is assumed that the infinite quantity of real numbers constitute these values. All the possible pairs of values for a and x then produce a value for y or $f(a, x)$. So we see that in this case $f(a, x)$ is a transformation, or mapping, which, given all the real number pairs, produces an equivalent set of real numbers. The given pairs are called the *domain*, and the resultant single numbers are called the *range* of the transformation. Coming now to the case of a single variable, we see immediately that it is a function of an unusually simple type, that is, $y = f(x) = x$. Here the domain is identical to the range, and it is customary to talk about the range of the variable x. That is, the range is the possible set of values which can be designated by use of the symbol x. The two situations just described can be illustrated diagrammatically as follows.

$$(1) \qquad y = ax^2 + 2$$

Domain	Range
a_1, x_1	$\longrightarrow$	y_1
a_1, x_2	$\longrightarrow$	y_2
a_1, x_3	$\longrightarrow$	y_3
$\vdots$		$\vdots$
a_2, x_1		
a_2, x_2		
a_2, x_3		
$\vdots$		

$$(2) \qquad y = x$$

x_1	$\longrightarrow$	y_1
x_2	$\longrightarrow$	y_2
x_3	$\longrightarrow$	y_3
$\vdots$		

As mentioned before, in the second case the columns of numbers, indicated by the numerically subscripted letters, are identical.

Even the symbol used to designate a constant in (1) above can now be understood as an even more specialized case of a function, that is, $y = f(2) = 2$. Thus, the symbol "2" may be regarded as a variable whose range is a single number. Moreover, as a convenience, the symbol used for this restricted variable is the range, i.e., the number itself. At this point, this may seem to be a very pedantic approach, but to fully understand a computing problem of any complexity it is important to distinguish between the symbols used and the range of values of these symbols.

Continuing the discussion of the elements of notation, we note that operations are designated by the familiar symbols $+$, $-$, $\times$, $\div$. These represent *binary* operations in that two operands are required to carry out the operations. Thus, for example, one writes $a + b$, $x \div y$, etc. Exponentiation is also a binary operation, but the symbol is merely implied by raised printing, a^b. It would have been more consistent to indicate exponentiation explicitly by introducing a symbol such as $a \uparrow b$, for example, but common usage has decreed otherwise. There are also *unary* operations in common use, absolute value and negation being the most familiar examples. These are called unary because they require only one operand, for instance, $|a|$, $-b$. One may well ask: Why these operations instead of others? This question will not be answered here or even pursued in any depth. The answer is indicated by the fact that the sum total of these symbols is called *algebraic* notation. There exists a system of formal rules which permit the definition of these familiar operations. This system is called an *algebra*. The real numbers, which are our primary concern when dealing with computational problems, constitute a model for this algebra. That is, the real numbers are a set of things for which these rules apply, and therefore these operations have been widely used. A glimpse of another *algebra*, which is not nearly as well known, but which has some very useful applications in formulating computing problems, is given in the next paragraphs.

The relations are designated by the symbols $=$, $\neq$, $<$, $\leq$, $>$, $\geq$. A relational expression, such as $a < b$, is often described as a question, namely: Is a less than b? There are only two answers to this question: either it is *true* for the specific elements in the ranges of a and b under consideration or it is *false*. Another way of describing this situation is to say that the value of the expression is *true* or *false*. Clearly, any two distinct symbols could be employed instead of these two words, and conventionally the symbols 1 and 0 are used to represent *true* and *false*. Expressions (and constants) of this kind then have a range of only two values, 0 and 1. There is another algebra, called Boolean after the mathematician Boole who developed the formal rules, for which two-valued elements are a model. Only two operations from this algebra will be considered here.

The operations of *and* ($\land$) and *or* ($\lor$) require two operands and are therefore binary. Since these two operands can have only two values, the simplest way to define these new operations is to exhaustively examine the domain and range of the defining functions. In distinction to the earlier examples of a function, we shall now enter the actual values.

(1) $$y = a \land b$$

Domain		Range
a	b	y
0	0	0
0	1	0
1	0	0
1	1	1

This formal definition corresponds to our intuitive meaning of the English word "and." If we have *a and b*, we mean that both objects are present and exclude the case where one or the other or both are missing. Thus there exists a correspondence in meaning since only when *a* and *b* are both 1, is the result 1.

(2)
$$y = a \vee b$$

Domain	Range
a *b*	*y*
0 0	0
0 1	1
1 0	1
1 1	1

This definition corresponds to one interpretation of the English word "or." If we have *a or b* we mean that at least one or the other is present, and possibly both. The result above is 1 in every case except the first where neither *a* nor *b* is one.

The tables above present the complete domain of the Boolean variables *a*, *b*. Other binary operations can be defined, but they are not of interest for the ordinary computational problem. (In fact, 14 others may be defined, giving a total of 16. In other words, as many operations can be defined as there are combinations of 0 and 1 that can be written in the column designating the range.)

Returning again to relations, we note that the initial one in the list, namely, the equals sign, requires some further discussion due to some ambivalence in its use. This symbol is used in mathematics primarily in the relational sense. For example, equation $x^2 + 2x + 1 = 0$ is a relational expression such as those mentioned in the preceding paragraphs. This relation is true or false depending upon what values from the range of *x* are selected. Identities such as $\tan x = \sin x / \cos x$ illustrate relations that are true for the entire range of the variable *x*. In general, then, an expression like $a = b$ can be determined to be true or false only if the values of *a* and *b* are independently given. Occasionally the symbol is used in the defining sense; i.e., an expression such as $a = b + 4$ is meant to define the variable *a*. We can indicate this variant of meaning by calling it "substitutional" equality. It is in this sense that the symbol is used when one evaluates a formula, and in this sense it occurs only in descriptions of algorithms. Ideally, in situations of this kind a separate symbol, such as ←, would be preferable.

In conventional notation, grouping marks, such as parentheses, braces, brackets, are used to delimit the scope of operations when expressions are used as operands. Thus parentheses are necessary to distinguish $(a + b) \times (c + d)$ from $a + b \times c + d$. Expressions such as the latter, however, are not ambiguous since there is an implied parenthesizing which is understood, that is, $a + b \times c + d \equiv a + (b \times c) + d$. Another way of describing this implicit parenthesizing is to say that the execution of the operation of multiplication takes precedence over the addition operation. Or, more simply, multiplication has precedence over addition. When operators of the same precedence are encountered in an unparenthesized expression, they are simply executed in left-to-right order. The relative precedence of the ordinary arithmetic operations is shown below. The top line is of highest precedence and the operations placed on the same line are of equal precedence.

Absolute value
Exponentiation
Negation (unary)
Multiplication, division
Addition, subtraction

The relations and the Boolean operations discussed are of lower precedence than those in the table above but may be relatively ranked as follows.

$$=, \neq, >, \geq, <, \leq$$
$\wedge$ (and)
$\vee$ (or)

Often operations are defined in terms of the elementary operations above, for which the operands are not single variables but sequences of variables. Vector multiplication is an example of such an operation. When the operation is carried out, the individual variables are used in a systematic order, and hence it is desirable to designate them by a common name, differing only by a constant subscript. The resulting set of variable names, such as

$$a_1, a_2, a_3, \ldots, a_{10}$$

is called a *linear array*, and a general element of such an array is designated by a_i. Here i is a subscript variable whose range is the set of integers (usually the nonnegative integers), and, obviously, to select a specific element from the array a, the subscript i must be assigned a value from its range.

A synonymous word for linear array is *vector*. Two common notational conventions are used to express the addition and multiplication of elements of linear arrays:

$$a_1 + a_2 + a_3 + \cdots + a_n = \sum_{i=1}^{n} a_i$$

$$a_1 \times a_2 \times a_3 \times \cdots \times a_n = \prod_{i=1}^{n} a_i$$

It is worth noting at this point that there exists an operation, although it is *not* common, which includes both these cases. Suppose that there is a repetition operator **R** which indicates that the first symbol written after the symbol **R** is the operation to be repeated. With this convention,

$$\sum_{i=1}^{n} a_i = \mathop{\mathbf{R}}_{i=1}^{n} + a_i$$

$$\prod_{i=1}^{n} a_i = \mathop{\mathbf{R}}_{i=1}^{n} \times a_i$$

This digression is included merely to introduce the idea that more general repetition operators might be useful.

Variables are organized in linear arrays because the variables have some common property (for example, they are coefficients of a polynomial) or are introduced systematically into a computation. One of these conditions almost always implies the other, as is the case with polynomial coefficients. The evaluation of an nth-degree polynomial can be indicated as follows:

$$a_0 + a_1 x + a_2 x^2 + \cdots + a_n x^n = \sum_{i=0}^{n} a_i x^i$$

It is interesting to observe that a polynomial can be evaluated with fewer operations if it is considered in the parenthesized form

$$(\cdots ((a_n x + a_{n-1})x + a_{n-2})x + \cdots + a_1)x + a_0$$

Evaluating a polynomial by starting with the inner parentheses and working outward is identical with evaluation by synthetic division. The indicated computation is repetitive, but cannot be expressed more concisely with the usual repetitive operators (i.e., $\sum$ and $\prod$).

Often array elements have more than one characteristic by which they are identified with other array elements. Another way of saying this is that a single variable may simultaneously be identified with two different linear arrays. For example, the coefficients of a group of polynomials have such a dual identification. A particular coefficient is part of, say, the ith polynomial but it also is the coefficient of the jth power of x in that polynomial. It would be very descriptive to refer to that coefficient as $a_{i,j}$. A similar example is provided by the coefficients of a system of linear equations. In that case the coefficient $a_{i,j}$ would be understood to be part of the ith equation as a multiplier of the jth variable. Such doubly-designated arrays are called *two-dimensional arrays*, or *matrices*. Writing out a system of linear equations using this notation will, perhaps, make it clearer.

$$a_{11}x_1 + a_{12}x_2 + a_{13}x_3 = b_1$$

$$a_{21}x_1 + a_{22}x_2 + a_{23}x_3 = b_2$$

$$a_{31}x_1 + a_{32}x_2 + a_{33}x_3 = b_3$$

Using the summation operator, we obtain

$$\sum_{j=1}^{3} a_{i,j}x_j = b_i \qquad \text{for} \qquad i = 1, 2, 3$$

Again i and j are variables, and only when they have been assigned values from their range is a particular variable designated.

The reader may observe that this brief review of notation is somewhat slanted. The references to evaluation and computation are really not germane when variables and functions are considered as transformations or mappings. The "computing" variable is similar in that it is a reference to a set of values, although the set is much more restricted than the real numbers. An evaluation can be regarded as a dynamic instance of a mapping.

A final remark on notation, which should be by now superfluous, is that subscripts are sometimes used on single variables for mnemonic effect. Thus for instance T_i is used to indicate *t*emperature at the *i*nlet or P_o is used to represent *p*ressure *o*ut, etc. Such variables should not be confused with array elements.

Elements of a Practical Language

The previous chapter reviewed, briefly, the elements of an existing language, mathematical notation; perhaps of two languages, since, in addition to the familiar *algebraic* notation, some of the notation of the less common *Boolean algebra* was introduced. To adapt these notations for use in producing descriptions of algorithms which are directly acceptable to a machine will require one innovation and one seemingly very restrictive limitation.

Before the appearance of machines capable of executing complicated procedures, algorithms were described solely for human consumption. The order of computation of the various sections of the algorithm were either assumed to be implicitly understood by the reader or, in cases of doubt, were clarified by such prose statements as "... after computing formula 1–1 repeat the cycle starting with formula 2–3." In an artificial language, such statements governing the order of computation must be removed from the realm of natural language and given an explicit syntax.

The limitation is that current machines can directly accept only a small set of characters. Although in coming years this set will expand, it will probably always be insufficient in the sense that the wealth of characters currently used in notation, upper-case and lower-case Roman, Greek, German, Hebrew, etc., cannot reasonably be included in the recognized set. A related limitation is that shifts in the line may not be acceptable as a means of conveying information. The language which we shall describe was designed to be expressible in the following character set (note that "space" is not included as a character).

```
A  B  C  D  E  F  G  H  I  J  K  L  M  N  O  P
Q  R  S  T  U  V  W  X  Y  Z  0  1  2  3  4  5
6  7  8  9  +  −  *  /  =  (  )  .  ,  $
```

In what follows, the MAD language (*M*ichigan *A*lgorithm *D*ecoder) will be introduced mainly as an example. The *MAD Manual* provides a more thorough description of the features of the language, and a technique for formal definition of the language is illustrated at the end of this section.

15

CONSTANTS

Constants are usually written in the following forms:

$$2, \quad -6.3, \quad +10.46983, \quad 31 \times 10^{-4}, \quad -0.683924 \times 10^{20}$$

All characters written in these forms are in the designated set. However, the designation of exponentiation by a superscript is not acceptable, and hence such forms as $\times 10^{-4}$ and $\times 10^{20}$ are expressed in a different manner. Since a number is assumed to be decimal, the $\times 10$ is simply replaced by E followed immediately on the same line by the exponent. The "E" was selected as a mnemonic label indicating that the number following it is an exponent. The example set of constants can be represented in the permissible character set as

$$2, \quad -6.3, \quad +10.46983, \quad 31\mathrm{E} - 4, \quad -0.683924\mathrm{E}20$$

Remember that subscript variables (and perhaps others) are restricted to an integer range. On some machines—for reasons which will become clear later—it is necessary to specify the difference between (1) an integer constant from an integer range and (2) an integer which is an element of the range of real numbers. A way of distinguishing these two cases is to write the first, for example, as 2 and the second as 2. or 2.0. This distinguishing convention is used in the language being defined.

VARIABLES

The paucity of admissible characters suggests that variables be designated by more than one character if desired. That such a convention admits the possibility of many more uniquely named variables is obvious; it also permits the use of mnemonic or suggestive strings of symbols, e.g., ALPHA for α, XBAR for $\bar{x}$, etc. The names are limited to six characters or less simply because this restriction was convenient for a particular machine. The permissible characters in the make-up of a name are the capital letters and the ten decimal digits. The first character *must* be a letter or else confusion with constants could arise. For reasons which should be obvious after the section on operations, special characters are not allowed. Some additional examples of simple variable names are: X1, ZA12, ZINIT, BETA, A, Y141. Variables may be designated as elements of arrays as indicated by the usual forms:

$$x_i, \quad z'_i, \quad m_{i,j}, \quad \alpha_{i+4,k-3}, \quad \beta_{3,1}$$

The letters appearing on the printing line are variable names and can be represented according to the rules above. The use of subscript characters is not permitted, and so the convention is adopted that expressions (variables and constants are simple forms of expressions) enclosed in parentheses and following a variable name are regarded as subscripts. Representations for the variables above could be:

$$X(I), \quad ZPRIME(I), \quad M(I, J), \quad ALPHA(I + 4, K - 3), \quad BETA(3, 1)$$

OPERATIONS

Some operations have already been implicitly introduced in the previous paragraphs. Operations are used in conjunction with variables and constants to form *expressions*. Taking the last sentence to be a definition of an expression, we can make a broader definition by saying that the conjunction of operations with variables, constants, and expressions forms expressions. This may seem like a circular definition for the term expressions, but such recursive definitions constitute an effective way of systematically defining artificial languages. An illustration of this technique applied to the MAD language is given at the end of this section.

The arithmetic binary operations of addition, subtraction, multiplication and division are represented by the symbols $+$, $-$, $*$ and $/$, respectively. A glance at the character set shows that this assignment exhausts the available single characters that may be used as operations. A multiple-character representation, distinguishable from variables, is needed to designate the remaining operations. One has therefore adopted the convention of using periods on both sides of a letter group which mnemonically suggests the operation. Thus the binary operation, exponentiation, is written as .P. ("to the *p*ower"). The unary operation, absolute value, is written .ABS. . The unary plus and minus use the same symbols as the analogous binary operations (i.e., $+$ and $-$) since this use can be distinguished from context and, moreover, is the accepted practice.

Left and right parentheses are the only permissible grouping marks. The use of these symbols in place of braces, brackets, etc., does not constitute any essential restriction since the conventional requirement that there be matching right and left parentheses eliminates any possible ambiguity. The previously stated use of parentheses for indicating subscripts, as well as the rules for forming variable names, imposes the requirement that the multiplication operator must always be written. Contrary to convention, adjacent variable names or adjacent names and parenthetical groups cannot indicate multiplication. Thus ab cannot be written AB but must be A$*$B, and $a(b + 4)$ cannot be written as A(B $+$ 4), which would be interpreted as a_{b+4}, but must be

$$A*(B + 4)$$

The implied parenthesizing conventions are the same as those discussed in the first chapter. The following examples illustrate the use of operations to form expressions, as well as the understood parenthesizing.

$(ALPHA/4.0) + Y$

$(X(I, J) - X(J, K))/X(K, K)$

$X142*Z1 + 8.0$ is the same as $(X142*Z1) + 8.0$

$A + B + C + D$ is the same as $((A + B) + C) + D$

$P/Q + R*S/T$ is the same as $(P/Q) + (R*S)/T$

The term *expression* has been repeatedly used and yet it has not been defined. This omission is intentional since the formal definition is quite involved and the intuitive understanding of an expression as being a combination of the basic elements, constants, variables, operations, and grouping marks which are properly grouped according to the rules of combination of the various operations, is sufficient. It is worthwhile to note, however, that a variable is an expression and a constant is an expression. This statement is the beginning of a formal recursive definition which can be pursued by observing in addition that

(1) a parenthesized expression is an expression;
(2) expressions conjoined by binary operators are expressions;
(3) expressions preceded by unary operators are expressions.

Another entity which must have notational distinction and is regarded as an expression is a function reference. To illustrate, let us suppose that $f(x) = x^2 + 2x + 2$ is defined; then the expression

$$y = (z^2 + 2z + 2) + (p^2 + 2p + 2) + 24$$

can be written

$$y = f(z) + f(p) + 24$$

The parenthesized expressions can conveniently be replaced by the function references. Note that a reference to f without the appended arguments is understood as a reference to the defining transformation and is not an evaluation. Some examples in common use are: $\exp(a + 4)$, $\sin x$, $\arctan (x, y)$. The rules for designating the function names are the same as those presented earlier for single variables, with the addition that a terminating period is required. (The total number of characters may therefore be as many as seven.) The examples can then be written: EXP.(A + 4), SIN.(X), ARCTAN.(X, Y). The terminating period, of course, permits the distinction between functions and array elements.

The formation of the *function name* according to the variable rules is appropriate in another sense. The function name, including the identifying period but not the list of arguments, is a variable of a special type. The range of this variable is an expression (or expressions). The rules of manipulation are very restricted, and it is not important here to formalize them. Nonetheless, it is another example of a variable of a different type which must be identified.

RELATIONS

Characters are not available for the relations, and hence a mnemonic letter group delimited by periods is used. The six relations are designated according to the following table.

Relations	Representation in MAD
= (equal)	.E.
≠ (not equal)	.NE.
< (less than)	.L.
≤ (less than or equal)	.LE.
> (greater than)	.G.
≥ (greater than or equal)	.GE.

The Boolean operations, which frequently use relational expressions as operands, are similarly written. The $\wedge$ operation (and) appears as .AND. and the $\vee$ operation (or) as .OR. . All the relations and operations considered in this section have a lower precedence than the arithmetic operations. Some of the effects of the precedence structure are illustrated in some of the following examples of Boolean expressions:

$$A \text{ .LE. } B$$
$$X \text{ .LE. EPS1 .AND. } Y \text{ .E. EPS2}$$

is the same as

$$(X \text{ .LE. EPS1) .AND. } (Y \text{ .E. EPS2})$$
$$X - Y \text{ .LE. E1 .AND. ALPHA} - 6.0 \text{ .G. } 20.0 \text{ .OR. Z1 .L. Z2}$$

is the same as

$$(((X - Y) \text{ .LE. E1) .AND. ((ALPHA} - 6.0) \text{ .G. } 20.0)) \text{ .OR. } (Z1 \text{ .L. Z2})$$

GROUPING MARKS

The principal grouping marks, paired parentheses, have been introduced in the preceding discussion. The remaining mark, a comma (,), has also been used in a natural way. Explicitly, the comma is used to separate elements of a *list*. The lists which have occurred thus far are lists of subscripts and lists of arguments of functions. In both instances, as can be seen in the following examples, the list elements may be variables, constants or expressions.

$$X(I, J)$$
$$X(I, 4)$$
$$X(I + 2, K*3)$$
$$F.(G, ALPHA + 4.0, 10.0)$$
$$G.((BETA + 2.0)*Y, Z1, N)$$

This concludes the examination of the basic elements of the notation written in the limited character set. The next step is to define useful statements formed from these elements which are uniquely identifiable by structure, or key words, or phrases. It should be noted at this point that so far as the structure of this artificial language is concerned, such key words could be considered as types of operators and represented by a single symbol or, alternatively, a small group of symbols. The choice of English words was made for the same reason that mnemonic letter groups are used. Namely, the words suggest the purpose of the construction, and hence are valuable aids facilitating the comprehension of the artificial language.

STATEMENT LABELS

In the next section, we shall discuss a number of statement types. It is often necessary to label those which are *executable*, i.e., cause some action in the execution of the algorithm, so that they may be referred to by other statements. These labels, which in the prose description of algorithms often appear as references to "formula 1–1," are, in a sense, a type of variable whose range is not a number, or set of numbers, but a single statement. Hence, the rules for forming these labels are the same as those for forming single variables. In addition, statement labels may be referred to as elements of a linear array. In such a case, **the** designating labels can have only subscripts that are integer constant**s. Ex**amples are:

$$LABEL, \quad STMNT, \quad \mathbf{ST(2)}, \quad ST(12)$$

BASIC COMPUTATIONAL STATEMENTS

The substitution statement. The general form of the substitution statement is $\upsilon = \varepsilon$, where υ is a variable name and ε is an expression. From this we see that the equal sign $(=)$ is used in the formula evaluation sense and is used only in this context. If a column of substitution statements are written, they are executed in sequence, i.e., from the top down. This statement is basic in computational programs since it provides the means of transforming the given data to produce the desired result. It is worth emphasizing that, to be meaningful, only a variable may be on the left of the equal sign—not an expression. To be sure, the variables may be array elements with subscript values given by expressions. Examples of substitution statements are:

$$X = Y + 4.0$$
$$Z(I) = ALPHA*BETA + Z(J)$$
$$I = I + 1$$
$$M(I + 1, J + 1) = ((A(3)*X + A(2))*X + A(1))*X + A(0)$$

The transfer statement. With only substitution statements in the repertoire, only one sequential, unrepeating computation could be described. To eliminate the sequential adjective, a transfer statement is required; that is, a statement which when inserted in a series of substitution statements indicates, by means of a statement label, the next statement to be executed. This transfer is the innovation alluded to earlier since, in the past, such instructions have been expressed in prose. The statement is of the form

TRANSFER TO s

where s designates a statement label. The rules for label formation were described earlier; however, here the linear subscript, if any, may be an expression since its integer value will be determined when the statement is executed. Some example statements follow:

TRANSFER TO ST
TRANSFER TO LABEL(2)
TRANSFER TO STMNT(K + 4)

The conditional prefix. The two statements thus far discussed do not yet permit any terminable repetition of statements. What is needed is the ability to alter the sequence of execution of statements dependent upon some condition. The conditional prefix may be used to qualify the two statements already described. This prefix is of the form

WHENEVER ℜ,

where ℜ is a relational expression. If the expression is *true*, the suffix statement is executed; if *false*, the next statement in sequence is immediately executed. Typical statements are:

WHENEVER S .L. EPSLON, TRANSFER TO END
WHENEVER Z1 − Z2 .L. O .AND. I .G. 10, X = P*Q

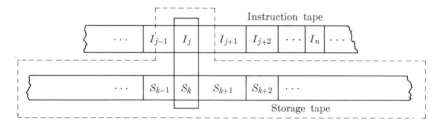

FIGURE 2–1

This basic group of statements is complete in the sense that they are sufficient to describe all computable algorithms (subject, of course, to finite storage limitations). That this is so can be shown by expressing the operations of the four-instruction Wang machine by means of these statements. Figure 2–1 shows how such a machine might be visualized. The sequence of instructions can be regarded as the array I; the current instruction is I_j. The storage tape is represented by the array S; the current symbol is S_k. The Wang machine uses only two symbols which were given in Chapter 1 as 0 and *. These symbols could just as easily be represented by the integers 0 and 1 as they will be here. Each of the elements of I are one of the four basic instructions, and these can now be expressed using the statements just defined.

(1) Operation ←   (Move storage tape left one symbol.)

Moving the tape left, i.e., making S_{k+1} the current symbol, is the same as increasing the subscript k by 1. Taking the next instruction in sequence is the same as increasing the subscript j by 1. In statement form these steps are:

$$K = K + 1$$
$$J = J + 1$$
$$\text{TRANSFER TO I(J)}$$

(2) Operation →   (Move storage tape right one symbol.)

$$K = K - 1$$
$$J = J + 1$$
$$\text{TRANSFER TO I(J)}$$

(3) Operation *   (Write a symbol on current position of storage tape.)

$$S(K) = 1$$
$$J = J + 1$$
$$\text{TRANSFER TO I(J)}$$

Since the symbol that can be written has been chosen to be 1, this operation consists of making the current symbol S(K) one and then advancing to the next instruction.

(4) Operation n (Jump to instruction number n if current symbol is 1, otherwise go to the next instruction.)

$$J = J + 1$$
$$\text{WHENEVER S(K) .E. 1, J} = N$$
$$\text{TRANSFER TO I(J)}$$

The first statement sets the instruction index J to the next instruction. The second instruction resets the index to N if the current symbol was 1, and then the transfer to another instruction is made.

To illustrate these operations, the following simple program makes a mark in every third symbol position of the storage tape. Programs are generally written vertically. To strengthen the analogy to the instruction tape, the individual operations are enclosed in a block.

1	←
2	←
3	*
4	1

In statement form, these instructions become:

I(1)	K = K + 1 J = J + 1 TRANSFER TO I(J)
I(2)	K = K + 1 J = J + 1 TRANSFER TO I(J)
I(3)	S(K) = 1 J = J + 1 TRANSFER TO I(J)
I(4)	J = J + 1 WHENEVER S(K) .E. 1, J = 1 TRANSFER TO I(J)

Since it has been proved (Turing *et al.*) that these four instructions are sufficient to describe *computable* problems, these basic statements are also sufficient.

The statements that remain to be described thus come under the heading of notational convenience rather than necessity. This, then, is an appropriate place to review the language definition process discussed thus far, and to indicate a more formal approach to this process.

RECURSIVE DEFINITION

By defining a metalanguage (meta means "middle") which is composed of characters not included in the character set of the artificial language, the recursive definition which has been alluded to earlier can be accomplished succinctly.

(1) Let matching pointed braces (⟨ ⟩) designate a set of entities whose descriptive name is included in the braces. Elements not in braces designate themselves, i.e., they are constants.

(2) The vertical stroke (|) means "exclusive or," i.e., $a|b$ allows either but not both a and b.

(3) The symbol := is used to mean "is defined to be."

(4) Adjacent elements not separated by a stroke imply concatenation.

With these definitions, it is now possible to present definitions describing the permissible constants and single variables in MAD.

⟨alpha character⟩ := A | B | C | D | $\cdots$ | Z
⟨digit⟩ := 0 | 1 | 2 | 3 $\cdots$ | 9
⟨character⟩ := ⟨alpha character⟩ | ⟨digit⟩
⟨character string⟩ := ⟨character⟩ | ⟨character⟩ ⟨character string⟩
⟨var name⟩ := ⟨alpha character⟩ | ⟨alpha character⟩ ⟨character string⟩
⟨digit string⟩ := ⟨digit⟩ | ⟨digit⟩ ⟨digit string⟩
⟨integer constant⟩ := +⟨digit string⟩ | −⟨digit string⟩ | ⟨digit string⟩
⟨simple constant⟩ := ⟨integer constant⟩ . ⟨digit string⟩
⟨exp constant⟩ := ⟨simple constant⟩ E ⟨integer constant⟩
⟨constant⟩ := ⟨integer constant⟩ | ⟨simple constant⟩ | ⟨exp constant⟩

As written, these definitions admit of variable names and constants having an infinite number of symbols, whereas there is, in fact, a limitation on both. The definitions do illustrate, however, the utility of this recursive approach when structural groups composed of an indefinite number of similar entities are to be dealt with. Expressions, which are often composed of expressions, are readily defined by this technique. The following definitions are not comprehensive enough to describe expression structure in

MAD, but they illustrate the first steps which, if pursued, could be elaborated to define the entire language.

⟨list⟩ := ⟨expression⟩ | ⟨expression⟩, ⟨list⟩
⟨variable⟩ := ⟨var name⟩ | ⟨var name⟩ (⟨list⟩)
⟨expression⟩ := ⟨constant⟩ | ⟨variable⟩ | (⟨expression⟩) | ⟨expression⟩
       + ⟨expression⟩ | ⟨expression⟩ − ⟨expression⟩ | ⟨expression⟩/
       ⟨expression⟩ | ⟨expression⟩*⟨expression⟩

A computer application of such syntax tables is given in the last chapter.

Statements
and
Flow Charts

The basic statement group just defined is sufficient to describe all algorithms (again subject to the limitations of storage) since they are capable of representing the Turing machine operations. The remaining statements then come under the heading of notational convenience, although the declaration statements described later permit such a simplification of algorithms that their proper use is mandatory.

ITERATION STATEMENTS

Incremental iteration statement. The usefulness of repetitive (or *iterative*) operators which apply in a simple fashion to elements of linear arrays is already established. The summation ($\sum$) and the product ($\prod$) operators are examples. In designing an artificial language one is faced with two possible approaches. (1) Include a profusion of very specialized and, hence, very succinct operators, with the result that algorithm expression will be compact, but the language will be more difficult to learn. (2) Include a few more general operators, with the result that, although the language will be easier to learn, algorithm expression will, in specific instances, be more lengthy. The latter seems to be the more appropriate criterion and is the one adopted for the iteration statements. To provide some motivation for the resultant statement form it is helpful to examine in detail an instance of the familiar summation operator:

$$y = \sum_{i=1}^{n} (a_i + b_i)$$

Note the following points.

(1) The expression to be repeatedly added is indicated by parentheses. The total expression might be called the *scope* of the operation.

(2) An iteration variable, i, is specified.

(3) The initial value, 1, of the specified variable is given.

(4) It is understood, or implied, that with each addition the specified variable is incremented by one.

(5) The terminal value of the specified variable is given, i.e., the iteration is terminated after the addition of the term for which the relational expression $(i = n)$ is true.

What are the possible avenues for generalization of an operator of this kind? In this example, the designated expression is *added* on each repetition. A more general statement might permit any operation, or sequence of operations, to be repeated. In addition, the five elements above could be expanded to include the following possibilities.

(1) The use of a label to designate the final expression (or statement) to be included in an iterative cycle.

(2) The designated variable may itself be an array element.

(3) The initial value may be given by an arbitrary expression.

(4) The incremental value can be made explicit and may be designated by an arbitrary expression.

(5) The termination of the repetition will be effected when an arbitrary relational expression, not necessarily involving the iteration variable, is true.

What remains is to define the operation as a statement within the bounds of the character set. The following form is adopted.

$$\text{THROUGH } s, \text{ FOR } v = \varepsilon_1, \varepsilon_2, \Re$$

Here s stands for a statement label designating the last of the immediately following statements to be repeated; v for a variable; ε_1 for an arbitrary expression which designates the initial value of the iteration variable; ε_2 for an arbitrary expression, the value of which is to be added to the iteration variable on each repetition; and $\Re$ is an arbitrary relational expression which, when true, causes the computation to continue from the statement labeled s.

Some example statements are:

THROUGH ST, FOR I = 1, 1, I .G. 100
THROUGH LABEL(2), FOR J = I, 1, I .G. 50 .OR. Y .L. EPS
THROUGH ALPHA, FOR D1 = B − A, −D1/2, .ABS. D1 .L. OMEGA

To emphasize earlier remarks, note that the first example above may be expressed in terms of basic statements.

```
        I = 1
        TRANSFER TO A
C       I = I + 1
A       WHENEVER I .G. 100, TRANSFER TO B
ST      :
        TRANSFER TO C
B
```

Operations such as the iteration statement are, on first encounter, somewhat difficult to comprehend from the prose description. It is useful, as it
often is with entire algorithms, to portray complicated operations in
graphic form. The depicting graphs, called *flow charts*, are widely used in
the description of algorithms for machine execution and many individual-
istic flow-charting conventions have evolved. The differences in these
techniques are of little importance as long as the resultant diagram is
sufficiently *visual* in character so that interpretation does not require
reference to a large set of written rules. In selecting the diagrammatic
forms presented here, care has been taken to ensure a close correspondence
between figures in the flow chart and statements in the resultant algorithm
description.

To regress for a moment, the substitution statement is charted by simply
including the statement in a rectangular box.

$$\boxed{\mathcal{V}_1 = \mathcal{E}_1}$$

A sequence of substitution statements are written in adjacent boxes with
directed lines to indicate the order of computation.

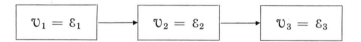

Since the order of computation of these three substitution statements is
always the same (i.e., there are no conditional transfers), the statements
may be written, for convenience, in a single box, with the understanding
that they are executed in top-to-bottom order.

$$\boxed{\begin{array}{c} \mathcal{V}_1 = \mathcal{E}_1 \\ \mathcal{V}_2 = \mathcal{E}_2 \\ \mathcal{V}_3 = \mathcal{E}_3 \end{array}}$$

From what has already been explained it is apparent that a directed line,
or arrow, fulfills the function of a transfer statement. When an algorithm
is long or complicated, then, instead of drawing long arrows, it is sometimes convenient to indicate such a remote connection as follows:

Any distinct symbol can be used in the circles.

The conditional prefix indicates a sequence which has one path in, but two possible paths out. One output corresponds to the case when the designated relation is *true*, and the other to the case where it is *false*. The triangle is a suitable figure for this three-part function.

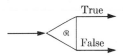

Rather than set a convention it is assumed that the output paths are always labeled. Combining diagrams, we find that a substitution statement with a conditional prefix becomes

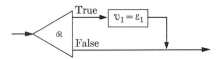

Returning now to the iteration statement, we note that the example which was written out in terms of basic statements has the flow-chart form shown in Fig. 3–1. Since these combined operations are represented as a single statement, a single-block condensation of the flow chart is suggested (Fig. 3–2). An iteration statement may contain within its scope one or more other iteration statements. Such an inclusion must be complete in the sense that the entire scope of the contained statement must be within the scope of the containing statement. (However, the scopes may terminate with the same statement.) The summation operation, $S = \sum_{i=1}^{10} (a_i + b_i)$, can be written as the following three-statement group.

$$S = 0$$
$$\text{THROUGH BETA, FOR I} = 1, 1, \text{I..G. } 10$$
$$\text{BETA} \quad S = S + A(I) + B(I)$$

The corresponding flow-chart form is shown in Fig. 3–3. The repeated product, $P = \Pi_{i=1}^{20} x_i$, has the same form. Here it is necessary to set the partial product variable initially to 1 instead of zero as was the case with

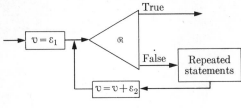

FIGURE 3–1

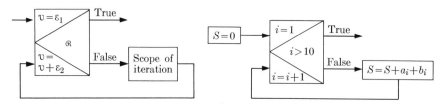

FIGURE 3-2   FIGURE 3-3

P = 1.0
THROUGH ST, FOR I = 1, 1, I .G. 20
ST   P = P*X(I)

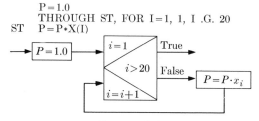

FIGURE 3-4

P = A(N)
THROUGH ST, FOR J = N−1, −1, J .L. 0
ST   P = P*X + A(J)

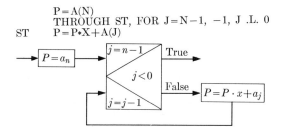

FIGURE 3-5

SUM = 0
THROUGH G, FOR I = 1, 1, I .E. N
THROUGH G, FOR J = I+1, 1, J .G. N
G   SUM = SUM + P(I)*Q(J)

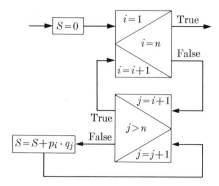

FIGURE 3-6

B   THROUGH B, FOR I=1, 1, X .E. A(I) .OR. I .G. K

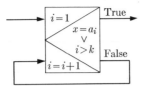

FIGURE 3-7

the partial sum in the example above (see Fig. 3-4). In both cases, the initial value of the partial variable (i.e., the partial sum or partial product) could have been initially set to the value of the first term, with the iteration variable, i, initially set to 2.

As mentioned before, the compact expression of the parenthesized or *nested* form of a polynomial presents difficulties. The following statements describe the evaluation of an nth-degree polynomial,

$$p = (\cdots((a_n x + a_{n-1})x + a_{n-2})x + \cdots + a_1)x + a_0$$

Here we have chosen to set the partial variable to a_n and the index variable initially to $n-1$. Alternatively, one could make the partial variable initially zero, with the index set to n (Fig. 3-5). As a final example, Fig. 3-6 shows the computation of contained or *nested* iterations whose scopes terminate on the same statements. The expression to be computed is

$$y = \sum_{\substack{i,j \\ j > i}}^{n} p_i q_j$$

$$= p_1 q_2 + p_1 q_3 + \cdots + p_1 q_n + p_2 q_3 + \cdots + p_2 q_n + \cdots + p_{n-1} q_n$$

The notation indicates that both index variables i and j are to be varied for all combinations of i and j for which $i \leq n$, $j \leq n$, and $j > i$.

The iteration statement is one of the most useful tools in the statement repertoire and, for this reason, has been explained and illustrated in considerable detail. It should be understood that although this statement is incremental, increments of zero or other terminating relations within the scope of an iteration are *not* excluded. It is possible for this statement to have as its scope the incremental and relational portions of the statement itself. An example of this type is the task of scanning a table for the purpose of comparing a given value x with the elements of a linear array, a_1, $a_2, \ldots, a_k$. The comparing procedure is halted whenever a matching value is found or k comparisons have been made (Fig. 3-7).

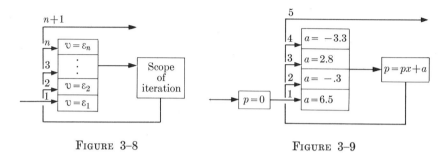

FIGURE 3–8   FIGURE 3–9

Fixed-list iteration statements. A less frequently used variant of the incremental iteration statement is useful when the values to be assigned to the iteration variable cannot be described in terms of some incremental variation. In such a case, one is given a list of expressions which determine the values to be assumed by the iteration variable. The scope of the iteration (the set of statements to be repeated) is executed for each of the designated values in the order in which they are written, and then the computation proceeds from the first statement after the scope. The form of the statement is

$$\text{THROUGH s, FOR VALUES OF } \upsilon = \varepsilon_1, \varepsilon_2, \ldots, \varepsilon_n$$

A diagrammatic representation is shown in Fig. 3–8.

An example, perhaps somewhat contrived, is the evaluation of the fixed coefficient polynomial $p = 6.5x^3 - 0.3x^2 + 2.8x - 3.3$, which is presented in Fig. 3–9.

Other typical statements are:

$$\text{THROUGH ALPHA, FOR VALUES OF A(I)} = \text{Z, Y} + 4, \text{X0}$$

$$\text{THROUGH D, FOR VALUES OF G} = \text{I, J*K} + 3, 10$$

COMPOUND CONDITIONAL STATEMENT GROUP

Although the conditional prefix is sufficient, it is not always convenient to use. This inconvenience is particularly evident when the conditional computation to be executed must be represented by a sequence of statements, rather than a single statement as the prefix allows. To facilitate the expression of this common construction and to allow the simple statement of a set of conditional, but mutually exclusive, sequences of statements, the compound conditional statement group is defined. The general

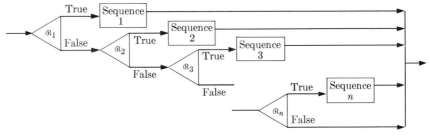

FIGURE 3–10

form of the group of statements is:

> WHENEVER $\Re_1$
> (Statement sequence 1)
>
> OR WHENEVER $\Re_2$
> (Statement sequence 2)
>
> OR WHENEVER $\Re_3$
> (Statement sequence 3)
> $\vdots$
> OR WHENEVER $\Re_n$
> (Statement sequence n)
>
> END OF CONDITIONAL

At this level of complexity the graphic representation (Fig. 3–10) becomes a better medium for description than the prose account of the intended meaning.

The first of the relational expressions $\Re_1$, $\Re_2$, $\Re_3$, . . . , $\Re_n$ found to be true results in (1) the execution of the immediately following sequence of statements followed by (2) a transfer to the terminal END OF CONDITIONAL statement.

Note that the diagram indicates that when all the relations are false, no execution takes place. A desirable variant is to permit the execution of a specified sequence when all the relations are false. This alternative is expressed by writing the desired sequence before the END OF CONDITIONAL in the form shown below.

> $\vdots$
> OTHERWISE
> (Unconditional statement sequence)
>
> END OF CONDITIONAL

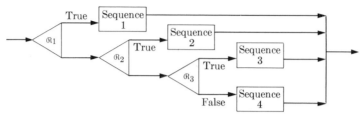

FIGURE 3–11

A somewhat more compact diagram for this case is presented in Fig. 3–11. Of course, the same result can be achieved by making sure that the last relation is always true, for instance, OR WHENEVER I .E. I. It is apparent that the END OF CONDITIONAL statement may be regarded as a common transfer point from the various sequences. Accordingly, it is possible to label and refer to this group-terminating statement.

One example of the use of this statement should suffice. Consider the problem of computing one root of the equation $ax^2 + bx + c = 0$ (a and b may not be simultaneously zero). The procedure is illustrated in Fig. 3–12.

The conditional sequences in a group may include other conditional groups, iterations, or nested iterations. Also, the scope of iteration statements may include conditional groups and nested conditional groups.

INPUT AND OUTPUT STATEMENTS

In the hypothetical Turing machine with its infinite storage, it was assumed that the input numbers or *data* required by an algorithm were initially encoded as marks in the storage tape. Similarly, the results of the execution of the algorithm were simply left encoded on the infinite tape. For a practical machine with finite storage, it is a virtual necessity —in order to extend the number of algorithms that may be executed—to be able to designate at what points in the computation data are to be introduced. Likewise, to increase the use of the limited storage, it must be possible to designate at what points storage may be freed by dispatching results to an external storage medium. In procedures where necessity does not demand these features, the statement of algorithms can often be simplified by considering them to be repetitions of an input-compute-output cycle.

One would expect that the nature of input and output operations would depend very heavily upon the specific media involved and, indeed, this is the case. Actually to fully utilize the features of the various readers, printers, and punches in use, it is necessary to devise an artificial language which is designed specifically to describe the *form* of the information to be

```
        IMAGX1 = 0.
WHENEVER A .E. 0
        REALX1 = −C/B
OR WHENEVER B*B−4.*A*C .L. 0
        REALX1 = −B/(2.0*A)
        IMAGX1 = ((4.*A*C−B*B) .P. .5)/(2.0*A)
OTHERWISE
        REALX1 = (−B+(B*B−4.0*A*C) .P. .5)/(2.0*A)
END OF CONDITIONAL
```

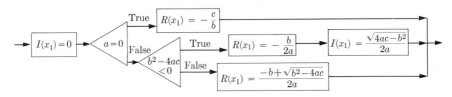

FIGURE 3–12

introduced into or produced from the computing process. Thus such a language is used for *format specification* and constitutes a language within the algorithm-describing language under consideration. A commonly adopted simplification of this function is to designate *standard* forms. This approach is taken here although the format specification sublanguage referred to is a part of the language being described.

The input information may be regarded as being a list of numbers, and either (1) the input (or *read* statement as it is called) must identify a subsequence of the list with the corresponding variables or (2) this identification must be an explicit part of the list. Assuming in both cases that the numbers are taken from the list sequentially, we note that in the second case it is also necessary to explicitly designate the length of the subsequence to be processed by a *read* statement. Case (2) is the convention adopted, and the input statement is simply composed of the two words:

READ DATA

The balance of the information is conveyed *in the data* and is an auxiliary part of the algorithm description. The data list is of the form $v_1 = n_1$, $v_2 = n_2, \ldots, v_k = n_k*$, where $v_1, \ldots, v_n$ are variable names and $n_1, \ldots, n_k$ are the values assigned to the variables. As a quick digression, observe that the list looks like a set of simple substitution statements. The asterisk (*) is the terminating mark which indicates the end of an input sequence. The values are expressed in the forms previously described for constants. For convenience, only the first element of consecutive array elements need be named. Thus $v_i = n_1, n_2, \ldots, n_k$ is the same as $v_i = n_1, v_{i+1} = n_2, \ldots, v_{i+k-1} = n_k$. The designated array elements may be linear or two-dimensional, and, in this context, the subscripts are limited to being integer constants. When the data are on a discrete medium, such as cards, it is assumed that one group $(v_j = n_j)$ does not extend from one card to another and that the asterisk, when it occurs, is the last mark on a card.

The output statement (often designated a *print* or *punch* statement) is the inverse of the *read* statement in that it governs the formation of a list of numbers. Only the option corresponding to (1) in the preceding paragraph is possible, however, since, quite obviously, the variables whose values are to be added to the list must be explicitly designated. The form of the printed output is directly analogous to the input in that all numbers, printed according to the rules for constants, are either individually labeled or are understood to be consecutive values of a previously labeled array element. The form of the output statement is

$$\text{PRINT RESULTS } \mathcal{L}$$

where $\mathcal{L}$ designates a list $v_1, v_2, \ldots, v_k$ of variable names. Here again a contracted version of the list is possible when consecutive array elements are to be specified. Consecutive elements $v_i, v_{i+1}, v_{i+2}, \ldots, v_k$ may be abbreviated in the list by $v_i \ldots v_k$. This notation resembles the ellipsis (...), but note that the preceding and succeeding commas of common usage are omitted. In this context the variable subscripts may be given by expressions.

By way of illustration a pair of "matching" input-output statements is included. We also present an appropriate data list, which is displaced from the *read* statement to emphasize the fact that such input values are conventionally listed after the algorithm-describing statements.

READ DATA

$\vdots$

PRINT RESULTS N, X1, ALPHA, B(1) ... B(N), XBAR

Data:

N = 4, X1 = 3.2, ALPHA = .216E − 5, B(1) = 6, 5, −3, 4,
XBAR = −784.27*

These statements constitute simple additions to flow charts.

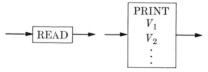

As a convenient reminder of what variables the *read* statement quantifies, it may be helpful to include a list in the input box also.

DECLARATION STATEMENTS

As their name implies, declaration statements are statements *about* the algorithm and do not describe any specific computation or specific order of computation as do the statements considered up to now. Declarations convey information about the range of variables. Strictly speaking, such information is not necessary, but with limited storage it may greatly simplify algorithms or, at the very least, introduce redundancy so that the executable statements may be checked to some extent for syntactical errors (i.e., errors in statement formation).

Dimension statement. It is intuitively apparent that consecutive elements in an array should occupy consecutive spaces in storage. No justification was needed, for instance, when, in simulating the Turing machine operations, consecutive spaces on the tape were labeled as consecutive elements of an array. Indeed, any other labeling would have greatly complicated the statement of the four basic operations. In a finite machine, to ensure the allocation of such consecutive blocks, the algorithm must include a statement of the largest and smallest possible values in the range of subscript expressions. The dimension statement accomplishes this purpose and is of the form

$$\text{DIMENSION } V_1(n_1), \ V_2(n_2), \ \ldots, \ V_k(n_k)$$

Here the $V_1, V_2, \ldots, V_k$ are array names and $n_1, n_2, \ldots, n_k$ are *positive integer constants* that are the largest values which will be assumed by the subscript expressions. It is understood that zero is the smallest possible value. An example of a dimension statement is

$$\text{DIMENSION } X(100), \ \text{BETA}(4), \ \text{XBAR}(50), \ K(10)$$

A restatement of the meaning in a more procedural form is that the parenthesized integer plus one gives the number of locations allocated to the immediately preceding array name.

Mode-declaration statements. Whereas the dimension statement gives the upper bound of the integer range of subscripts, the *mode* declaration statements distinguish between different classes of variable ranges. Variable modes already introduced are real, integer, Boolean, statement label, and function name. The latter two are language-oriented innovations, and the application of variables of this type will not be pursued. Variables in Boolean mode are also infrequently encountered in ordinary numerical problems. To be sure, relations are Boolean expressions, but the variables involved are generally real or integer. Only when a variable assumes the value of a relation does the notion of Boolean mode become relevant. A substitution statement such as

$$Z = X \text{ .GE. EPSLON}$$

defines Z to have only the true-false (or 0, 1) range and hence must be of Boolean mode. The infrequent use of such variables places the primary emphasis on the real and integer modes. The predominance of real variables in physical problems leads to the convention that variables are understood to be real unless they are declared to be of some other mode. For the reasons indicated above, the only statement introduced here is one which declares variables of integer mode; the form is

$$\text{INTEGER } \mathcal{L}$$

where $\mathcal{L}$ designates a list of variables having integer range. All elements of an array must have the same range, and hence only the array name— no subscripts—need appear on the list. For instance,

$$\text{INTEGER I, J, M41, CRITIC}$$

Any of these variables, let us say J, for example, may designate an array, that is, J(I), J(22), J(M41 + 2), etc., could appear in executable statements.

It should be possible to identify the modes of variables from their context in statements, and, with the exception of a few cases, an extensive analysis could produce the lists given in mode declarations. The exceptions arise from the adoption of conventional usage, which is somewhat less than precise. For instance, the symbol / is used to represent real division and also integer division. Strictly speaking, integer division is not defined; given the integers a, b, the function $f(a, b) = a/b$ does not have an integer range. What is meant, but is not stated, is that $f(a, b) = $ greatest integer in (a/b) (a and b are presumed to be positive). In such a case, to execute a/b correctly one needs to know the modes of a and b. Primarily, the mode declarations provide only redundancy—a statement of what could be derived. When the derived result differs from the declared result, an error in either statement formation or declaration has occurred.

Functions
and
Example Programs

CHAPTER

FOUR

In computing parlance the set of statements which describe an algorithm is called a *program* and the language used for the description is a *programming language*. The specifications of such a language, undertaken in the previous chapters, is virtually complete. All that remains is to indicate how function *definitions* are given; the notations for function *references* have already been covered.

FUNCTIONS

The expressions and relations which are used to define a function can be given in the forms already discussed. What is needed, in addition, are ways to (1) indicate the set of statements which constitute the definition (i.e., the *scope* of the definition), (2) designate the name(s) assigned to identify the function, and (3) designate the *dummy* variables whose occurrences in the definition are to be replaced by the given arguments during the execution of a function *reference*. The last item deserves some amplification, and recourse to ordinary notation may help. When one writes, for instance,

$$f(x, y) = x^2 + axy + 4$$

the resulting expression is not construed as a specific calculation to be carried out, but rather as the definition of a pattern of computation. Then, in a computational *reference* to the function named f, for example, $f(z - 2, 8)$, the values of the two *arguments* given are substituted in the pattern for x and y, and the subsequent evaluation produces a single numerical result. Conventionally, the function reference is treated as a name for this result:

$$q = d + f(z - 2, 4) = d + (z - 2)^2 + a(z - 2)4 + 4$$

In the scope of the definition, the symbols x and y are not genuine variables but are *dummy* variables (or, alternatively, *bound* variables and sometimes *parameters*, although this latter use is poor). Note, however, that a is an

39

actual variable and must in some way be quantified with a value from its range before the expression indicated above can be evaluated.

Mathematical notation also permits vector functions; these are functions which are defined by rules for computing the value, not of a single expression but of many expressions; in fact, of one expression for each element of an array. From the foregoing discussion it appears that this usage is not permitted since the function reference, with arguments, is treated as an expression which when evaluated produces a single number as a result. Indeed, this is the case, since any other usage would mean that the arithmetic operations would have to be defined for operands which consisted of entire arrays (not array elements!), as well as of single variables. However, a simple extension of function notation permits the effective use of vector functions even though it is then not possible to consider the function reference as an expression.

Conventionally, in defining a pattern for $f(x, y)$ the dummy variables x and y are used to represent the variables upon which the expression depends. The notation is now extended to permit the inclusion of symbols representing variables *depending upon* the defined expressions. Since more than one expression may now be defined, the defining sequence must permit the labeling of expressions, and this is done by indicating substitutional equality. For example,

$$f(x, y, z) = x^2 + axy + 2 \qquad \text{and} \qquad z = y^2 + 2x$$

A reference to f is understood to be the value of the first expression, but the same reference causes the argument inserted for z to take the appropriate value of the second expression. As defined, a reference can be used in an expression, for example,

$$p = 41.2 + qr + f(q + 4, 8, s)$$

Note that it is not meaningful for the third argument to be an expression or a constant since the function reference will give it a value. If, instead, this function were defined,

$$f(w, x, y, z):$$
$$y = w^2 + awx + 2$$
$$z = x^2 + 2w$$

the reference could not be included in an expression since it was not designated to have the value of some expression. Note, however, that it is now meaningful for the function reference to stand alone since the reference itself causes the last two variables named as arguments to assume new values. In this last form the application as a vector function is apparent.

$$f(w, x, a):$$

$$a_1 = w^2 + awx + 2$$

$$a_2 = x^2 + 2w$$

It is possible for any (or all) dummy variables to designate arrays.

$$f(w, a):$$

$$a_1 = w_1^2 + aw_1w_2 + 2$$

$$a_2 = w_2^2 + 2w_1$$

Some descriptive term is needed as a name for the expression which is referred to by the function reference (if any). This expression is called the *direct result* of the function. The dichotomy of input and output dummy variables which has been implicit thus far is not necessary. A dummy variable may be used both to evaluate an expression and to be given the value of some expression, for example,

$$g(k):$$

$$k = k + 1$$

All that remains now is to introduce into the programming language statements which provide the three essential ingredients of function definition. The scope of the definition is indicated by preceding the relevant sequence of statements with the words

EXTERNAL FUNCTION $(V_1, V_2, \ldots, V_n)$

and terminating the sequence with

END OF FUNCTION

The dummy variables $(V_1, V_2, \ldots, V_n)$ are listed, enclosed by parentheses and separated by commas, immediately after the initial words EXTERNAL FUNCTION. The input and output dummy variables need not be separated and can be in any order in the list. The function name(s) is indicated by inserting a label immediately before the first statement of the function being defined. The use of multiple names allows the simple definition of related functions within one inclusive scope of definition. The statement form utilized is ENTRY TO $\mathfrak{F}$, where $\mathfrak{F}$ is a function name including the necessary final period. Dummy variables which

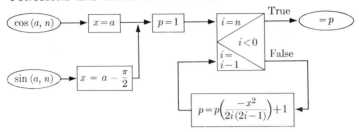

FIGURE 4–1

represent output variables will at some point in the definition appear to the left of an equals sign in a substitution statement. The direct result cannot be indicated by a substitution statement because there is no dummy variable to which it corresponds. The statement

FUNCTION RETURN ε

must be the last statement executed in a particular reference and the value of the expression ε is taken as the direct result. (When there is no direct result, no expression is written in this statement.) These inclusions can best be illustrated by writing the definitions for two simple, related functions:

$$\cos (x, n) = 1 - \frac{x^2}{2!} + \frac{x^4}{4!} - \cdots + (-1)^n \frac{x^{2n}}{(2n)!}$$

and

$$\sin (x, n) = \cos \left(x - \frac{\pi}{2}, n \right)$$

Before proceeding to the flow chart, we should formulate a plan of attack for computing the cosine series. The series is an nth-degree polynomial in x^2 and hence could be evaluated by the nesting methods discussed earlier. The coefficients cause a slight additional complication which perhaps can be resolved by writing the first four terms in nested form:

$$1 - \frac{x^2}{2!} + \frac{x^4}{4!} - \frac{x^6}{6!} = \left(\left(\frac{-x^2}{6 \cdot 5} + 1 \right) \frac{-x^2}{4 \cdot 3} + 1 \right) \frac{-x^2}{2 \cdot 1} + 1$$

If we consider that in this case, $n = 3$, the procedure for arbitrary n is clear (Fig. 4–1).

The initial elliptic figure may be regarded as the terminus of a special kind of remote connection, i.e., one which quantifies the appropriate variables listed in it. The output of a direct result is encircled and may be construed as the initiation of a remote connection, one which assigns the value of the expression following the equals sign to be the one which a function reference represents. The equivalent statements are:

```
          EXTERNAL FUNCTION (A, N)
          INTEGER N, I
          ENTRY TO COS.
          X = A
          TRANSFER TO COMP
          ENTRY TO SIN.
          X = A − 1.5707963
COMP      P = 1.0
          THROUGH ITER, FOR I = N, −1, I .L. 0
ITER      P = P*(−X*X/((2*I)*(2*I − 1))) + 1.0
          FUNCTION RETURN P
          END OF FUNCTION
```

References to this function would appear as expressions or subexpressions, such as

$$Z(4) = \text{BETA} + \text{SIN.(ALPHA, 3)}*Y$$

To understand the implications of the adjective EXTERNAL it is helpful to look again at the first function example,

$$f(x, y) = x^2 + axy + 4$$

The definition of an external function must include statements which when executed would quantify the ordinary variables in the expressions. The variable a above would have to be given a value by some substitution before a function reference could be executed. For example, one might write

$$f(x, y) = x^2 + axy + 4, \qquad \text{where} \quad a = 6$$

although in such a simple case it would be more appropriate to write the constant 6 instead of a. A function definition for which such quantifying steps are not required in the scope of definition is called an *internal* function.

The distinction between the two cases can be restated as follows. In external functions ordinary variables are defined only within the scope of definition of the function, but in internal functions the symbols used for such variables have the same meaning outside the scope of definition. Apparently, then, an internal function can be *embedded* in some larger program, such as an external function, while an external function, except for the linkages introduced by the dummy variables, is a completely independent program. Note that the ordinary variables involved in the cos-sin external function, namely X and P, are quantified during execution by the statements X = A, X = A − 1.5707963, P = 1.0.

To turn the example into an internal function, let us assume for simplicity that only the cosine is of interest, and that n is to be a program-wide variable having the same definition outside the scope of the function.

$$\vdots$$

```
        INTERNAL FUNCTION (X)
        ENTRY TO COS.
        P = 1.0
        THROUGH RPT, FOR I = N, −1, I .L. 0
RPT     P = P*(−X*X/((2*I)*(2*I − 1))) + 1.0
        FUNCTION RETURN P
        END OF FUNCTION
```

$$\vdots$$

Here N is not quantified by a statement in the scope of the definition but by some statement in the program in which this function is embedded.

Whenever an internal function definition is simple enough to be written as a single expression, a one-line definition is permissible. The form is

$$\text{INTERNAL FUNCTION } \mathfrak{F} \ (V_1, \ldots, V_n) = \mathcal{E}$$

where $\mathfrak{F}$ is the function name, $V_1, \ldots, V_n$ is the list of dummy variables, and $\mathcal{E}$ is the defining expression. As a concrete example, the cosine series below, which terminates with $n = 3$, is defined in this style.

$$\text{INTERNAL FUNCTION COS. (X)} = ((−X*X/(30) + 1)*(−X*X)/ \\ (12) + 1)*(−X*X)/(2) + 1$$

The mode of dummy variables must be declared if the mode is other than real. Dummy variables should not be dimensioned, however. Since the function reference is regarded as a name for the direct result of a function, the function reference itself must be classified in regard to mode. This classification is accomplished by including the function names in the list of a mode declaration if the direct result is not real. For example, the declaration

$$\text{INTEGER N, J, G., NFAC.}$$

states that the direct results of the functions named G. and NFAC. are integers.

In the earlier exposition of functions, an example of a function which did not define a direct result was included. Such a function is not an expression but, rather, it is analogous to a set of substitution statements.

A reference to such a function can be made as a separate statement by simply preceding the function reference with the word EXECUTE. Thus, an internal function which adds the elements of a linear array A to the corresponding elements of linear array B to produce a new array C (i.e., vector addition) could be referred to by:

EXECUTE VECADD. (A, B, C)

In the definition of more complex multiple-expression functions, such as those which require the use of an EXECUTE statement, it is often useful to be able to specify one or more possible changes in the order of computation following the function reference. In other words, what is needed is the possibility of designating statements other than the next in sequence to be executed after the function reference. Since statement labels are variables, all that is needed to accomplish this result in a function definition is to declare one or more dummy variables to be in statement label mode (by a STATEMENT LABEL $\mathcal{L}$ declaration) and then insert transfers to these dummy variables at the appropriate points in the scope of the definition. A frequently repeated relation can be written as an internal function to illustrate this point. Suppose that a program contains many relations of the form

WHENEVER ε .G. 0 .AND. (ε .G. K .OR. ε .L. 100), TRANSFER TO s

These occurrences can be replaced by a function reference COND. (ε, s) with the following definition. (As before, ε and s refer to arbitrary expression and statement label, respectively.)

$\vdots$

INTERNAL FUNCTION (A, S)
INTEGER A
STATEMENT LABEL S
WHENEVER A .G. 0 .AND. (A .G. K .OR. A .L. 100), TRANSFER TO S
FUNCTION RETURN
END OF FUNCTION

$\vdots$

The final statement of external functions *may* be END OF FUNCTION, but for other programs the statement END OF PROGRAM *must* be last. These terminal statements may be labeled, must be the physical end, and may be the last in the execution of an algorithm. An alternative way of terminating execution is to transfer to a *read* statement after the input data list has been exhausted.

USE OF THE PROGRAMMING LANGUAGE

As a summary, and for the purpose of exhibiting some complete programs, three computational problems from the realm of analytic geometry are presented and programs for their solution developed. These problems are representative of a large class of similar geometrical problems which provide good introductory examples of programming. The subject matter needs no explanation, and yet the algorithms are sufficiently uncommon so that neither experience nor ready reference to texts provides a substitute for reasoning through the expression of the procedure.

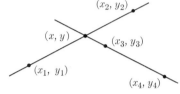

Problem 1. Given two pairs of Cartesian points, determine the point of intersection of the straight lines passing through the points (Fig. 4–2). Test for, and indicate, the case when the lines are parallel or coincident.

FIGURE 4–2

Analysis. Determining the point of intersection of two straight lines is tantamount to solving two linear equations in two unknowns. If one line is given by the slope-intercept equation $y = \bar{a}_1 x + \bar{b}_1$ and the second by $y = \bar{a}_2 x + \bar{b}_2$, then their intersection is given by the simultaneous solution of the expressions

$$-\bar{a}_1 x + y = \bar{b}_1$$

$$-\bar{a}_2 x + y = \bar{b}_2$$

Actually, the slope-intercept form is not applicable in the special case when the slope becomes infinite (that is, x is constant), and the implicit form of the lines is more useful:

$$a_1 x + b_1 y = 1$$

$$a_2 x + b_2 y = 1$$

Now it is necessary to determine the coefficients a_1, b_1, a_2, b_2. If the points (x_1, y_1) and (x_2, y_2) determine line 1, then

$$a_1 x_1 + b_1 y_1 = 1$$

$$a_1 x_2 + b_1 y_2 = 1$$

Solving these linear equations by Cramer's rule, one obtains

$$a_1 = \frac{y_2 - y_1}{x_1 y_2 - x_2 y_1} \quad \text{and} \quad b_1 = \frac{x_1 - x_2}{x_1 y_2 - x_2 y_1}$$

Similarly, if points (x_3, y_3) and (x_4, y_4) are used to determine the second line, then

$$a_2 = \frac{y_4 - y_3}{x_3 y_4 - x_4 y_3} \quad \text{and} \quad b_2 = \frac{x_3 - x_4}{x_3 y_4 - x_4 y_3}$$

Making these substitutions into the original equations, one has

$$\left[\frac{y_2 - y_1}{x_1 y_2 - x_2 y_1}\right] x + \left[\frac{x_1 - x_2}{x_1 y_2 - x_2 y_1}\right] y = 1$$

$$\left[\frac{y_4 - y_3}{x_3 y_4 - x_4 y_3}\right] x + \left[\frac{x_3 - x_4}{x_3 y_4 - x_4 y_3}\right] y = 1$$

Again, by making use of Cramer's rule, one can solve the equations and obtains the desired expression for the point of intersection in terms of the given coordinates. The manipulation is a little simpler if both equations are multiplied by the denominators:

$$(y_2 - y_1)x + (x_1 - x_2)y = (x_1 y_2 - x_2 y_1)$$

$$(y_4 - y_3)x + (x_3 - x_4)y = (x_3 y_4 - x_4 y_3)$$

Solving produces

$$x = \frac{(x_3 - x_4)(x_1 y_2 - x_2 y_1) - (x_1 - x_2)(x_3 y_4 - x_4 y_3)}{(x_3 - x_4)(y_2 - y_1) - (x_1 - x_2)(y_4 - y_3)}$$

$$y = \frac{(y_2 - y_1)(x_3 y_4 - x_4 y_3) - (y_4 - y_3)(x_1 y_2 - x_2 y_1)}{(x_3 - x_4)(y_2 - y_1) - (x_1 - x_2)(y_4 - y_3)}$$

The denominator of these expressions is the determinant of the system of two linear equations and, if zero, indicates that the equations are not independent but represent parallel or coincident lines.

Flow chart. The flow chart (Fig. 4–3) in this case is very simple. The only condition to be considered in the computation is whether or not the

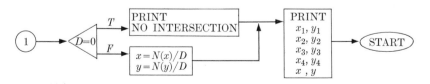

FIGURE 4–3

determinant is zero. For conciseness the numerators of the expressions for x and y are represented by $N(x)$ and $N(y)$. As written the computation will continue until the input data list is exhausted.

Program. To print the words, another extremely simple kind of print statement is introduced. The statement PRINT COMMENT $\$@\$$ causes the string of alphabetic, numerical, and special characters (except $) designated by $@$ to be printed. Note that the previously unused character, $, is now employed to delimit a sequence of the other characters. This statement also permits some control of the vertical spacing of the comment on the printed page. The first character after the left dollar sign, a blank in the example below, designates the spacing of the line. The admissible space control codes are:

Blank — — single space before the comment
0 — — double space before the comment
1 — — print the comment at the top of a page
2 — — print the comment at the next half-point position on the page
4 — — print the comment at the next quarter-point position on the page

The program has the following form.

```
START   READ DATA
        DET = (X3 − X4)*(Y2 − Y1) − (X1 − X2)*(Y4 − Y3)
        WHENEVER DET .E. 0, TRANSFER TO PAR
        X = ((X3 − X4)*(X1*Y2 − X2*Y1)
            − (X1 − X2)*(X3*Y4 − X4*Y3))/DET
        Y = ((Y2 − Y1)*(X3*Y4 − X4*Y3)
            − (Y4 − Y3)*(X1*Y2 − X2*Y1))/DET
PR      PRINT RESULTS X1, Y1, X2, Y2, X3, Y3, X4, Y4, X, Y
        TRANSFER TO START
PAR     PRINT COMMENT $ NO INTERSECTION $
        TRANSFER TO PR
        END OF PROGRAM
```

Typical data:

$$X1 = 1.0, \quad Y1 = 1.0, \quad X2 = 3.0, \quad Y2 = 3.0,$$
$$X3 = 1.0, \quad Y3 = 3.0, \quad X4 = 3.0, \quad Y4 = 1.0*$$

Problem 2. Define an external function which has as dummy variables the coordinates of the end points of two line segments and produces a direct result of unity if the segments intersect, and zero otherwise. In addition,

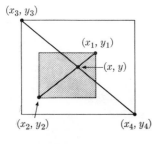

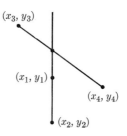

FIGURE 4–4   FIGURE 4–5

the function produces the coordinates of the point of intersection of the segments if its exists.

Analysis. The problem is very similar to the previous one, with the additional condition that, after the computation is performed, the point of intersection of the *lines* must be examined to see whether it is contained in both line segments. This condition is equivalent to the graphical question of whether the point of intersection is in the smallest included rectangle formed by passing horizontal and vertical lines through the end points (Fig. 4–4). The points are arbitrarily labeled, and hence no assumptions, such as $x_2 > x_1$ or $x_3 < x_4$, can be made. The relation which must be true if x lies within the end points of the first line is

$$\{(x \geq x_2) \wedge (x \leq x_1)\} \vee \{(x \geq x_1) \wedge (x \leq x_2)\} = X_1$$

The same relation for the second line is

$$\{(x \geq x_3) \wedge (x \leq x_4)\} \vee \{(x \geq x_4) \wedge (x \leq x_3)\} = X_2$$

If both relations are true simultaneously ($X_1 \wedge X_2$), then the x-coordinate lies in the required range. Except for one situation, finding the x-coordinate in the required range is the same as determining that the intersection point is in the proper rectangle. The exceptional case occurs when one of the lines is vertical (Fig. 4–5). Here the point of intersection is included in the range of the abscissas, but is not included in both segments. It is, of course, possible to determine whether $x_1 = x_2$ or $x_3 = x_4$, or whether there is inclusion in the rectangle, by testing, as is done here, whether the ordinate of the intersection point is included in the proper range. These relations determining whether y lies within the range of line segment 1 (Y_1) and within the range of segment 2 (Y_2) are symmetrical in form to the relations above.   If all these relations are simultaneously true ($X_1 \wedge X_2 \wedge Y_1 \wedge Y_2$), the point of intersection is contained in both

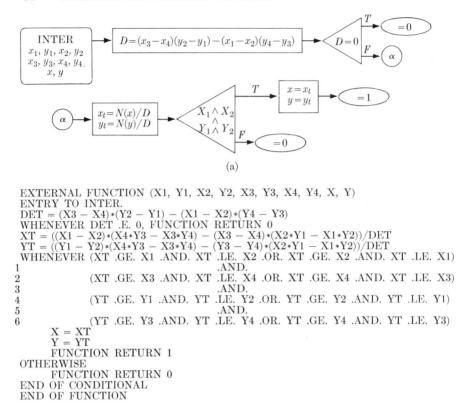

(a)

```
EXTERNAL FUNCTION (X1, Y1, X2, Y2, X3, Y3, X4, Y4, X, Y)
ENTRY TO INTER.
DET = (X3 − X4)*(Y2 − Y1) − (X1 − X2)*(Y4 − Y3)
WHENEVER DET .E. 0, FUNCTION RETURN 0
XT = ((X1 − X2)*(X4*Y3 − X3*Y4) − (X3 − X4)*(X2*Y1 − X1*Y2))/DET
YT = ((Y1 − Y2)*(X4*Y3 − X3*Y4) − (Y3 − Y4)*(X2*Y1 − X1*Y2))/DET
WHENEVER (XT .GE. X1 .AND. XT .LE. X2 .OR. XT .GE. X2 .AND. XT .LE. X1)
1                        .AND.
2            (XT .GE. X3 .AND. XT .LE. X4 .OR. XT .GE. X4 .AND. XT .LE. X3)
3                        .AND.
4            (YT .GE. Y1 .AND. YT .LE. Y2 .OR. YT .GE. Y2 .AND. YT .LE. Y1)
5                        .AND.
6            (YT .GE. Y3 .AND. YT .LE. Y4 .OR. YT .GE. Y4 .AND. YT .LE. Y3)
        X = XT
        Y = YT
        FUNCTION RETURN 1
OTHERWISE
        FUNCTION RETURN 0
END OF CONDITIONAL
END OF FUNCTION
```

(b)

FIGURE 4–6

line segments. The appropriate flow chart and the program are presented
in Fig. 4–6. Since this program is not a complete algorithm in itself (it is a
function definition) and no *read* statement is included, there is no associated data list. The use of this function is illustrated in the following
problem.

Note: In all the example programs that appear as part of the text, the
continuation of statements is indicated by simply indenting the subsequent
lines. When such statements are punched in cards, the cards after the first
must be designated as continuations by having a single-digit integer
punched in column 11 of the card (see Appendix A). The continuation of
the statements in the figures is indicated in this way.

Problem 3. Using the function defined in the previous problem, write
a program which reads, as elements of linear arrays, the end points of n line
segments and then determines the number of triangles that can be formed

	1	2	3	4	5
1		0	0	0	0
2	0		1	0	1
3	0	1		0	1
4	0	0	0		0
5	0	1	1	0	

FIGURE 4–7

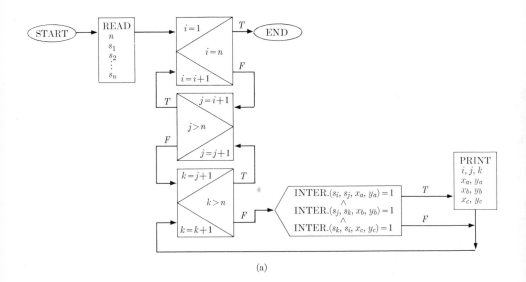

(a)

```
      INTEGER I, J, K, N, INTER.
      DIMENSION X1(100), Y1(100), X2(100), Y2(100)
      READ DATA
      THROUGH ST, FOR I = 1, 1, I .E. N
      THROUGH ST, FOR J = I + 1, 1, J .G. N
      THROUGH ST, FOR K = J + 1, 1, K .G. N
ST    WHENEVER INTER.(X1(I), Y1(I), X2(I), Y2(I), X1(J), Y1(J), X2(J), Y2(J), XA, YA) .E. 1
1         .AND. INTER.(X1(J), Y1(J), X2(J), Y2(J), X1(K), Y1(K), X2(K), Y2(K), XB, YB) .E. 1
2         .AND. INTER.(X1(K). Y1(K). X2(K), Y2(K), X1(I), Y1(I), X2(I), Y2(I), XC, YC) .E. 1,
3         PRINT RESULTS I, J, K, XA, YA, XB, YB, XC, YC
      END OF PROGRAM

Typical data
    X1(1) = 1, 3, 1, 1, 0, 3, 1, 1, 1, 2
    Y1(1) = 1, 1, 1, 0, 0, 1, 1, 0, 3, 1
    X2(1) = 3, 1, 3, 3, 1, 1, 3, 0, 3, 3
    Y2(1) = 3, 3, 3, 2, 1, 3, 3, 1, 1, 3 *
```

(b)

FIGURE 4–8

from the segments. The program should print the numbers of the triangle-forming line segments and the coordinates of the vertices.

Analysis. Four numbers are required to designate a line segment. To utilize the previously defined function, four linear arrays must be defined where the first element of each array defines line segment 1, the second element of each array line segment 2, etc. The problem then is to examine systematically all combinations of three line segments, say segment i, segment j, and segment k. When i intersects with j, a further search is warranted to find a $k \neq i$ which intersects with j. If, in addition, k intersects with i, the three form a triangle. To avoid finding the same triangle twice, only combinations of the three values should be examined —not permutations. To illustrate this point consider an "intersection" matrix whose rows and columns are labeled with the segment numbers. If segments i and j intersect, the ith row and the jth column element would be 1 and otherwise zero. As a specific case, let us suppose that 2 intersects with 5, 5 intersects with 3, and 3 intersects with 2. These three segments then form a triangle. The triangle is represented twice in the square array shown in Fig. 4–7, and only the combinations represented by the part of the array above the crosshatched diagonal (or, alternatively, below it) need be examined. The diagonal positions are not considered since a line segment is coincident with itself, and this fact is regarded as a special case of parallelism.

To simplify notation, the ith group of elements from the coordinate arrays which defines the ith segment will be called s_i. The flow chart and program are presented in Fig. 4–8.

A somewhat more efficient computation is produced if the iteration on k is not undertaken unless segments i and j intersect. The advantage is not so great as it seems at first glance, however, because in the conjunction of relations the first one found to be false eliminates the necessity of examining the remaining ones. From the definition of the .AND. operation (i.e., conjunction), it follows that if one of the variables is zero, the value of the other does not matter since the result will be zero in either case.

The Design of a Practical Machine

CHAPTER

FIVE

The earlier remarks on the relation of the terms "language" and "machine" suggest the conclusion that, once a suitable language has been defined, a machine is constructed which accepts as operations and operands the elements of this artificial language, and that further discussion concerning the nature of the machine is unnecessary. The obvious and often-mentioned fact that physically realizable machines are finite in itself precludes this happy state of affairs. Also, from a technological point of view, it becomes increasingly difficult to design a machine to respond to very concise operations (i.e., an artificial language with high information content per symbol). The imposed finitude means that the real numbers, which have been so freely referred to, cannot be represented since this would require an infinity of digits, but must be approximated by rational numbers. Such approximation introduces error, and it is necessary to know in detail the number representations of a machine to determine the magnitude of the introduced error. Also, it is obvious that not all integers can be represented, but in practice, this limitation does not often result in approximation.

This is, perhaps, an appropriate point at which to discuss the distinction between two fundamental types of machines, *digital* and *analog*. The digital machine, which is the principal concern of this text, cannot represent a continuous real function but only the value of the function at discrete points. For, to represent all the values in an interval, say (0, 1), would require the infinite storage necessary to represent real numbers. On the other hand, the analog machine represents continuous functions by analogy to a varying physical quantity (generally time-varying) such as voltage, pressure, speed, etc. Here no approximation of real variables is necessary since all the intermediate values, say between 0 volts and 1 volt, are possible. Such machines are very useful, particularly in the solution of problems from the realm of ordinary differential equations. However, the forced approximation of the digital system is not necessarily damaging since the approximation error can often be made negligibly small, and the continuous representation of the analog case is not a panacea since the physical variables can frequently be measured only to fractions of one-percent accuracy. Also, due to the fact that time is generally the independent variable, it becomes difficult in analog machines to represent functions of several independent variables.

The Wang machine previously discussed will be used as a point of departure for the development of a more realistic digital computing machine. This approach is not so abstract as it might at first appear; many features of present-day computers can be viewed as a logical outgrowth of operations with the more primitive machines. More importantly, perhaps, this evolution makes explicit the decisions, which, if the alternatives were taken, would lead to a sufficient but quite different machine organization.

By way of review the basic machine has a doubly infinite storage tape (i.e., it has no beginning) and a control unit which can accept the following four basic instructions:

(1) Move storage tape right one space $\rightarrow$
(2) Move storage tape left one space $\leftarrow$
(3) Make a mark (*)
(4) If current space is marked, take the nth instruction, otherwise take next instruction in sequence (n).

The sequence of instructions can also be regarded as coming from a tape. Schematically this machine is represented as before by a storage tape and a control device (Fig. 5–1). The instructions are on a separate tape that is read by the control unit.

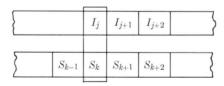

FIGURE 5–1

A *program* for this machine is a sequence of instructions which may be regarded as a sequence of symbol pairs. The first symbol in a pair is an integer which designates the cell number in the instruction tape and the second designates the instruction. For simplicity, when instruction number (4) is used, only the integer n is written since this clearly distinguishes the instruction from the other three, $\leftarrow$, $\rightarrow$, and *. An example of a routine that does nothing (effectively stops) but write a mark and then repeat ad infinitum the testing to see whether the mark is there is

$$1 \quad *$$
$$2 \quad 2$$

TABLE 5–1

1	←	7	←	13	←
2	10	8	*	14	*
3	←	9	n	15	7
4	12	10	←	16	←
5	←	11	16	17	*
6	←	12	←	18	6

The routine given below finds the first blank cell to the right (on the tape) of the current one under scan.

1	←
2	1

A more difficult problem and, in fact, one that cannot be executed without writing marks on the section of the tape just searched or using an infinite number of instructions is to find the first marked cell to the right. Consider now a routine to carry out a very elementary addition, that is, to add two digits whose values may be zero or one to produce the possible sums 0, 1, or 2. Two marks will be needed on the tape to represent 2; the complete addition table is given below.

$$a + b = c$$

a	b	c	
0	0	0	0
0	*	0	*
*	0	0	*
*	*	*	0

A zero designates the absence of a mark on the tape. To specify the problem more completely the storage tape can be visualized as illustrated in Fig. 5–2, which shows that it contains the initial values of a and that space is allotted for the result c. There will always be a mark following c, and the cell to the left of a is initially under scan. The operation is prescribed in Table 5–1, where n is some integer designating the next instruction to be executed after this program.

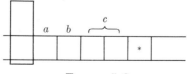

FIGURE 5–2

TABLE 5–2

a	b	Carry	c
0	0	0	0 0
0	0	*	0 *
0	*	0	0 *
0	*	*	* 0
*	0	0	0 *
*	0	*	* 0
*	*	0	* 0
*	*	*	* *

The foregoing routine, or the tabular representation, may be familiar since it is the addition of two binary digits. An addition problem is a recursive problem in that one repeatedly performs simple additions to complete one complex addition. Thus, in adding $973 + 368$, three simple additions are performed:

(1) $8 + 3 = 11$,   (2) $6 + 7 + 1 = 14$,   (3) $9 + 3 + 1 = 13$

When a carry is involved, there are three single-digit operands. If the addend and augend, as well as the carry digit, are restricted to values of 0 and 1, as before, then the eight possible operand combinations and the corresponding sums are as shown in Table 5–2. When all three digits are 1, i.e., the last line of the table, the resultant sum, $c = 3$, is encoded as **.

It is possible to write the program to carry out this three-digit addition and by repeated use of that routine perform the addition of numbers of arbitrary size. The routine which performs binary addition will be frequently used, and it is convenient to represent it by a single symbol, say I_+, in the sequence of instructions where it is used rather than write it out in detail every time. A frequently used routine of this kind is called a *subroutine*. Such sets of "packaged instructions" require the adoption of some conventions as to where the operands and the control are initially and where the result is to be written. Assumptions similar to the example program (Table 5–1) are adopted here. The operands are initially adjacent on the storage tape, and the result is written immediately to the right of these operands.

A natural question can be raised in this context. Would it not be useful—in fact, an economy of storage—to consider a more complicated symbol manipulator which permits the use of more than one kind of symbol? For instance, a device permitting one to write

$$*, \square, /, \ldots$$

or, more suggestively,

$$0, 1, 2, 3, \ldots, 9$$

The answer is that it would indeed be useful, but with current technology it is not feasible to build such a device. To achieve high-speed operation of a machine, inertia-less electronic and magnetic devices must be used. For any consistently reliable operation, these must be treated as two-state devices, i.e., current is passing through a transistor or it is not, a condenser is charged or it is discharged, a magnet has north-south polarity or south-north polarity. It is natural, then, to consider these bistable devices as representations of the two symbols 0 and * (or, more conventionally, 0 and 1). As noted in the earlier discussion of hypothetical machines, this situation does not preclude the possibility of representing symbols as combinations of this elementary pair. The decimal digits can be represented by four marks on the tape:

0	0000	5	0*0*
1	000*	6	0**0
2	00*0	7	0***
3	00**	8	*000
4	0*00	9	*00*

In fact, such a representation is common, and the four-mark groups are called binary-coded decimal characters (BCD). If, in building a machine, the decision is made not to consider individual marks but to treat them in groups of four as above, the machine could be called a *decimal* machine. In such cases it becomes a matter of philosophy whether the four-mark groups are single characters or not, but, in any event, in any electronic machine the basic representation is always composed of two-possibility symbols. In contrast, the mechanically rotating counterwheels in adding machines, tabulators, and the like, provide an example of a multistate device. These wheels are geared so that they can come to rest in ten possible positions. For electronic machines, economy of storage argues against such an encoding scheme for three reasons: (1) The routine required to add two encoded decimal digits to produce the two-digit sum in the same form is considerably more complicated than the equivalent binary addition. (2) The representation in itself does not convey the maximum amount of information. There are 16 possible combinations of 0's and *'s in four spaces, but only ten are utilized. (3) For Boolean variables (or relational expressions) there are only two alternatives, and the encoding requires that four marks be used to represent them. The powerful argument for such decimal coding is, of course, the familiarity of the decimal system.

Returning now to the basic machine, we may assume that other sequences of instructions are designated as subroutines. The other arithmetic operations, subtraction, multiplication, and division, are obvious candidates and will be referred to as I_-, $I_\times$, $I_\div$. Without the ability to

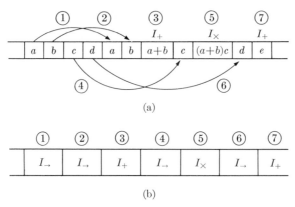

(a)

(b)

FIGURE 5-3

erase even the simplest problem will consume large amounts of the available instruction and storage tapes. Remembering that the subroutines require that the operands be adjacent on the tape and that the result of the operation is written after the second operand, consider the storage tape for the computation $e = (a + b)c + d$ (Fig. 5–3a). The arrows indicate a *store* or number transfer operation which it will also be convenient to represent as the subroutine $I\rightarrow$. The instruction tape for this problem is shown in Fig. 5–3(b). Certainly space could be conserved if the a-, b-, and c-operand and result cells could be reused and if, instead of inserting for every addition the long sequence of elementary instructions, a single set could be reexecuted for every occurrence. It is fairly obvious that the former can be achieved by providing for erasure or writing over portions of the storage tape, but the latter requires more explanation. Note that in the short routine written, the steps $(\ldots, 8\ *, 9\ n, \ldots)$ constitute an unconditional transfer to instruction n. Thus, by executing a similar sequence it is possible to repeat a set of instructions. The apparent problem is to follow each repetition with a *different* sequence of instructions, i.e., to make an unconditional transfer to a different instruction after each repetition. To achieve this variation one enters a different value for n in the final instruction of the repeated sequence before executing it. To insert this new value one must be able to write on the instruction tape also and to erase and write over previous values for n.

If the operands of the subroutines are multidigit binary numbers, then there arises a serious question about the subroutines; namely, how does one determine where an operand ends? Let us illustrate the problem by the following example. The *store* subroutine apparently searches the tape until it finds the first blank spot in which to insert a number; however, a series of blanks is a valid number $(000 \ldots 0)$, and hence the problem

FIGURE 5–4

cannot be solved unless there are some marks, or set of marks, which cannot be interpreted as numbers. This, then, is a design problem, and there are two solutions both of which have been implemented in actual machines.

The first solution is to permit numbers of varying length and follow each number with a special set of marks which designate the end of the number. In the strictly binary case, this special set must have at least one mark more than the maximum number of marks used to represent numbers—or else the mark itself cannot be distinguished from a number. The problem is less severe in the coded decimal scheme since in that case one of the six unused character positions is used as a number-terminating mark. Machines which have been built utilizing variable number length have been decimal machines.

The second solution, and the one adopted here, is to postulate that the storage tape has a structure similar to the instruction tape; that is, the storage is composed of equal-sized, numbered cells. With this arrangement, the *store* subroutine (as well as the arithmetic operations) is a much simpler procedure since the difference of the integer labels (addresses) of the storage cells provides the needed number of shifts to be carried out when moving a number from one spot on the tape to another.

The fixed number length, as well as the previously discussed need to alter instructions, suggests that instruction and data be combined into a common storage. The revised schematic (Fig. 5–4) reflects this change in organization. The finite common storage, here represented by an enclosed block, is organized as a sequence of fixed size storage cells (each containing the same number of marking positions) which accommodate both the instruction sequences and the data-storage sequences. An instruction, or some integral number of instructions, must be representable in the space allotted to one of the basic storage cells. The cells labeled a, b, and c are the operand and result positions used by the arithmetic subroutines and hence are called *arithmetic registers*. These same registers are referred to by the store subroutine $(I\rightarrow)$ whose primary function is to introduce numbers into the operand arithmetic registers (a, b) or to transfer the contents of the result register (c) for subsequent use as an operand. The subroutines are composed of many elementary operations and, as mentioned before, for such instruction sequences to be repeatedly used, it is

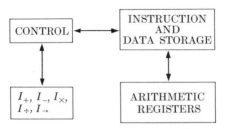

FIGURE 5–5

necessary to modify the terminating unconditional transfer. Since the storage is shared by instructions and data, this modification can be accomplished, as the arrows indicate, by permitting the control unit to erase and mark the instructions. With the use of subroutines permitted, the sequence of instructions $I_1, I_2, \ldots, I_N$ will consist primarily of subroutine references, rather than the four basic operations.

The foregoing suggests that the arithmetic registers and the subroutines, due to their great utility, be considered as an integral part of the machine and be removed from the realm of common storage. Organized in such a fashion, the resulting block diagram (Fig. 5–5) begins to take the form characteristic of large present-day digital computers. The basic arithmetic subroutines are not, in general, expressed by a written set of elementary operations but are represented physically in the machine by wires, transistors, etc. To the person writing a program, this distinction is nebulous since all that is apparent when an instruction is written which calls for execution of an arithmetic operation is that a sequence of more elementary steps (a *microprogram* as it is sometimes called) is carried out—by what means is unimportant. This notion of a subroutine, that is, defining complex operations once and for all in terms of more elementary sequences of instructions, is fundamental in computing.

A TYPICAL MACHINE

As a representative of a binary, fixed-length storage cell machine (the term *word* is generally used when referring to such a cell), the machine organization of International Business Machines' 704, 709, 7090 series of computers will be described. The character set introduced for the purpose of defining a language is, by no coincidence, acceptable by this group of machines as well as by others. Rather than refer to the elementary two-state positions as binary digits, the contracted term *bit* will be used. Machines in this category can be represented by the general block diagram shown in Fig. 5–6. As indicated in the figure, the machine can be divided

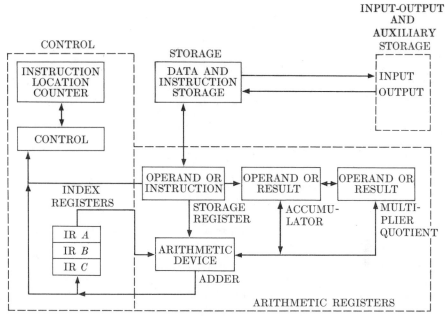

FIGURE 5–6

into four areas of interest:

(1) storage,
(2) control,
(3) input-output (and auxiliary storage),
(4) arithmetic registers.

These four sections will be given a cursory explanation so that an example program can be written. Subsequently, the physical process of storage will be described, and an extended discussion of arithmetic operations will be included.

Storage. The basic word size in storage is 36 binary digits, or bits. The number of words in storage varies from machine to machine, but it is always some multiple of $2^{12} = 4096$, i.e., 4096, 8192, 16,384, or 32,768 words. The words are uniquely numbered, or *addressed*, so that a particular word may be designated by giving the number of its location (i.e., its address). Conceptually, it is useful to think of the storage in serial fashion, as one big linear array, which is numbered starting with zero.

0000	0001	0002			4095

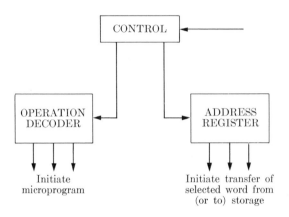

FIGURE 5–7

The storage *access time* is the time needed to transfer the contents of an arbitrary address to another section of the machine or, alternatively, to transfer from another section to storage. This time is measured in microseconds (1 μsec = 0.000001 sec). For the type 704 and 709 computers it is 12 μsec, and for the type 7090 it is approximately 2 μsec.

Control. Since instruction words and data words share the same storage, one or more instructions must be expressible in the basic 36-bit word size. Instructions as referred to here are macroscopic in the sense that they cause the execution of some elementary microprogram which is composed of a very few basic instructions. From the preceding references to storage it is apparent that many bits will be required simply to designate the address of an operand. (Fifteen bits are required to represent the numbers from 0 to 32,768). Other bits are needed to specify the particular operation to be carried out (i.e., to designate the microprogram to be selected). The basic 36-bit instruction word is organized as follows:

Operation		Address

S 1 2   · · ·   17 18–20 21   · · ·   35

The leading bit is labeled S to indicate that its two possibilities are often interpreted as the algebraic sign + or −. With this structure in mind, the control box in the block diagram can be elaborated, as shown in Fig. 5–7. This format permits the specification of only one operand, and the machine is accordingly categorized as processing *single-address* instructions. This

INDEX REGISTER INVOLVED

OPERATION	CONSTANT	✓	INSTRUCTION ADDRESS
S 1 2 3 . . .		17 18–20	21 . . . 35

FIGURE 5–8

is, of course, not a restriction, but the traditional three-operand form, such as $a + b = c$, will require three single-address instructions for its execution.

The arithmetic operations, along with the store operation, were fairly obvious candidates for expression in subroutine form and for the ultimate implementation of these subroutines or microprograms by actual physical circuitry. The question arises whether there are other operations of frequent occurrence and sufficient simplicity to warrant their inclusion as circuitry also. Without computing experience the question is hard to answer. Somewhat dogmatically then, although conventional notation bears out this conclusion, operations involving subscript variables are considered to meet these criteria. Accordingly, special registers called *index registers* are included. These index registers (A, B, C) contain the values of subscript variables, and special instructions are included in the instruction repertoire, which initially set, increment, and test these variables. Testing and incrementing often involve a constant. Thus, for example, in computing $y = \sum_{i=1}^{10} a_i$, incrementing involves the constant 1, and terminating the relation involves the constant 10. To facilitate such operations involving index registers and constants, a variant of the previous instruction format is built into the machine (Fig. 5–8.)

The summation example above illustrates another use of index registers, namely as a means of selecting elements of linear arrays. If consecutive elements of linear arrays occupy consecutive storage locations and if

OPERAND OR INSTRUCTION (STORAGE) REGISTER

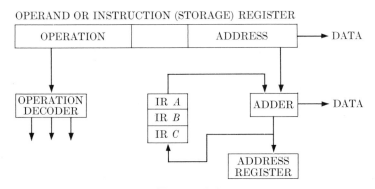

FIGURE 5–9

there is a zeroth element in the array, say a_0, then the address of a_i is the address of a_0 plus the value of i. If the value of the subscript variable i is in an index register, the address of a_i is obtained by adding the value of the index register to the address of a_0. In the first instruction format, the insertion of an index register number in positions 18–20 ($A = 001$, $B = 010$, $C = 100$) will cause the address given in the instruction to be modified by adding (or subtracting) the current value of the designated index register. The block diagram can be expanded (Fig. 5–9) to make this address-modifying feature of the index registers more apparent. The time of execution of the different instructions varies, but the majority take two storage access cycles and therefore, depending on machine types, vary from 4 to 24 μsec.

The purpose of the Instruction Location Counter is virtually described by its name. Instructions are executed in sequence, that is, from consecutive storage locations, until a conditional (or unconditional) transfer instruction is encountered. At that point, if the condition is met, the address given in the instruction designates the next instruction to be executed. This procedure can be simply implemented by a counter which is set to some instruction-location number and then is incremented by one each time an instruction is executed. A transfer instruction simply resets this counter to the address, which is included as part of the instruction. A machine operating in this fashion is called *sequential* as opposed, for instance, to a machine with an instruction code which requires each instruction to contain the address of the succeeding instruction. Note that the Instruction Location Counter fulfills the role of the instruction number n in the Wang machine program (Table 5–1). This counter contains the location of the next instruction to be executed after the current microprogram has been completed. In brief summary, the machines under consideration can be described as fixed-word-length, binary, sequential, single-address machines.

Input-output. The introduction of information into the computing process and the subsequent production of results give rise to two questions: (1) In what form does information directly enter and leave the storage? (2) What representations do human users of the machine employ to introduce instructions and data and to view results? From the operating speeds indicated, it would seem that data input would require an extremely high rate-of-information transfer device. Since machine instructions are executed at rates from 40,000 to 250,000 instructions per second, information whose rate of introduction is measured in seconds (or large fractions of seconds) will produce long delays in computing. Accordingly, magnetic tape with transfer rates varying from 90,000 to 375,000 bits per second is the computer's primary input and output medium. Since magnetic tape does not meet the requirements imposed by human users, equipment *peripheral* to the computing machine is needed to take information from manually produced cards or punched paper tape and transfer these data to magnetic tape. Peripheral equipment is also required to perform the opposite transformation, i.e., to print (or graph) the contents of a magnetic tape for visual inspection. The physical characteristics of these media will be considered in more detail later.

Arithmetic registers. The basic purpose of the arithmetic registers was illustrated by the Wang-machine example program, where the registers were the data-tape cells called a, b, and c. By having the same pair of registers contain the operands for an arithmetic operation and by having the result of the operation always placed in the same location, the arithmetic operations could be simply written as subroutines. The introduction of the *store* subroutine then permitted the use of results as subsequent operands and the introduction of new operands. As indicated earlier, it is a natural development for the arithmetic subroutines and these special registers to be built as distinct elements (i.e., *hardware*) of the machine rather than be a part of common storage. In designing this hardware, an economy can be effected if it is not required that the original operands be preserved upon completion of the operation—as the elementary example did. (Since the operands came from storage, they are still available there for subsequent use.) In addition and subtraction, two full-word-length (36 bits) registers are sufficient, i.e., a can be added to b and the result left in b. The appropriate block diagram is shown in Fig. 5–10. The ADDER is the physical device which repeatedly carries out the elementary binary addition program given in Table 5–1. Two sequences of bits, a and b, pass into the adder, and one sequence, the sum $a + b$, is transmitted from the adder.

Multiplication may be regarded as a repeated addition, but the resultant sum (i.e., product) may be twice full-word size, and the multiplier, which designates the number of additions to be made, must also be stored. At first glance, this situation seems to require two more registers than the simple case of addition does. Actually one additional register, satisfying both the requirements above, can be included. This dual function is possible since the number of digits in the multiplier, which is not preserved,

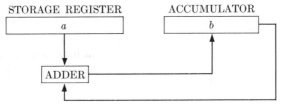

FIGURE 5–10

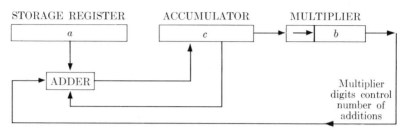

FIGURE 5–11

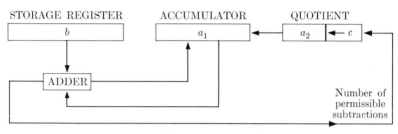

FIGURE 5–12

can be reduced as fast as the product increases in digit size (Fig. 5–11). The accumulating product is shifted right into the multiplier unit at the same time that the low-order multiplier digits are transmitted to control the number of addition cycles.

Division is the reverse process: the divisor is repeatedly subtracted from the dividend, and the number of possible subtractions before a sign change at each digit position is recorded as the quotient. Due to the repeated subtraction, the number of digit positions in the dividend decreases as the number of quotient digits increases and, as would be expected, the same register has a dual role. The operation is $a/b = c$ (Fig. 5–12).

The dividend can be a double-length word ($a_1 + a_2$) and is initially in the accumulator and the quotient register. Upon completion of the operation, the remainder will be in the accumulator, and the quotient will occupy the entire right register, appropriately called the multiplier-quotient register.

The use of these special-purpose registers is certainly not an innovation with electronic machines. The conventional desk computer has a very similar structure. The diagram presented in Fig. 5–13 illustrates the similarities. These mechanical machines have a fixed word length (almost invariably ten decimal digits) and, in performing the basic arithmetic operations, one operand is always entered in the keyboard, which performs the same function as the storage register. For addition, the other operand is in the double-length accumulator, i.e., it has the capacity of

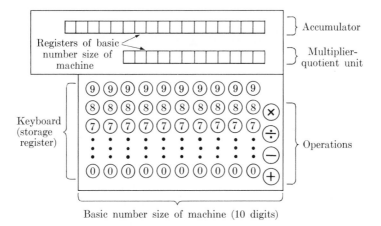

Basic number size of machine (10 digits)

FIGURE 5–13

20 decimal digits. To perform multiplication, a step is required to enter the multiplier into the 10-digit multiplier register; after the multiplication has been completed the product appears in the accumulator. In division, the dividend is entered into the accumulator, and the quotient is developed in the multiplier-quotient register. To initiate an operation, a button must be depressed to make the proper mechanical linkages. In such a "system," the human operator is the instruction and data storage, makes all conditional transfers, and "decodes" the instructions by depressing the proper buttons in the correct sequence.

Machine Language and Components

Since the form of instructions has now been established, it is possible, after explicit definition of a few instructions, to write a program using this basic machine language. In agreement with the instruction format, the operation was designated by as many as 18 binary digits, that is, an 18-bit binary number. Such a string of zeros and ones is not particularly convenient to write or to comprehend, and hence the *octal* representation of binary numbers is almost universally used. In this form, groups of three bits, starting from the right, are replaced by decimal characters according to the following code:

Binary 3-bit group	Decimal character
000	0
001	1
010	2
011	3
100	4
101	5
110	6
111	7

Thus the 18-bit number 101110001101010001 is written 561521. Often the leftmost bit is interpreted as a sign (0 = + and 1 = −), and an equivalent representation of the number above is then −161521. In contexts where confusion with decimal numbers is possible, the octal numbers are enclosed in parentheses with a subscripted eight; for instance, $(561521)_8$.

In describing the specific machine instructions, the following abbreviations will be used: AC for Accumulator; MQ for the Multiplier-Quotient register; ILC for the Instruction Location Counter; IR1, IR2, IR4 for Index Registers A, B, C, respectively. The symbol A will be used to indicate an arbitrary address in storage and C( ), to indicate the *contents of* the register or address enclosed in the parentheses. Thus C(A) means

68

the contents of some address A, and C(AC) means the contents of the accumulator. The role of the storage register is that of an intermediary register between storage and control, or storage and the arithmetic registers, which can now be expressed as (1) C(A) → C(SR) and (2) C(SR) → C(AC). Since the storage register was only an intermediary, this transfer of a word from address A to the accumulator is more simply expressed as C(A) → C(AC). When such a transfer takes place, the source location is not erased, and the value is retained for subsequent use, if desired.

The operation definitions given in Table 6–1 contain a suggestive three-character mnemonic code, the prose description, the symbolic description, and the octal representation of the binary operation.

The first seven instructions may be indexed, i.e., if one of the three index registers is specified as an octal digit (1, 2, or 4) to the right of the operation, the current value of that index register is *subtracted* from the given address before the entire instruction is executed. This subtraction is contrary to human practice, but it is convenient in the design of the machine and raises no essential difficulty.

The last instruction in the list deserves some additional comment. Let us recall for a moment, from the earlier discussion on subroutines, that to avoid rewriting a subroutine on each occurrence it is necessary to alter the final unconditional transfer in the subroutine. Without this possibility of change, the subroutine would, of course, always return to the same sequence of instructions after executing the subroutine. The last instruction facilitates the alteration of the terminal transfer instruction by setting the return point (the n of the elementary subroutine example) in an index register. To illustrate this facility and also for the purposes of writing an example program, a symbolic form of these octal instructions is introduced. A transfer to location $(1000)_8$ setting index register 4 at the same time is written in octal form as 007400 4 01000. Using the mnemonic codes and allowing a slight rearrangement, a more readable form is TSX 1000, 4. The operation is written first, then the address, then the index register (if any), then the constant D (often called the decrement) if applicable. Returning now to the subroutine entry and exit illustration, consider the sequences given below.

Location	Instruction			Location	Instruction	
700	CLA	1200	$C(IR4) = -701$	1000	STO	1006
701	TSX	1000, 4		1001	LDQ	1006
702	STO	1201		1002	MPY	1006
	⋮			1003	STQ	1006
				1004	CLA	1006
		$C(ILC) = 1 - (-701)$		1005	TRA	1, 4
		$= 702$		1006		

TABLE 6-1

Prose description	Symbolic description	Octal representation
(TRA) Transfer—The next instruction to be executed will be the contents of the given address.	$A \to C(ILC)$	$(002000)_s$
(CLA) Clear and Add—The contents of the address given are transferred to the accumulator.	$C(A) \to C(AC)$	050000
(STO) Store—The contents of the accumulator are stored in the address given.	$C(AC) \to C(A)$	060100
(LDQ) Load Multiplier-Quotient—The contents of the address given are transferred to the multiplier-quotient.	$C(A) \to C(MQ)$	056000
(STQ) Store Multiplier Quotient—The contents of the multiplier-quotient are transferred to the address given.	$C(MQ) \to C(A)$	−060000
(ADD) Add—The contents of the address given are added to the contents of the accumulator, and the result is left in the accumulator.	$C(A) + C(AC) \to C(AC)$	040000
(MPY) Multiply—The number in the multiplier-quotient unit is multiplied by the contents of the given address and the product is left in the accumulator and multiplier quotient unit (least significant digits in MQ).	$C(MQ) \times C(A) \to C(AC) + C(MQ)$	020000
(AXT) Address to Index True—The index register designated (k) is set to the true value (as opposed to negative) of the address given.	$A \to C(IRk)$ $k = 1, 2,$ or 4	$077400k$
(TXI) Transfer with Index Incremented—(1) The contents of the address given will be the next instruction. (2) The index register designated (k) will be increased by the constant (D) given.	(1) $A \to C(ILC)$ (2) $C(IRk) + D \to C(IRk)$ $k = 1, 2,$ or 4	1 D k (5 octal digits)
(TXL) Transfer if Index Less or Equal—If the contents of the index register designated (k) are less than or equal to the given constant D, the next instruction will be $C(A)$; otherwise the next instruction in sequence will be executed.	If $C(IRk) \leq D$ $A \to C(ILC)$ otherwise $C(ILC) + 1 \to C(ILC)$ $k = 1, 2,$ or 4	3 D k (5 octal digits)
(TSX) Transfer and Set Index—The next instruction to be executed will be the contents of the given address, and the negative of the address of the current instruction becomes the contents of the designated index register (k).	$-C(ILC) \to C(IRk)$ then $A \to C(ILC)$ $k = 1, 2,$ or 4	$007400k$

Starting in location 1000 is a subroutine which squares whatever number is in the accumulator. It is assumed that the digits of the resultant square do not exceed the capacity of one word; this value is left in the accumulator. However, the important feature is that the final unconditional transfer is determined by the setting of index register 4 and, since the values of index registers are subtractive, the last instruction is, in this case, effectively a transfer to location 702. As an example, the following problem will be programmed. For simplicity it is assumed that the initial data are already in storage, and the problem will be considered completed when all results are stored.

Problem. Given a value for the variable x and values for the linear array $a_0, a_1, a_2, \ldots$, compute the values of a linear array

$$y_i = \sqrt{a_j x^2 + a_{j+1} x + a_{j+2}}$$

where $i = 1, 2, \ldots, 6$ and $j = 0, 3, 6, \ldots$ The appropriate flow chart is presented in Fig. 6–1. The square-root operation required in this computation was not included in the list of definitions (Table 6–1). Hence, square roots are computed by subroutine, that is, a sequence of the operations defined, which is in storage and which is executed by use of the TSX operation, as illustrated earlier, with the square-root operand (i.e., argument) in the accumulator. As an aid in visualizing the storage allocation the block diagram in Fig. 6–2 may be useful. In writing the program, one

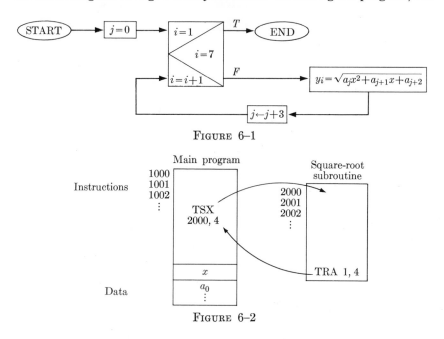

FIGURE 6–1

FIGURE 6–2

TABLE 6–2

Binary form (octal representation)		Symbolic form		
Location	Numerical instruction	Location	Symbolic instruction	Remarks
$(1000)_8$	077400 1 00000	$(1000)_8$	AXT 0, 1	Set j(IR1) to zero
1001	077400 2 77777		AXT −1, 2	Set i(IR2) to −1
1002	−377771 2 01022	TEST	TXL END, 2, −7	Is $i \leq -7$?
1003	056000 1 01034		LDQ A, 1	
1004	020000 0 01024		MPY X	Compute $a_j x$
1005	−060000 0 01023		STQ TEMP	
1006	050000 0 01023		CLA TEMP	
1007	040000 1 01035		ADD A + 1, 1	Compute $a_j x + a_{j+1}$
1010	060100 0 01023		STO TEMP	
1011	056000 0 01023		LDQ TEMP	
1012	020000 0 01024		MPY X	Compute $(a_j x + a_{j+1})x$
1013	−060000 0 01023		STQ TEMP	
1014	050000 0 01023		CLA TEMP	
1015	040000 1 01036		ADD A + 2, 1	Compute $(a_j x + a_{j+1})x + a_{j+2}$
1016	007400 4 02000		TSX 2000, 4	Enter subroutine
1017	060100 2 01025		STO Y, 2	Store square root
1020	177775 1 01021		TXI NEXT, 1, −3	$j = j - 3$
1021	177777 2 01002	NEXT	TXI TEST, 2, −1	$i = i - 1$
1022	002000 0 01022	END	TRA END	Halt
1023		TEMP		Reserve a working location
1024		X		Reserve x
1025		Y	BSS 7	Reserve a block of length 7
1026				
1027				
1030				
1031				
1032				
1033				
1034		A		A-array starts

simply assumes that the subroutine is in storage starting at location $(2000)_8$. The program written in binary (octal representation) and corresponding symbolic forms are presented in Table 6–2. Some observations about this program are:

(1) The locations were assigned sequentially from the starting location, and for convenience only the starting location (or *origin*) was written in the symbolic version. The symbols which were written in the location column (TEST, NEXT, END, TEMP, X, Y, A) are identified with the proper sequentially-assigned location. The octal representation of binary counting produces a carry at 7; that is, the next number after 111 (7) is 1000 (10).

(2) Since the index registers subtract rather than add, the indexing is done negatively to produce an effective addition $(A - (-1) = A + 1)$.

(3) The negative constants appear in complement form; that is, the digits of the constant are subtracted from 7; however, the rightmost nonzero digit is subtracted from 8. The complement of 3 is $77778 - 00003 = 77775$.

(4) Sequential locations are reserved for the data by simply appending the variables at the end of the instructions. When linear arrays are reserved, it is convenient to designate the number of elements in the array. Thus, Y BSS 7 may be expanded to read, "Reserve a block of 7 locations and the starting address is to correspond to the symbol Y." This is an example of a *pseudo-operation*, one which is not really an instruction but gives information about the program or storage allocation.

(5) It is assumed in this problem that the values of A and X are such that none of the intermediate results will exceed the capacity of a register or storage location; i.e., no result will require more than 36 bits.

The numerical columns in the program above are actual machine instructions which, if introduced into the control unit as electronic impulses representing the bits, would cause the execution of the algorithm described. The symbolic columns are not in such a directly acceptable form, but require processing to produce the numerical form before the computation described can be carried out. This initial processing is straightforward and can itself be described in terms of a computer program. The steps, in brief, are:

(1) Starting with the given origins, sequentially assign locations to each line of the symbolic program.

(2) As the assignment is carried out, set up a symbolic correspondence table, entering the symbols and the corresponding locations.

(3) After the symbolic correspondence table has been formed, replace all the symbols with their numerical equivalents, including a proper substitution for the three-letter operation code.

A program designed to carry out this reduction of the symbolic instructions is called an *assembly* program, and the symbolic form of the instructions constitutes an *assembly language*. In practical languages of this sort, numbers are represented in decimal form and the proper conversion is carried out by the program. Virtually no programs are written in numerical machine instructions, but many are written in an assembly language since this form permits one to utilize the special features of the machine. The group of machines under discussion have from 90 to 190 built-in instructions, only eleven of which have been described. Quite obviously, many of these instructions are very specialized and accomplish operations which would require many steps in a more limited instruction repertoire. However, most problems that are readily expressible in mathematical notation are written in a statement type language similar to what has already been described. It should be apparent that such statements must also be translated to basic machine instructions. A program which reduces the statements to these elementary machine-language instructions is called a *translator* or *compiler*.

LANGUAGE HIERARCHY AND TRANSLATION

If an attempt were made to place a machine language, such as the one just described, in the spectrum of languages ranging from Turing machine operations to mathematical notation, it would probably be inserted closer to the former than the latter. As in the Turing machine, the machine operations are not modified by their predecessors or successors; they do not depend on context. That the differences are relatively minor, however, can be illustrated by the descriptions below which show how an expression is evaluated in the two languages.

(1) $y = (a + b \times d)c + (b - d)/c$ (2) Take b
                                                                   Subtract d

  Divide by c

  Store result in t

  Take b

  Multiply by d

  Add a

  Multiply by c

  Add t

  Store result in y

In the first case the order of execution of the arithmetic operations is given by the grouping marks (parentheses) and the context (e.g., in an unparenthesized group multiplication precedes addition). If the calculations can be done only serially—not simultaneously—it is implied from the structure of the expression that the value of some subexpression must be stored. The second description of the computation is essentially the single-address structure of machine language where only one operand is specified; the second operand is assumed to be the result of the immediately preceding step except for the "take" operation which initiates a sequence. Note here that the order of computation is sequential and that the necessary storage of partial results is explicit. The process of translating statements to machine language instructions is essentially that of transforming (1) into (2). The algorithm carrying out this transformation is not very complicated, but at the present time most computer control units are not capable of executing the process. However, one phase of the process, the insertion of the necessary storage steps in a sequential evaluation, is being implemented. There is an intermediate form between (1) and (2) above, which is a statement form (i.e., a horizontal string of symbols) but which requires no grouping marks to determine the order of computation. In this form (*Polish prefix* or *parentheses-free* notation) the calculation proceeds from the right. The rule for writing expressions in this form is to write the operator first, followed immediately on the right

TABLE 6–3

Operation	Current list structure
(1) Put c on the list	$\begin{cases} c \\ d \\ b \end{cases}$
(2) Put d on the list	
(3) Put b on the list	
(4) Perform $-bd = t_1$ and put t_1 on the list in place of d and b	$\begin{cases} c \\ t_1 \end{cases}$
(5) Perform $/t_1c = t_2$ and replace this operation with t_2 on list	t_2
(6) Put c on the list	$\begin{cases} t_2 \\ c \\ d \\ b \end{cases}$
(7) Put d on the list	
(8) Put b on the list	
(9) Perform $\times bd = t_3$ and replace this operation with t_3 on list	$\begin{cases} t_2 \\ c \\ t_3 \end{cases}$
(10) Put a on the list	$\begin{cases} t_2 \\ c \\ t_3 \\ a \end{cases}$
(11) Perform $+at_3 = t_4$ and replace operation on list	$\begin{cases} t_2 \\ c \\ t_4 \end{cases}$
(12) Perform $\times t_4c = t_5$ and replace operands on list	$\begin{cases} t_2 \\ t_5 \end{cases}$
(13) Perform $+t_5t_2 = t_6$ and replace operation on list	t_6
(14) Put y on list	$\begin{cases} t_6 \\ y \end{cases}$
(15) Perform $= yt_6$, completing the evaluation	

by one operand and then the other. Before displaying the example expression in this form, we present some simpler examples which might be helpful.

$$a + b = +ab$$
$$a + b + c = ++abc$$
$$a + b \times c = +a \times bc$$

Expression (1) rewritten in this form is

$$(3) \qquad = y + \times + a \times bdc \; / \; -bdc$$

When this notation is used, the indicated evaluation can be carried out by circuitry, which will insert the proper storage steps for intermediate values. At present a program is still necessary to translate form (1) to form (3).

The following prose description and list structure give an indication of the steps which the circuitry must carry out to perform the right-to-left evaluation of (3). A working linear array, called the *list*, is used in the process. The procedure bears some similarlity to an elementary tape machine in that the control initially points to the rightmost character and then proceeds to the left:

$$= y + \times + a \times bdc \; / \; - bdc$$

In Table 6–3 the phrase, "to put variables on the list," means, "put the current values of the variables on the list."

Since technology permits the construction of a physical machine (as opposed to a sequence of elementary instructions) which carries out such a complicated procedure, perhaps machines can someday be designed to implement a specific language. In any event the problems caused by finite storage will remain.

PHYSICAL DEVICES

It is not the purpose of this section to present a technical exposition of the physical devices used in digital computers, but, simply as a matter of interest rather than necessity, give a general description.

Input-output. Punched cards and paper tape are the most common input media. An example card is reproduced in Fig. 6–3. Note that all the permissible characters have been punched. A card can contain up to 80 characters and each character is represented in a binary-coded form. Since each character position (a column) contains twelve possible punching positions, each character representation requires 12 bits. The particular code adopted is called *Hollerith* code and is not efficient from the point of view of bit utilization since only 46 of the 4096 bit possibilities are used. Although the code was designed years before the advent of electronic computers for use with electromechanical accounting machines, it is the most popular form of input. Punched cards are prepared on a typewriter-like machine called a keypunch. Cards are usually read (i.e., the punched hole code is converted to electrical impulses) electromechanically by passing the card between a row of wire brushes and a solid, conducting

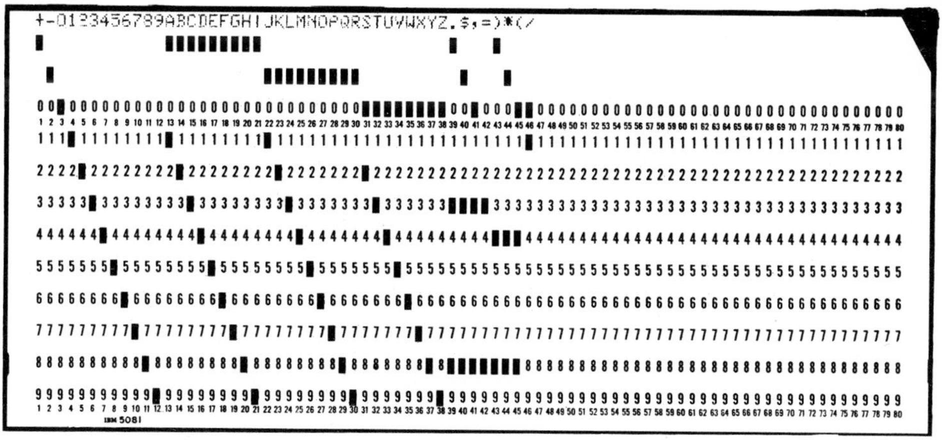

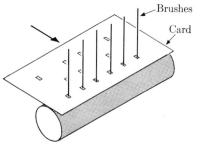

(punch card image)

```
+-01234567 9ABCDEFGHIJKLMNOPQRSTUVWXYZ.$,=)*(/
```

IBM 5081

FIGURE 6–3

platen. The brushes making contact with the platen through the holes
complete an electrical circuit (Fig. 6–4). Cards may be read in this fashion
at a rate of 250 to 1000 cards per minute. The use of cards for output requires a punching machine which is faster than the manually operated
keypunch. Such machines punch cards at rates of 100 to 250 cards per
minute.

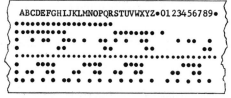

Brushes

Card

FIGURE 6–4

Punched paper tape is the other commonly used input medium. Figure
6–5 presents a section of an 8-channel tape showing the code for the
alphabet and numbers. Actually only six of the channels are used to

ABCDEFGHIJKLMNOPQRSTUVWXYZ●0123456789●

FIG. 6–5. Example tape. The characters on this tape are typewritten.

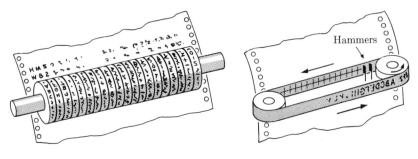

FIGURE 6–6   FIGURE 6–7

represent characters; one is used as a check bit and another is reserved for use as a tape-feeding indicator. The remaining six positions across the tape provide $2^6 = 64$ possibilities of which 46 are utilized. Note that the numbers are represented by the binary-coded-form which was described earlier. The tape is prepared by a typewriter which produces normal printed copy as well as the tape. Such tapes are read at 150 to 1000 characters per second and are machine-punched (not manual) at 15 to 60 characters per second.

The ultimate output is, of course, the printed page, although punched cards or tape may be regarded as an intermediate form of output. A typewriter can print at the rate of ten characters per second. Line printers, which are constructed in a variety of ways, can print 150 to 1000 lines per minute, with one line containing 120 to 132 characters. The slowest of these printers has rotary printing wheels which are positioned and then pressed against a platen (Fig. 6–6).

Higher speeds are attained by chain or wire printers. In a chain printer the type faces are on a continuously moving horizontal chain and are individually pressed against the platen at the proper time (Fig. 6–7). The wire printer does not have a set of type faces, but the proper character is made by impressing a number of wires, selected from a 5×7 grid, against the paper. Figure 6–8, which shows the ends of the wires, illustrates how the character "B" would be printed; i.e., the wires represented by dark dots would be forced against the paper through an inked ribbon.

FIGURE 6–8

These brief descriptions refer to direct printing processes. Higher output rates are possible if photographic (or electrographic) techniques are used. For instance, the characters can be displayed on a cathode-ray tube, similar to a television picture tube, and the display is then automatically photographed. Extremely high outputs can be achieved by this method, but additional processing is required.

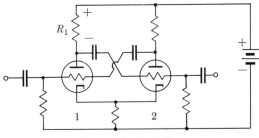

FIG. 6–9. Flip-flop.

Storage. The idea of storing numbers for automatic calculation is not new. In the 1850's, Charles Babbage, an Englishman, designed and built a mechanical "Analytical Engine" which stored numbers by positioning wheels, and then operated on these numbers by gearing sets of such positioned wheels together. The machine was not successful because the complicated mechanical linkages required could not be produced accurately or efficiently enough to permit proper operation. It wasn't until equivalent electronic circuits were developed, which permitted the amplification and reshaping of the impulses used to represent the numbers, that the automatic digital computer became practical. During World War II, the ENIAC computer was developed to compute fire-control tables. In this machine, each decimal digit stored required ten vacuum tubes. These tubes were connected as two-state devices; they were conducting or they were not, and of the ten the one which was conducting indicated which of the ten possible digits was being represented. Circuits of this type are called flip-flops; an example schematic is presented in Fig. 6–9. Suppose that 1 is the cutoff tube (i.e., the grid ($-\!\!\bigwedge\!\!\bigwedge\!\!\bigwedge\!\!$) is sufficiently negative so that the electron current cannot pass from the cathode ($\bigcap$) to the plate ($\perp$) as the battery tends to force it). If the grid of the cutoff tube is made positive by introducing a positive impulse, it will conduct, and the resultant current through it will cause a negative voltage drop across R_1. If this voltage drop is transmitted to the grid of tube 2 as indicated, the second tube will be cutoff. The conducting tube, 1, can be regarded as the *stored* positive impulse.

This type of storage is not very economical when tens of thousands of digits are involved. Indeed, among the necessary hundreds of thousands of tubes, there would always be a sufficient number of tube failures to make such a scheme unworkable. One obvious improvement was to utilize the equipment more effectively by using the binary system of number representation rather than the extremely inefficient one-out-of-ten binary coded decimal. Also, there was a definite need for replacing the arrangement consisting of a complete vacuum tube circuit for each bit by simpler bistable physical elements. Several devices have been tried but variations

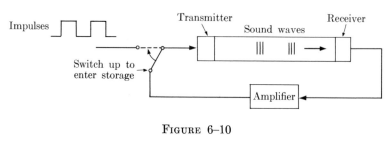

FIGURE 6–10

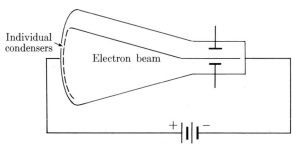

FIGURE 6–11

of magnetic storage have been the most successful. Before considering these variants it is worth while to mention two other types of storage which have been successfully used.

With *circulating* storage the impulse (unit of information) is transformed into a wave which is propagated through some time-consuming medium, received at the other end, retransmitted through the medium, received, etc. Acoustic delay lines have been used as storage in this manner, as illustrated in the diagram of Fig. 6–10.

Electrostatic storage elements have also been used. The basic element is the condenser whose charged or discharged state provides the two alternatives. This principle has been used most successfully in conjunction with cathode-ray tubes where individual spots on the face of the tube (which is similar to the picture tube in a television set) are the individual capacitors. The beam of electrons in the tube can be regarded as a conductor which can be readily connected to any of the tiny individual condensers, either to charge them or determine their state of charge (see Fig. 6–11).

Magnetic devices take more power to operate than electrostatic ones, but magnetically stored information is more permanent (electric charges tend to recombine and redistribute), and there is a certain built-in threshold in magnetic materials which helps to distinguish information from random currents, impulses, etc.

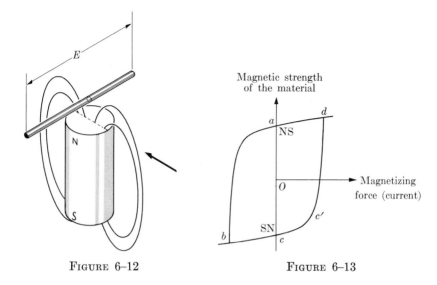

FIGURE 6-12   FIGURE 6-13

The physical facts relevant to magnetic storage are:

(1) Faraday's law. A voltage, E, is induced in a conductor which has some relative motion with respect to some magnetic lines of force (Fig. 6-12). The voltage is induced by physically moving the conductor or the source of the magnetic lines, or by the alteration of the lines of force.

(2) Ferromagnetic materials can be permanently magnetized and tend to saturate; that is, continuously increasing the magnetizing force applied to a material does not increase the resultant magnetization indefinitely. This fact can be expressed as a graph (Fig. 6-13). If the material is initially a south-north magnet (point c), changing its polarity to north-south requires sufficient magnetizing force to get to point d. When this force is removed, the material will be magnetized north-south at point a. An insufficient force would trace the curve only to c' and would not result in a polarity reversal. This threshold or "hysteresis" property is used for high-speed magnetic storage.

Both magnetic tapes and drums involve motion of the magnetic material so that conductors, or perhaps more descriptively, small electromagnets, near the moving surface can be used to *write* local magnets on the surface by passing currents through the conductors, and *read* the magnetized areas by sensing the induced voltage in the conductors as a magnetized area passes by (Fig. 6-14). The local magnets on these ferromagnetic drum and tape surfaces can be written very densely, from 200 to 1400 per linear inch. Magnetic-tape transfer rates have already been discussed. A typical transfer rate for a drum is 96 μsec per 36-bit number. Note that the drum is cyclical, i.e., a mark that is written will be under scan for potential read-

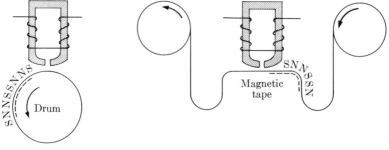

FIGURE 6–14

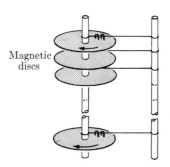

FIGURE 6–15

ing at every revolution of the constant speed drum. Such relatively ready access to stored information suggests that the drum be organized in locations or addresses, as previously described, so that each number may be individually referred to. The tapes, however, require a time-consuming mechanical reversal of the rotating reels to read information which has already been written. The implication of this fact is that tapes are generally used to store information which can be treated serially and in large blocks. Hence each position on the tape is not assigned a unique address but is simply a sequential list of large blocks of information.

Another device which depends on motion is a cross between drum and tape storage. This so-called *disc* storage is a constantly rotating set of discs whose surfaces may be magnetized. Aside from the much larger recording surface, disc storage differs from drum storage in that the reading and writing electromagnets (called *heads*) are movable along a radius of the discs and require mechanical positioning (Fig. 6–15). With this type of equipment the worst access time, the maximum time required to position the reading-writing heads, is measured in milliseconds, while the worst case with magnetic tape spacing (over 2400 feet of tape) requires about a minute.

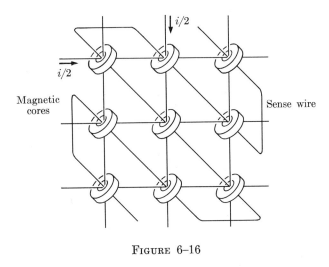

FIGURE 6–16

FIGURE 6–17

All these devices involve mechanical motion and suffer from the relatively long attendant delays. By far the most successful (but not the least
expensive) high-speed magnetic storage is core storage, which uses the
hysteresis properties of small ferromagnetic toroids to create a stationary
storage medium.   These magnetic cores are arranged in square arrays,
generally 64 on a side for a total of 4096 in an array, and information can
be stored or read as the magnetic state of only one core at a time.   This one-
at-a-time restriction means that for rapid access there would be one core
plane for every bit of a binary number to be stored.   Thirty-six such planes
would permit the storage of 4096 36-bit numbers.   To illustrate the operation, a small 3×3 plane is drawn in Fig. 6–16.   The cores can be regarded
as circular magnets whose lines of magnetic force can have two possible
orientations, clockwise or counterclockwise.   A current, provided it is
large enough, passing through the center of a core is sufficient to magnetize
the core in one of the two polarities.   A current in the opposite direction will
produce the other polarity (Fig. 6–17).   If the hysteresis properties of these
cores are such that a current of $i/2$ passing through the core does not
change its magnetic state, but a current of magnitude i does, the state of a
single core in a plane array can be set or ascertained.   As indicated in the
core-plane diagram (Fig. 6–18), if a current of magnitude $i/2$ is passed

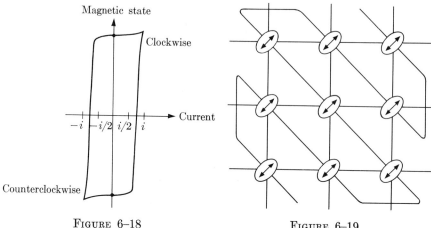

FIGURE 6–18   FIGURE 6–19

through one horizontal wire and one vertical wire, only the core in which they intersect will enclose a current of i sufficient to change its state, and by this means one bit is "written" in a core. To "read," a current i is passed through a selected core in the same way. If the core is already in the state which the current i would produce, there is no change in magnetic state, hence no change in the magnetic lines of force, and therefore no induced voltage in the diagonal sense wire. Alternatively, if the current causes a state reversal, there is a complete switch in the magnetic lines, inducing a voltage in the sense wire. In this manner, the state of the interrogated core is determined. Since the determination may destroy the information, it is necessary to automatically rewrite the information, and this is done. The cores vary in diameter from 0.080 inches to 0.020 inches, and switching times of the order of one microsecond are attainable.

As a preview of things to come, laboratory work is under way investigating techniques of depositing very thin films of magnetic materials which would permit faster switching times. Instead of toroids, thin circular spots (thickness measured in terms of angstroms, i.e., wavelengths of light) are deposited from vapor on some supporting stratum. The spots are deposited in the presence of a strong magnetic field and have a preferred magnetic orientation. The reading and writing wires do not pass through the spots but underneath the spots as shown in Fig. 6–19. As before, the spot can be magnetized in only two states and coincident current is required to switch states. The reduced dimensions permit less power consumption and much faster storage access. Information can be written, i.e., a magnetic state changed, in approximately one nanosecond (1 nanosecond = 10^{-9} seconds).

Arithmetic registers. The detailed structure of arithmetic devices is beyond the scope of this text. The following material has been included to illustrate (1) that arithmetic operations are expressible in terms of the basic logical or Boolean operations and (2) that the basic Boolean operations can be simply implemented by physical devices.

The operations of *and* ($\wedge$) and *or* ($\vee$) were defined by means of a table, often called a *truth* table, which displayed all the possible values of the operands and result. The elementary binary addition problem for the Wang-machine program was defined in the same way. It is possible to express this addition problem in terms of the Boolean operations by introducing another unary Boolean operation, *not* ($\neg$).

a	$\neg a$
0	1
1	0

Using this operation with the others, one can represent the simple addition as a Boolean function. The table below develops the resultant expression from right to left by taking the original operands, a and b, and applying the logical operations.

Desired result		Operands		(1)		(2)	(3)	(4)	(5) $(a \wedge \neg b)$ $\vee (\neg a \wedge b)$
c_1	c_2	a	b	$\neg a$	$\neg b$	$a \wedge \neg b$	$\neg a \wedge b$	$a \wedge b = c_1$	$= c_2$
0	0	0	0	1	1	0	0	0	0
0	1	0	1	1	0	0	1	0	1
0	1	1	0	0	1	1	0	0	1
1	0	1	1	0	0	0	0	1	0

Thus the two one-digit results of the binary addition $a + b$ can be expressed as

$$c_1 = a \wedge b$$
$$c_2 = (a \wedge \neg b) \vee (\neg a \wedge b)$$

The corresponding flow chart is shown in Fig. 6–20. If the boxes labeled

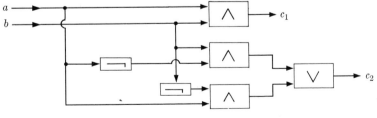

FIGURE 6–20

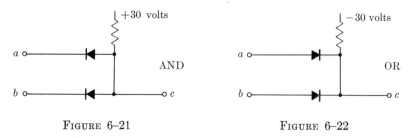

FIGURE 6–21   FIGURE 6–22

with the Boolean operators can be implemented by circuits, they can then be connected as shown in the figure, and the simple addition accomplished. The *and* and *or* circuits can be made from elements called diodes (━◄━◄±) which conduct current in the direction of the arrow if the arrow side is positive with respect to the other side; otherwise the diode will not conduct. If 1 is considered to be +5 volts and zero as −5 volts, the circuit shown in Fig. 6–21 produces the *and* operation. If either a or b is at −5, a current path exists which puts point c at −5 (i.e., 0) but if both are at + 5, the result c will be at +5 (i.e., 1).

A circuit to implement the *or* operation is presented in Fig. 6–22. Since the diodes are turned around if either a or b is at +5, a path exists to make c = +5 also, i.e., the result is c = 1. The *not* operation is simply an inversion, the substitution of +5 for −5 and vice versa. A simple tube amplifier or transistor circuit can accomplish such functions. Elementary circuit packages such as these can be combined to produce the necessary arithmetic and control registers.

Number Systems and Arithmetic

Binary numbers have been repeatedly mentioned, and yet this notation has not been formally explained. Before proceeding with this explanation, it may be worth while to indulge in some theoretical discussion of numbers and counting. Certainly the most elementary representation of counts or natural numbers is simply to make a mark for each item counted; the totality of marks can then be regarded as a symbol for the number. One method of condensing such symbols is to represent groups of marks by a separate symbol and use such a symbol as a replacement for the designated number of marks, e.g., twenty-three represented by XXIII. Rather than write a multiplicity of the same symbol, a more systematic approach is to write a sequence of simple numbers which are understood multipliers of basic groups of marks. As an example, in the British monetary system a typical price (i.e., the number of pennies or pence) is written 2/16/8, meaning 2 pounds, 16 shillings, and 8 pence. But a pound is 240 pence, and a shilling is 12 pence; so in pence this price is $2 \times 240 + 16 \times 12 + 8 = 680$ pence. The forms 2/16/8 and 680 are different representations of the same number; the difference is due to the grouping assumptions used in counting. In both instances, there are understood multipliers which are determined by the *position* of the digits, 240, 12 and 1 for the first form, and 100, 10, 1 for the second. The multipliers in the second case are systematic in that they can be expressed as integral powers of one number, i.e., 10. It is systematic notation of this type that is of interest here, although this monetary example illustrates that there are other possibilities. Although it hardly bears mention, a notation to be useful must be capable of representing all numbers. It is quite useless to represent the pounds-shillings-pence price by three adjacent decimal digits (e.g., $364 = 3/6/4$) since, with only ten distinct decimal digit symbols, 10 or 11 pence cannot be represented nor can 10 to 19 shillings.

With systematic positional notation, a number composed of an integral and fractional part is written $d_n d_{n-1} \ldots d_0 . d_{-1} d_{-2} \ldots d_{-m}$ and means

$$d_n b^n + d_{n-1} b^{n-1} + \cdots + d_0 + d_{-1} b^{-1} + d_{-2} b^{-2} + \cdots + d_{-m} b^{-m}$$

The point, often called the radix point, separates the integral from the fractional part. The integer b is called the base, and there must be b distinct symbols to represent the digits which are labeled d (digits). Since the notation is positional, that is, the position of the digit relative to the point determines the power of b by which the digit is to be multiplied, one of the b symbols must correspond to a null multiplier, or zero. Such a symbol is needed simply to mark the position; considered as a multiplier, it has no effect on the magnitude of the number being represented.

As a concrete example, consider the decimal number

$$107.375 = 1 \times 10^2 + 0 \times 10^1 + 7 \times 10^0 + 3 \times 10^{-1}$$
$$+ 7 \times 10^{-2} + 5 \times 10^{-3}$$

In the decimal system the base $b = 10$, and there are ten symbols, 0, 1, 2, . . . , 9, which are used as digits. The same number expressed in binary form ($b = 2$) requires only two symbols, 0 and 1.

$$(107.375)_{10} = (1101011.011)_2$$
$$= 1 \times 2^6 + 1 \times 2^5 + 0 \times 2^4 + 1 \times 2^3 + 0 \times 2^2 + 0 \times 2^1$$
$$+ 1 + 0 \times 2^{-1} + 1 \times 2^{-2} + 1 \times 3^{-3}$$
$$= 64 + 32 + 8 + 2 + 1 + \tfrac{1}{4} + \tfrac{1}{8}$$
$$= 107\tfrac{3}{8} = 107.375$$

The question is sometimes raised as to why it is permissible to use decimal numbers in the exponential terms of the expanded polynomial form of the binary number above. The answer is simply convenience. The factors are *understood* in the positional form of the number, and our built-in preference for the decimal system makes 2^6 more understandable than its binary equivalent 10^{110}.

The next steps are to go through some examples of binary arithmetic and then consider the problem of conversion from one number system to another. The binary system is emphasized because of its utility in electronic digital computers; it should be understood that any integer base can be selected for use with positional notation so long as the appropriate number of symbols is used. It is worth noting at this point that the conversion of binary numbers to other bases which are powers of 2 (i.e., 4, 8, 16, . . .) is very simple and, as indicated before, involves only a grouping of the binary digits. For instance, since every third power of 2 is a power of 8, three binary digits, starting at the radix point, may be written as an octal (base 8) digit, and the resultant number is octal. The first eight binary integers are repeated below to illustrate such a regrouping conversion.

000	0	100	4
001	1	101	5
010	2	110	6
011	3	111	7

By making these substitutions in the example previously cited, one obtains the octal equivalent:

$$(1\ 101\ 011.011)_2 = (153.3)_8$$
$$(153.3)_8 = 1 \times 8^2 + 5 \times 8 + 3 + 3 \times \tfrac{1}{8}$$
$$= 64 \quad + 40 \quad + 3 + \tfrac{3}{8} = 107.375$$

When there is no simple power relationship between bases, the conversions cannot be accomplished by grouping but must be done arithmetically.

BINARY AND OCTAL ARITHMETIC

Addition. The binary addition table has already been displayed, but it is included here in the more conventional form, i.e. the possible digits head the columns and rows, and the results appear in the body of the table.

+	0	1
0	0	1
1	1	10

The octal addition table is presented in Table 7–1.

TABLE 7–1

+	0	1	2	3	4	5	6	7
0	0	1	2	3	4	5	6	7
1	1	2	3	4	5	6	7	10
2	2	3	4	5	6	7	10	11
3	3	4	5	6	7	10	11	12
4	4	5	6	7	10	11	12	13
5	5	6	7	10	11	12	13	14
6	6	7	10	11	12	13	14	15
7	7	10	11	12	13	14	15	16

Since all positional notation is just a shorthand form of writing a polynomial involving powers of the base, it is apparent that the familiar rule of "lining up the point before adding" is simply another way of saying that the coefficients of like powers of the base are added. In the arithmetic examples that follow, the problem is done in decimal, octal, and binary arithmetic, and carries are indicated where they occur.

Decimal	Octal	Binary
1		11 11
27.125	33.1	11011.001
+ 9.5	+ 11.4	+ 1001.1
$(36.625)_{10}$	$(44.5)_8$	$(100100.101)_2$

Note that the octal result could be obtained from the binary sum by making the appropriate 3-bit substitutions.

Subtraction. Subtraction could also be described by writing subtraction tables and then repeatedly applying the tables to problems, borrowing when necessary, to produce the difference. However, it is instructive to describe subtraction in the manner in which it is carried out in most computers, i.e., by complementing and adding. This procedure permits the same economy of operation that is desirable in the machine. A simple transformation on negative numbers eliminates the need for a subtraction table, and only the addition table is needed. This scheme works only when the numbers are of fixed length (as they are in the computer described earlier), and some decimal examples using five decimal-digit numbers are shown to illustrate the procedure.

$$17326 - 8140 = 17326 + (100000 - 8140) - 100000$$

The term in parentheses is $(100000 - 8140) = 91860$. Adding,

$$\begin{array}{r} 17326 \\ + 91860 \\ \hline 109186 \end{array}$$

and subtracting 100000 by simply dropping the high-order 1, one obtains the correct result, 9186. The number 91860 is called the 10's complement (or, more generally, the radix complement) and is obtained by the rule of "starting from the right, subtract the first nonzero digit from 10 and all succeeding digits to the left from 9." In summary then, if the largest of the fixed-size decimal numbers under consideration is $10^n - 1$, the subtraction problem $a - b$ is changed to $a + (10^n - b) - 10^n$, where $10^n - b$ is the 10's complement of b. The complementing rule given above, and hence the corresponding circuitry, can be simplified if the *radix-diminished* complement is formed which, for the decimal case, is the 9's complement. With this approach, the example problem becomes:

$$17326 - 8140 = 17326 + (100000 - 1 - 8140) - (100000 - 1)$$
$$= 17326 + (99999 - 8140) - 100000 + 1$$
$$= 17326 + 91859 - 100000 + 1$$
$$= \begin{array}{r} 17326 \\ 91859 \\ \hline 109185 \end{array} - 100000 + 1$$
$$= 09185 + 1 = 9186$$

Note that the process of subtracting 100000 and adding 1 may be considered as simply an "end-around" carry from the leftmost digit into the units digit, as shown below:

$$109185 = 9186$$

It is seen that the complement above is much more easily obtained since every digit is treated alike, i.e., simply subtracted from 9. The general form of decimal-diminished complement subtraction is

$$a - b = a + (10^n - 1 - b) - 10^n + 1$$

The parenthesized term can be formed without formally subtracting (digit by digit complementing), and the subtraction of 10^n and addition of 1 is implemented as an end-around carry. Reversing the signs on the example illustrates the production of a negative result.

$$\begin{array}{r} 8140 \\ -17326 \end{array} \qquad \text{9's complement} \qquad \begin{array}{r} 8140 \\ +82673 \\ \hline 090813 \end{array}$$

The fact that the leftmost digit is zero (no end-around carry) indicates that it is a complement; it is less than 10^5. By complementing and appending a minus sign one obtains the conventional form of this result:

$$\begin{array}{r} 99999 \\ -90813 \\ \hline 09186 \end{array} \rightarrow -09186$$

The following subtraction problems are carried out by adding the diminished complement.

Decimal	Octal	Binary
27.125	33.1	11011.001
− 9.5	− 11.4	− 1001.1

$$\downarrow \qquad\qquad \downarrow \qquad\qquad \downarrow$$

Decimal	Octal	Binary
^{11} 27.125	^{11} 33.1	^{1111} ^{11} 11011.001
+ 90.499	+ 66.3	+ 10110.011
117.624	121.4	110001.100

| $(17.625)_{10}$ | $(21.5)_8$ | $(10001.101)_2$ |

The octal-diminished complement is formed by subtracting each digit from 7 and the binary, by subtracting each digit from 1. Binary complementation is particularly simple since it amounts to reversing every bit to 1 if it is 0, and to 0 if it is 1. The same problems with reversed signs become:

Decimal	Octal	Binary
9.5	11.4	1001.1
− 27.125	− 33.1	− 110011.001

$$\downarrow \qquad\qquad \downarrow \qquad\qquad \downarrow$$

Decimal	Octal	Binary
^{11} 9.5	^{1} 11.4	^{1} ^{11} 1001.1
+ 72.874	+ 44.6	+ 001100.110
082.374	056.2	010110.010

| Complement | Complement | Complement |
| $(-17.625)_{10}$ | $(-21.5)_8$ | $(-01001.101)_2$ |

Multiplication. The binary multiplication table is equally simple.

×	0	1
0	0	0
1	0	1

If this table were arranged in columnar form to define $a \times b = c$, one would recognize that it is the same as the *and* operation which has already been discussed. As a result of this similarity, the *and* is often called the

TABLE 7–2

×	0	1	2	3	4	5	6	7
0	0	0	0	0	0	0	0	0
1	0	1	2	3	4	5	6	7
2	0	2	4	6	10	12	14	16
3	0	3	6	11	14	17	22	25
4	0	4	10	14	20	24	30	34
5	0	5	12	17	24	31	36	43
6	0	6	14	22	30	36	44	52
7	0	7	16	25	34	43	52	61

logical product and, where the context is clear, is indicated by the operators ·, ×, or simply by juxtaposition of the operands. The octal multiplication table is presented in Table 7–2. Since in multiplication the sign of the result is determined from the signs of the operands according to the table below (note that this table refers to single-digit sums, neglecting the

Sign a	Sign b	Sign c
+	+	+
+	−	−
−	+	−
−	−	+

carry), examples of multiplications involving only positive numbers will suffice.

Decimal	Octal	Binary
107.5	153.4	1101011.1
× 8.75	10.6	1000.11
5375	12050	11010111
7525	1534	11010111
8600		11010111
$(940.625)_{10}$	$(1654.50)_8$	$(1110101100.101)_2$

The binary case is particularly simple; it is effectively just a matter of shifting and adding.

Division. Division tables are not conventionally employed since this operation is not "closed." The latter term means that division, unlike addition and multiplication, does not necessarily produce integral results if integral operands are used. Division is the inverse of the multiplication operation and can be carried out by repeated subtractions. The complement-and-add procedure described could be used to perform the necessary subtractions, but to shorten the problems illustrated, direct subtraction will be used. In spite of the fact that no subtraction tables have been introduced, the steps should be apparent. As before, positive operands are used since the signs of the operands and results in $a/b = c + R$ (R is the remainder) are simply determined according to the table below.

Sign a	Sign b	Sign c	Sign R
+	+	+	+
+	−	−	+
−	+	−	−
−	−	+	−

The following examples are the reverse of the multiplication problems, and therefore no remainders are produced. In all these examples the determination of the point position is directly analogous to the familiar decimal rules, as it must be, since moving the point in positional-notation numbers corresponds to multiplying by some power of the base.

Decimal	Octal	Binary
8.75	10.6	1000.11
1075 | 9406.25	1534 | 16545.0	11010111 | 11101011001.01
8600	1534	11010111
8062	12050	101000010
7525	12050	11010111
5375	0	11010111
5375		11010111
0		0

Division by zero is, of course, not possible, and divisors must be large enough in magnitude relative to the dividend so that the quotient does not exceed the fixed word size of the machine.

Conversion. The procedure of converting a number from one base to another is readily understandable if the polynomial form of a positional number is borne in mind:

$$d_n b^n + d_{n-1} b^{n-1} + \cdots + d_0 + d_{-1} b^{-1} + d_{-2} b^{-2} + \cdots + d_{-m} b^{-m}$$

It is important to remember that the coefficients are all less than b. Consider for the moment only the integer portion (i.e., only the nonnegative subscripts):

$$N = d_n b^n + d_{n-1} b^{n-1} + \cdots + d_1 b + d_0$$

If N is divided by the base b, the remainder will be the rightmost digit d_0

TABLE 7–3

Decimal integer to octal	Decimal integer to binary

Decimal integer to octal:

$$7$$
$$8\,\overline{)\,59}$$
$$\underline{56}$$
$$3 \;=\; \text{Remainder 1}$$

$$0$$
$$8\,\overline{)\,7} \;=\; \text{Remainder 2}$$

$$\therefore\ (59)_{10} \;=\; (73)_8$$

Decimal integer to binary:

$$29$$
$$2\,\overline{)\,59}$$
$$\underline{58}$$
$$1 \;=\; \text{Remainder 1}$$

$$14$$
$$2\,\overline{)\,29}$$
$$\underline{28}$$
$$1 \;=\; \text{Remainder 2}$$

$$7$$
$$2\,\overline{)\,14}$$
$$\underline{14}$$
$$0 \;=\; \text{Remainder 3}$$

$$3$$
$$2\,\overline{)\,7}$$
$$\underline{6}$$
$$1 \;=\; \text{Remainder 4}$$

$$1$$
$$2\,\overline{)\,3}$$
$$\underline{2}$$
$$1 \;=\; \text{Remainder 5}$$

$$0$$
$$2\,\overline{)\,1} \;=\; \text{Remainder 6}$$

$$\therefore\ (59)_{10} \;=\; (111011)_2$$

since b divides evenly into all other terms:

$$\frac{N}{b} = d_n b^{n-1} + d_{n-1} b^{n-2} + \cdots + d_1 + \frac{d_0}{b}$$

Now, if N/b is again divided by b, the remainder will be the digit d_1. Continuing to divide by b in this fashion will isolate as a remainder every one of the digits of the number expressed in the base b. To carry out the division, N was originally expressed in some base (presumably different from b), and the division just described would have to be carried out using the arithmetic rules appropriate for the original base of N. As examples of integer conversion, Table 7–3 shows the conversion of $(59)_{10}$ to octal and binary notations.

The obvious way for a human to convert *to* decimal form is to evaluate the polynomial by means of decimal arithmetic, e.g.,

$$(237)_8 = 2 \times 64 + 3 \times 8 + 7 = (159)_{10}$$

A binary machine cannot use decimal arithmetic, but the method of division by the new base (i.e., 10) remains applicable.

Octal integer to decimal
(by octal arithmetic)

$$
\begin{array}{r}
5 \\
12\,\overline{)73} \\
62 \\
\hline
11
\end{array}
= \text{Remainder } 1 = (9)_{10}
$$

$$
\begin{array}{r}
0 \\
12\,\overline{)5}
\end{array}
= \text{Remainder } 2 = (5)_{10}
$$

$$\therefore (73)_8 = (59)_{10}$$

Binary integer to decimal
(by binary arithmetic)

$$
\begin{array}{r}
101 \\
1010\,\overline{)111011} \\
1010 \\
\hline
10011 \\
1010 \\
\hline
1001
\end{array}
= \text{Remainder } 1 = (9)_{10}
$$

$$
\begin{array}{r}
0 \\
1010\,\overline{)101}
\end{array}
= \text{Remainder } 2 = (5)_{10}
$$

$$\therefore (111011)_2 = (59)_{10}$$

The conversion of fractions is also a repetitive procedure, but to isolate digits it is necessary to multiply:

$$F = d_{-1}b^{-1} + d_{-2}b^{-2} + \cdots + d_{-m}b^{-m}$$
$$bF = d_{-1} + d_{-2}b^{-1} + \cdots + d_{-m}b^{-m+1}$$

By multiplying by the base, the leftmost digit becomes the integral part of the resultant product. Now, however, there is no guarantee that the process will terminate even if the fraction F expressed in the original number system was a terminating decimal. For example, consider the conversion of the decimal fraction 0.8 to octal and binary.

Decimal fraction to octal		Decimal fraction to binary	
$8 \times 0.8 = 6.4$	Integer 1 = 6	$2 \times 0.8 = 1.6$	Integer 1 = 1
$8 \times 0.4 = 3.2$	Integer 2 = 3	$2 \times 0.6 = 1.2$	Integer 2 = 1
$8 \times 0.2 = 1.6$	Integer 3 = 1	$2 \times 0.2 = 0.4$	Integer 4 = 0
$8 \times 0.6 = 4.8$	Integer 4 = 4	$2 \times 0.4 = 0.8$	Integer 5 = 0
$8 \times 0.8 = 6.4$	Integer 5 = 6	$2 \times 0.8 = 1.6$	Integer 6 = 1
$\vdots$	$\vdots$	$\vdots$	$\vdots$

$$\therefore (0.8)_{10} = (0.631463146\ldots)_8 \qquad (0.8)_{10} = (0.1100110011001100\ldots)_2$$

Again, the most natural way of converting in the other direction, i.e., *to* decimal, is to evaluate in decimal arithmetic the polynomial involving powers of $1/b$ that the fraction represents. The other approach is to use the proper arithmetic for the given form of the fraction and convert by multiplication as shown above. It is useful here to proceed by the first method since the term-by-term evaluation of the polynomial, starting with the constant term, shows how many terms (digits) are needed to make an accurate reconversion.

Octal fraction to decimal
(by decimal arithmetic)

$$(0.631)_8 = 6 \times \tfrac{1}{8} + 3 \times \tfrac{1}{64} + 1 \times \tfrac{1}{512}$$
$$= 0.75 + 0.046875 + 0.001953125$$
$$= (0.7988228125)_{10}$$

Binary fraction to decimal
(by decimal arithmetic)

$$(0.110011 = \tfrac{1}{2} + \tfrac{1}{4} + \tfrac{1}{32} + \tfrac{1}{64}$$
$$= 0.5 + 0.25 + 0.03125 + 0.015625$$
$$= (0.796875)_{10}$$

If the decimal results were to be rounded to two decimal places, two digits of the octal fraction would be sufficient to give correct results; but six digits would be required in the binary fraction. From the equivalence of the octal and binary digits this is what one would expect. A rule of thumb is that three and one-third binary digits are required for each decimal digit.

SCALING

When only a fixed number of digits are available to represent a number, as in a fixed word-length machine, the range of numbers which can be represented is quite limited unless *understood multipliers* are assumed. To elaborate on this statement and to illustrate what follows, decimal numbers expressed by ten digits and a sign will be used, but the comments apply to fixed-length numbers using bases other than 10. It would be just as applicable, though not as familiar, to use a 35-bit binary word and sign. In fact, the rule of thumb concerning the ratio of $3\tfrac{1}{3}$ binary bits per decimal digit indicates that the number ranges would be about the same as the 10-digit decimal examples.

In ten decimal digits the largest and smallest numbers (in absolute value) which can be represented exclusive of zero are 9999999999. and 0.0000000001 or $10^{10} - 1$ and 10^{-10}. These extremes seem generous, but in physical problems it is not unusual to encounter numbers outside this range. Moreover, it is not possible to express numbers near the low end of this range to a large number of significant digits. For instance 1.2683×10^{-8} is within the range, but cannot be represented in ten digits unless some multiplicative factor is assumed, for example, $0.000000012683 = 0.0000012683 \times 10^{-2}$. Since a number is simply a polynomial in the base b, multiplication by an integral power of b (1) results in a shift of the number relative to a fixed decimal point and (2) increases or decreases the magnitude of the number, i.e., it is a *scale factor*. Thus every number can have an understood scale factor (which may be $10^0 = 1$) and hence the basic number can be regarded as written with the decimal point in a fixed place. Among the possible choices for this standard form, the two most obvious alternatives are to treat all numbers either as integers (with implied scale factor) or as fractions (with implied scale factor). The fractional representation is most often accepted, so that a number is written $\pm.d_1d_2 \ldots d_{10}$ ($\times 10^n$), where 10^n does not appear explicitly but is understood.

The evaluation of an expression can be implemented in two distinct parts: (1) the digit-by-digit applications of the arithmetic rules to fractions, called *arithmetic processing*. (2) The appropriate manipulation of the scale factors of the fractional operands to produce a scale factor for the result, called *scaling*. As a simple example, consider the evaluation of 2.168×3.2.

$$0.0000002168 \ (\times 10^7) \times 0.0000000032 \times (10^9)$$

(1) $0.0000002168 \times 0.000000032 = 0.00000000000000069376$
(2) $10^7 \times 10^9 = 10^{16}$

Result: $0.00000000000000069376 \times 10^{16} = 6.9376$

This problem would be somewhat simpler if the operands were written in *normalized* form, that is, with the scale factors adjusted so that the leftmost fractional digit is nonzero.

$$0.2168 \ (\times 10^1) \times 0.32 \ (\times 10^1)$$

(1) $0.2168 \times 0.32 = 0.069376$
(2) $10^1 \times 10^1 = 10^2$

Result: 0.069376×10^2

To put this result in normalized form, multiply the fraction by 10^1 and the scale factor by 10^{-1},

$$(0.069376 \times 10^1) \times (10^{-1} \times 10^2) = 0.69376 \times 10^1$$

or, more simply, shift the fraction one digit to the left and reduce the scale-factor exponent by one.

As an example of the scaling analysis of a more complicated expression, consider $e = (a \cdot b) + c/d$, where the operands in every instance of evaluation are of the following decimal form:

$$
\begin{aligned}
a &= xxx.xx = \bar{a} \cdot 10^3 \\
b &= x.xxx \ \ = \bar{b} \cdot 10^1 \\
c &= xxx.xx = \bar{c} \cdot 10^3 \\
d &= xx.x \ \ \ = \bar{d} \cdot 10^2
\end{aligned}
$$

The x's represent any decimal digit, including zero (although the digits of the divisor d may not be all zero) and the overlined letters represent the fractional part of the number (i.e., $a = .xxxxx \cdot 10^3$). Entering the scale-factored form of the numbers in the expression, one can determine the resultant scale factor:

$$
\begin{aligned}
e &= (\bar{a} \cdot 10^3 \cdot \bar{b} \cdot 10^1) + (\bar{c} \cdot 10^3)/(\bar{d} \cdot 10^2) \\
&= \overline{ab} \cdot 10^4 + \overline{c/d} \cdot 10^1
\end{aligned}
$$

Two numbers can be added only if they have the same scale factor; hence one must multiply the fraction $\overline{c/d}$ by 10^{-3} and its scale factor by 10^3 to make the two terms consistent:

$$
e = \overline{ab} \cdot 10^4 + \overline{c/d} \cdot 10^{-3} \cdot 10^4 = \bar{e} \cdot 10^4
$$

The possibility exists that the addition of two fractions produces a sum which is not a proper fraction, e.g., $0.8 + 0.7 = 1.5$. If this "overflow" occurred, the result, to be in fractional form, would have to have a scale factor of 10^5. There is another step in the analysis which has been glossed over—the division $\overline{c/d}$ will produce a quotient equal to or greater than one if $\bar{d}$ is less than or equal to $\bar{c}$ in magnitude. Therefore c and d must be scaled so that the quotient will not overflow for any possible combination of values of c and d.

In summary, if enough is known about the range of the operands, the scaling at each step of a computation can be determined in advance. The arithmetic processing can then be regarded as involving only fractions (or *digital* numbers as they are sometimes called). The final result is multiplied by the scale factor which was previously determined.

The difficulties with this approach are quite apparent. If the calculations are long and involved, the scaling analysis is extremely tedious or perhaps even impossible. Unless the ranges of the variables, as well as the combinations of values, are very well known, the scale factors of intermediate values may have such a range of values that steps must be inserted to test for overflow and alter the scale factors during the arithmetic processing. This latter possibility suggests the solution to these difficulties, namely, incorporation of the scale-factor computation as an explicit part of the arithmetic processing. To use this mode of operation, the scale factor must be a part of the number. One way of incorporating this factor into ten decimal digits with a single sign is to add a positive constant to the exponent of the scale factor, for example, $\pm.d_1d_2d_3d_4d_5d_6d_7d_8 \cdot 10 \pm f_2f_1$ is represented in ten digits as $\pm g_2g_1d_1d_2d_3 \ldots d_8$, where $g_2g_1 = 50 + f_2f_1$. The additive constant 50 ensures that the two digits devoted to the exponent will always be positive. Note that since g_1g_2 represents the range 00 to 99, the actual scale-factor exponent ranges from -50 to $+49$.

Numbers in the form described above are called *floating-point* numbers and are a standardized variant of so-called scientific notation. In a *normalized* floating-point number, the leftmost digit of the fractional part is nonzero unless the number is identically zero. To handle floating-point numbers in a machine, there must be available either subroutines which perform the arithmetic operations on floating-point numbers or, preferably, built-in floating-point operations. In either case, the operations will use normalized floating-point numbers as operands and produce normalized results. The possible shifts which were mentioned in the scaling example will be automatically made and the scale factor adjusted. Some decimal examples of floating-point operations are given below; in each case, the conventional form, as well as the 10-digit encoded form, is illustrated. Subtraction (or addition involving negative numbers) deserves special attention since shifts and scale-factor adjustments of more than unity are possible with this operation.

Floating-point addition

(1) $0.1284 \times 10^3 + 0.6892 \times 10^2 = 0.19732 \times 10^3$
$$+ 5312840000 + 5268920000 = +5319732000$$

(2) $0.75 \times 10^4 + 0.82 \times 10^4 = 0.157 \times 10^5$
$$+ 5475000000 + 5482000000 = +5515700000$$

Floating-point subtraction

(1) $0.3189 \times 10^{-4} - 0.2124 \times 10^{-2} = -0.209211 \times 10^{-2}$
$$+ 4631890000 - 4821240000 = -4820921100$$

(2) $0.31416 \times 10^1 - 0.31415926 \times 10^1 = 0.74 \times 10^{-5}$
$$+ 5131416000 - 5131415926 = + 4574000000$$

Floating-point multiplication

(1) $0.41 \times 10^{24} \times 0.318 \times 10^{10} = 0.13038 \times 10^{34}$
$$+ 7441000000 \times +6031800000 = +8413038000$$

(2) $-0.84 \times 10^3 \times 0.674 \times 10^{-2} = -0.56616 \times 10^1$
$$- 5384000000 \times +4867400000 = -5156616000$$

Floating-point division

(1) $-0.643422 \times 10^2 \div 0.2 \times 10^{12} = -0.321711 \times 10^{-9}$
$$- 5264342200 \div +6220000000 = -4132171100$$

(2) $-0.56616 \times 10^{12} \div -0.674 \times 10^6 = 0.84 \times 10^6$
$$- 6256616000 \div -5667400000 = +5684000000$$

For bases other than ten, the representation of floating-point numbers is done in an analogous way. Obviously, in other number systems the scale factors are not powers of ten but are powers of the base.

The representation of binary floating-point numbers is of primary interest and, although the use of octal digits to write binary numbers is useful in this context, it is helpful to examine how a 36-bit binary word is directly allocated to the exponent and fractional parts.

S	12345678	9 10 35

Sign   Exponent   Fraction
of
scale factor

Thus the numbers $(000)_{10}$ to $(255)_{10}$ can be represented by eight bits. Assuming, as before, that a constant is added to the exponent to ensure that it will always be positive, one sees that the obvious choice for such a constant is the middle of this range, or $(128)_{10} = (10000000)_2$. From this choice it follows that the effective exponent range is $(-128)_{10}$ to $(+127)_{10}$ or, alternatively, the scale factors range from 2^{-128} to 2^{127} In decimal terms, the latter range is approximately 10^{-38} to 10^{+38}. Both the fraction and exponent bits can be grouped in threes and written in octal form. (Note, however, that the leftmost octal digit has the range 0 to 3 since it is representing only two bits.) However, the exponent so written cannot be interpreted as a power of eight since not all integral powers of 2 are integral powers of 8. As illustrations, consider the following examples.

(1) $\frac{3}{4} \times 2^4 = (.11)_2 \times 2^{(100)_2} = 01000010011000 \ldots 0$

Sign Exponent Fraction

$$= (+204600000000)_8$$

(2) $-\frac{5}{8} \times 2^{21} = -(.101)_2 \times 2^{(10101)_2} = 11001010110100 \ldots 0$

Sign Exponent Fraction

$$= (-225500000000)_8$$

(3) $\frac{11}{16} \times 2^{-10} = .1011 \times 2^{-(1010)_2} = \underbrace{0}\underbrace{0111011}\underbrace{010110 \ldots 0}$

Sign Exponent Fraction

$$= (+166540000000)_8$$

[*Note:* The augmented exponent was obtained by subtracting $(1010)_2$ from the positive constant $(10000000)_2$.]

The conversion of floating-point numbers to the equivalent decimal form is a fairly straightforward but tedious manual procedure. The steps are illustrated here by converting example (1) above.

$$+204600000000 = .6_8 \times 2^4$$

(a) Convert the fraction to a decimal fraction:

$$.6_8 = \tfrac{6}{8} = 0.75_{10}$$

(b) Convert the scale factor to decimal floating-point form:

$$2^4 = 16 = 0.16 \times 10^2$$

(c) Multiply the two decimal numbers:

$$0.75 \times 0.16 \times 10^2 = 0.12 \times 10^2$$

(d) Adjust the floating-point decimal number to normalized form, if necessary.

Most scientific calculations are carried out by means of floating-point numbers. Numbers with *understood* scale factors are called *fixed point*. Integers, a special case of fixed-point numbers, are used for subscript and index variables. Variables whose range is the real numbers are almost always represented by floating-point numbers.

Computational Error

We have seen in the preceding chapter that real numbers, with their infinite string of digits, cannot be represented in the finite number of storage locations in a digital computer; they must be approximated by rational numbers, for example,

$$\pi \approx \frac{31415926}{10000000} = 3.1415926$$

This inability to represent real numbers is not the only source of error in a computational problem. The four categories listed below are in the realm of conscious error as opposed to mistakes. Since these errors are known to exist, the assumption is that they cannot be eliminated but that, hopefully, their magnitudes may be estimated.

(1) The equations and expressions which are used to describe physical processes are, in general, approximations or idealizations which at the outset introduce a disparity between the physical problem and its computational analog. Such errors could be called *formulation* errors.

(2) In actual fact, a digital computer is limited to performing the arithmetic operations on a limited set of rational numbers. Or, stated differently, only rational functions can be evaluated, where *rational function* is defined to mean any function that can be evaluated by operating on numbers using only addition, subtraction, multiplication, and division. The function

$$g(x) = \frac{4x^2 + 3}{3x^3 - 2x^2 + x - 8}$$

is an example. Functions which are defined by limiting processes, such as

$$\ln x = \int_1^x \frac{dt}{t}$$

must somehow be represented by a rational function, and thus an error is introduced. This error is called a *truncation* error since the rational function is often obtained by truncating (i.e. terminating) an infinite series after a specified number of terms.

(3) The already mentioned fact that an infinite number of digits cannot be used to represent a number gives rise to what is called *round-off* errors.

Remembering that a number is a polynomial, one sees that this type of error arises from the truncation of terms in this polynomial. However, it should be kept in mind that the term "truncation error" refers to the error arising from functional approximation, not number approximation.

(4) Physical quantities can be measured only to a limited accuracy. When such values are used in computations, their indefinite value, or error, is frequently more restrictive than the limited number of digits available to express these measures. Such errors could be called *measurement* errors.

There is no way to estimate formulation error other than to check by observation how well the mathematical expression predicts the physical case. When the formulation error is admittedly large, then, occasionally, a great deal of effort is expended to reduce the other types of error. It would seem that the following corruption of an old adage would apply in such cases: "A thing not worth doing at all is not worth doing well."

Estimation of truncation errors is one of the main tasks of numerical analysis. Examples of such estimation are given in later sections.

Round-off and measurement errors have a similar effect even though the causes differ. The precision with which a number can be expressed is limited. The magnitude of the error caused by this imprecision is relatively simply determined in detail for individual operations and is the principal concern of this chapter. However, the determination of the error in the result of a complicated calculation (even though the error in the original quantities is known) is a vexing problem which cannot always be solved. As the last statement implies, error is propagated; that is, if one or both operands in an operation are approximate, then the result of the operation is approximate or in error. If this result is then used as an operand, the error is propagated to the value of another expression, etc. In addition to the error propagated at each step of a calculation, an error may also be *generated* because the operations themselves (not the operands) are only approximations. The most obvious example of an inexact operation is division, where, unless the divisor divides evenly into the dividend, the quotient will have an infinite number of digits. Restricting the number of quotient digits makes the operation an approximation. One also uses approximate multiplication, i.e., one retains not all the product digits but only a specified number of the most significant digits (generally, as many digits as the word size permits). In floating-point arithmetic, even addition and subtraction are often approximated. When numbers with different scale factors (or possibly even with the same scale factor) are added, not all the sum digits can be accommodated in the basic number size of the machine, and hence the least significant sum digits are dropped. In the following discussion such *generated* errors are not considered; the discussion is limited to the propagation of errors due to inaccurate operands.

SIGNIFICANT NUMBERS

The most common way of indicating the degree of precision of a number is to write only those digits which are known accurately or, in other words, are *significant*. The rightmost digit that is written can be in error by at most half a unit because a greater error would mean that rounding would produce a different final digit. Writing the significant number 1.2932 implies that the "true" value represented by this number is less than or equal to 1.293249999 . . . and greater than or equal to 1.29315. If these extreme values are rounded or "half-adjusted" to four decimal places by adding .00005 and then droppping the digits from the fifth decimal place on, the result is 1.2932. Alternatively, this range can be indicated by writing 1.2932 $\pm$ 0.00005, which in turn can be written 1.2932 (.5), where the number enclosed in parentheses is understood to be in units of the rightmost place. Another alternative expression which allows the error amount to be written as an integer is 1.29320 (5). The shortcomings of significant number notation become apparent if one now supposes that the example number is not known quite so accurately and the range of indefiniteness is, say, 7 units in the first place dropped, i.e. 1.29320 (7). But this representation is no longer a significant number, and the next larger significant number which includes this range (1.29313 to 1.29327) is 1.2930 (5) = 1.29300 (50), whose range is 1.29250 to 1.29350. This notation forces one to designate more variation than is known to exist in the given approximation. An alternative approach is to deal directly with the range of the numbers, as was done above, rather than use the significant number notation. Before the discussion turns to *range numbers*, it should be noted that when an integer with trailing zeros, say 92600, is written, it is not clear how many of the digits are significant. To clear up this ambiguity one must either explicitly state the significance or adopt some writing convention, such as 9260×10^1, which indicates, in this example, that the rightmost zero is not significant.

RANGE NUMBERS

In range number form, a number N is replaced by a pair, the largest and smallest possible values in its range. These high and low values are bracketed and displayed one above the other as shown below.

$$\begin{bmatrix} N_H \\ N_L \end{bmatrix}$$

The significant number 1.2932 becomes

$$\begin{bmatrix} 1.29325 \\ 1.29315 \end{bmatrix}$$

If a number is known exactly, the extremes of the range are the same:

$$6\tfrac{3}{8} = \begin{bmatrix} 6.375 \\ 6.375 \end{bmatrix}$$

The arithmetic operations expressed in terms of range numbers and some numerical examples are shown below.

Addition

$$x + y = \begin{bmatrix} x_H \\ x_L \end{bmatrix} + \begin{bmatrix} y_H \\ y_L \end{bmatrix} = \begin{bmatrix} x_H + y_H \\ x_L + y_L \end{bmatrix}$$

$$1.29(6) + 7.81(4) = \begin{bmatrix} 1.35 \\ 1.23 \end{bmatrix} + \begin{bmatrix} 7.85 \\ 7.77 \end{bmatrix} = \begin{bmatrix} 9.20 \\ 9.00 \end{bmatrix}$$

Subtraction. If the signs are considered to be a part of the numbers, the problem becomes one of addition.

$$1.29(6) - 7.81(4) = \begin{bmatrix} 1.35 \\ 1.23 \end{bmatrix} + \begin{bmatrix} -7.77 \\ -7.85 \end{bmatrix} = \begin{bmatrix} -6.42 \\ -6.62 \end{bmatrix}$$

Multiplication

$$x \cdot y = \begin{bmatrix} x_H \\ x_L \end{bmatrix} \times \begin{bmatrix} y_H \\ y_L \end{bmatrix} = \begin{bmatrix} x_H \cdot y_H \\ x_L \cdot y_L \end{bmatrix}$$

$$3.46(7) \times 2.120(5) = \begin{bmatrix} 3.53 \\ 3.39 \end{bmatrix} \times \begin{bmatrix} 2.125 \\ 2.115 \end{bmatrix} = \begin{bmatrix} 7.50125 \\ 7.16985 \end{bmatrix}$$

In this instance negative signs, if any, should precede the brackets since the objective is to produce the products that are largest and smallest in absolute value. As an example consider

$$\begin{bmatrix} -3.39 \\ -3.53 \end{bmatrix} \quad \text{to be} \quad -\begin{bmatrix} 3.53 \\ 3.39 \end{bmatrix}$$

Division

$$x \div y = \begin{bmatrix} x_H \\ x_L \end{bmatrix} \div \begin{bmatrix} y_H \\ y_L \end{bmatrix} = \begin{bmatrix} y_H \div y_L \\ x_L \div y_H \end{bmatrix}$$

Here again signs should be placed outside the brackets so that the values within are highest and lowest in absolute value.

$$4.246(8) \div 0.120(5) = \begin{bmatrix} 4.254 \\ 4.238 \end{bmatrix} \div \begin{bmatrix} 0.215 \\ 0.115 \end{bmatrix} = \begin{bmatrix} 36.992 \\ 33.904 \end{bmatrix}$$

The quotients should be truncated so that no possible quotients are excluded from the range. Thus the quotient $4.254 \div 0.115 = 36.9913\ldots$ was adjusted to 36.992 to be included in the range $36.9913\ldots$ (Note that 36.991 would have excluded this value.)

If the extremes of the range are of different sign, zero is included in the range. This inclusion is not permissible if the range number is a divisor, and will require adjustments in the rules above for the other cases. However, all the rules given can be subsumed under one general rule prescribing the procedure of obtaining the range number of the result of an operation: Of the four possible combinations of the range number pairs which are operands, select the two giving the largest range to designate the resulting range number.

Range numbers are useful to demonstrate the propagation of errors. The following evaluation employing significant numbers illustrates this point.

$$y = 0.12 \times 236.4 - (63.8 \times 2.01) \div 25$$

$$= \begin{bmatrix} 0.125 \\ 0.115 \end{bmatrix} \times \begin{bmatrix} 236.45 \\ 236.35 \end{bmatrix} - \begin{bmatrix} 63.85 \\ 63.75 \end{bmatrix} \times \begin{bmatrix} 2.015 \\ 2.005 \end{bmatrix} \div \begin{bmatrix} 25.5 \\ 24.5 \end{bmatrix}$$

$$= \begin{bmatrix} 29.55625 \\ 27.18025 \end{bmatrix} - \begin{bmatrix} 128.65775 \\ 127.81875 \end{bmatrix} \div \begin{bmatrix} 25.5 \\ 24.5 \end{bmatrix}$$

$$= \begin{bmatrix} 29.55625 \\ 27.18025 \end{bmatrix} - \begin{bmatrix} 5.251336 \\ 5.012500 \end{bmatrix}$$

$$= \begin{bmatrix} 24.543750 \\ 21.928914 \end{bmatrix}$$

If this result is adjusted to two decimal places, it becomes

$$\begin{bmatrix} 24.55 \\ 21.92 \end{bmatrix}$$

As a significant number this range is represented by 2×10^1, i.e., by only one significant figure. Except for limited hand calculation, the utility of range numbers is restricted to such demonstrations. For the determination of error bounds, it is desirable to express the amount of the error explicitly. Moreover, the error from the approximation of infinite decimal numbers does not appear in range numbers, i.e.,

$$\tfrac{1}{3} = 0.3333 = \begin{bmatrix} 0.3333 \\ 0.3333 \end{bmatrix}$$

Since the error is known, there is no range; the *approximation-error* form corrects these deficiencies.

APPROXIMATION—ERROR NUMBERS

As the name implies, numbers in approximation-error form consist of two parts, the approximation and the error. For instance, $\frac{1}{3} = 0.3333 + \frac{1}{3} \times 10^{-5}$, and, in general, $x = \bar{x} + \epsilon$. More often than not the actual error is not known; only the range is known. Hence, the 1.2932, the significant number previously used as an example, is in this form:

$$1.2932 + \epsilon, \qquad -0.00005 \leq \epsilon < 0.00005$$

Thus a complete statement is $x = \bar{x} + \epsilon$, where $-\eta \leq \epsilon < \eta$. The basic arithmetic operations are expressed in this form as follows.

Addition

$$x + y = (\bar{x} + \epsilon_1) + (\bar{y} + \epsilon_2) = (\bar{x} + \bar{y}) + (\epsilon_1 + \epsilon_2)$$

The errors are additive. If n numbers are added,

$$x_1 + x_2 + x_3 + \cdots + x_n$$

the error of the sum will be

$$\epsilon_1 + \epsilon_2 + \epsilon_3 + \cdots + \epsilon_n$$

If, in addition, the individual errors have a common range, that is, $-\eta \leq \epsilon_i < \eta$ for $i = 1, 2, \ldots, n$, then

$$\epsilon_1 + \epsilon_2 + \cdots + \epsilon_n = \sum_{i=1}^{n} \epsilon_i < n\eta.$$

As a simple example, suppose that the significant numbers 11, 12, 13, ..., 20 are added. The error for each number is less than 0.5, and the total error for the sum of the ten numbers is less than ten times that upper bound:

$$\epsilon_{\text{total}} < 10 \cdot 0.5 = 5.$$

Subtraction

$$x - y = (\bar{x} + \epsilon_1) - (\bar{y} + \epsilon_2) = (\bar{x} - \bar{y}) + (\epsilon_1 - \epsilon_2)$$

Since the values of ϵ_1 and ϵ_2 may be positive or negative, the determination of the maximum error is the same as in addition.

Multiplication

$$x \cdot y = (\bar{x} + \epsilon_1)(\bar{y} + \epsilon_2) = (\bar{x} \cdot \bar{y}) + (\epsilon_2 \bar{x} + \epsilon_1 \bar{y} + \epsilon_1 \epsilon_2)$$

Since the errors are usually small compared to the approximation numbers, the $\epsilon_1 \epsilon_2$-term is very often neglected. As before, to determine the maximum error that can be made in a multiplication, the positive upper bounds for the errors are used, together with the absolute values of the approximating numbers. Assuming that $-\eta_1 \le \epsilon_1 < \eta_1$ and $-\eta_2 \le \epsilon_2 < \eta_2$, one has

$$\epsilon_2 \bar{x} + \epsilon_1 \bar{y} < \eta_2 |\bar{x}| + \eta_1 |\bar{y}|$$

Division. This operation is a little more complicated.

$$\frac{x}{y} = \frac{\bar{x} + \epsilon_1}{\bar{y} + \epsilon_2} = \frac{\bar{x}(1 + \epsilon_1/\bar{x})}{\bar{y}(1 + \epsilon_2/\bar{y})} = \frac{\bar{x}}{\bar{y}} \left(1 + \frac{\epsilon_1}{\bar{x}}\right) \left(1 + \frac{\epsilon_2}{\bar{y}}\right)^{-1}$$

The rightmost term can be expanded by means of the binomial theorem to yield the common series

$$\frac{1}{1 + z} = 1 - z + z^2 - z^3 + \cdots$$

Then

$$\frac{x}{y} = \frac{\bar{x}}{\bar{y}} \left(1 + \frac{\epsilon_1}{\bar{x}}\right) \left(1 - \frac{\epsilon_2}{\bar{y}} + \frac{\epsilon_2^2}{\bar{y}^2} - \cdots\right)$$

If all second- and higher-order terms are neglected, i.e., those involving products of the ϵ's, then

$$\frac{x}{y} \cong \frac{\bar{x}}{\bar{y}} \left(1 + \frac{\epsilon_1}{\bar{x}} - \frac{\epsilon_2}{\bar{y}}\right) = \left(\frac{\bar{x}}{\bar{y}}\right) + \left(\frac{\epsilon_1 \bar{y} - \epsilon_2 \bar{x}}{\bar{y}^2}\right)$$

The maximum error can be obtained by replacing the errors with their upper bounds and using the absolute values of the approximations:

$$\frac{\epsilon_1 \bar{y} + \epsilon_2 \bar{x}}{\bar{y}^2} < \frac{\eta_1 |\bar{y}| + \eta_2 |\bar{x}|}{\bar{y}^2}$$

where

$$-\eta_1 \le \epsilon_1 < \eta_1 \quad \text{and} \quad -\eta_2 \le \epsilon_2 < \eta_2$$

To illustrate this kind of analysis, the error in evaluating a second-degree polynomial, $a_2 x^2 + a_1 x + a_0$, will be computed. This error estimation will be carried out for the evaluation done in nested form, that is, $(a_2 x + a_1)x + a_0$. The approximation-error forms used are:

$$a_2 = \bar{a}_2 + \epsilon_2$$
$$a_1 = \bar{a}_1 + \epsilon_1$$
$$a_0 = \bar{a}_0 + \epsilon_0$$
$$x = \bar{x} + \epsilon_x$$

$$(a_2 x + a_1)x + a_0 = ((\bar{a}_2 + \epsilon_2)(\bar{x} + \epsilon_x) + \bar{a}_1 + \epsilon_1)(\bar{x} + \epsilon_x) + \bar{a}_2 + \epsilon_0$$
$$\approx (\bar{a}_2 \bar{x} + \epsilon_2 \bar{x} + \epsilon_x \bar{a}_2 + \bar{a}_1 + \epsilon_1)(\bar{x} + \epsilon_x) + \bar{a}_0 + \epsilon_0$$
$$\approx \bar{a}_2 \bar{x}^2 + \bar{a}_1 \bar{x} + \bar{a}_0 + [\epsilon_2 \bar{x}^2 + 2\epsilon_x \bar{a}_2 \bar{x} + \epsilon_1 \bar{x} + \bar{a}_1 \epsilon_x + \epsilon_0]$$

The second-order terms (those involving products of errors) are neglected. Applying this result to a specific case,

$$6.80x^2 + 3.25x + 8.24$$

one can compute the maximum error. Assume that x is in the range $0.00 < x \leq 10.00$ and that all the numbers are significant numbers. Then

$$\text{Error} = \epsilon_2 \bar{x}^2 + 2\epsilon_x \bar{a}_2 \bar{x} + \epsilon_1 \bar{x} + \bar{a}_1 \epsilon_x + \epsilon_0$$

Since all the maximum errors are the same (0.005) and all the numbers are positive, the maximum error of the expression can be obtained by substituting 0.005 for ϵ_2, ϵ_1, ϵ_0, ϵ_x and the maximum value 10.00 for $\bar{x}$.

$$\text{Max error} = 0.005(10^2 + 2(6.80)10 + 10 + 3.25 + 1)$$
$$= 0.005(100 + 136 + 14.25) = 1.25125$$

AN ERROR-LIMITED PROBLEM

A final numerical example is included here to illustrate that computations can be limited by the lack of precision of the input numbers and, moreover, that carrying extra digits in the various steps of calculation does not eliminate the difficulty. Consider the simultaneous equations

$$2.00x + 3.00y = 5.00$$
$$0.65x + 1.07y = 1.68$$

Assuming that the coefficients and the terms on the right-hand sides are significant numbers, one computes the solutions twice, once to determine the maximum value of x and y and once to determine the minimum. The solutions are obtained by determinants (Cramer's rule):

$$x_{max} = \frac{\begin{vmatrix} 5.005 & 2.995 \\ 1.675 & 1.075 \end{vmatrix}}{\begin{vmatrix} 1.995 & 3.005 \\ 0.655 & 1.065 \end{vmatrix}} = 2.325, \quad y_{max} = \frac{\begin{vmatrix} 2.005 & 4.995 \\ 0.645 & 1.685 \end{vmatrix}}{\begin{vmatrix} 1.995 & 3.005 \\ 0.655 & 1.065 \end{vmatrix}} = 1.001$$

$$x_{min} = \frac{\begin{vmatrix} 4.995 & 3.005 \\ 1.685 & 1.065 \end{vmatrix}}{\begin{vmatrix} 2.005 & 2.995 \\ 0.645 & 1.075 \end{vmatrix}} = 1.146, \quad y_{min} = \frac{\begin{vmatrix} 1.995 & 5.005 \\ 0.655 & 1.675 \end{vmatrix}}{\begin{vmatrix} 2.005 & 2.995 \\ 0.645 & 1.075 \end{vmatrix}} = 0.283$$

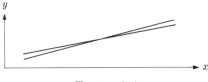

FIGURE 8–1

The imprecision of the original coefficients leads to this wide range of results. The calculation is sensitive to the changes in values permitted by
the range of the numbers, and no better solution is possible unless the
original numbers are known to higher accuracy. This problem corresponds
geometrically to the intersection of two lines which are almost parallel.
Any slight change in coefficients (and therefore slopes) causes a marked
change in the location of the point of intersection (Fig. 8–1). In such
cases, one equation is "almost" the same as the other, except for a multiplicative constant. Systems of equations of this type are called *near-
singular*.

Taylor's Series
and
Divided Differences

CHAPTER

NINE

The subject of numerical analysis has been facetiously subtitled, "Numerical Analysis or 1001 Applications of Taylor's Series." Although this is a gross oversimplification, it is true that the Taylor series representation of functions is a very common point of departure when estimates of the magnitude of truncation errors are sought. The terms of a series are generally rational functions, and the sum of the neglected terms, or error, provides a measure of the "goodness" of the rational approximation represented by the retained terms. To develop and illustrate the use of such error terms for (1) the case when the function and its derivatives are known and (2) the case when only values of the function are known, three background theorems from calculus are needed.

1. The differential mean-value theorem. If a function $f(x)$ is continuous in $a \le x \le b$ and differentiable in $a < x < b$, then there exists at least one point, ζ, in the interval at which

$$f'(\zeta) = \frac{f(b) - f(a)}{b - a}$$

where $f'(\zeta)$ denotes the derivative evaluated at the intermediate point ζ.

In less formal terms, the theorem states that at some point in the interval the tangent to the graph of $f(x)$ has the same slope as the straight line passing through the points $(a, f(a))$ and $(b, f(b))$. See Fig. 9–1.

A variant of this theorem is Rolle's theorem which states, in addition, that if

$$f(a) = f(b) = 0, \qquad \text{then} \qquad f'(\zeta) = 0$$

(see Fig. 9–2). A repeated application of Rolle's theorem permits one to say that if there are n abscissas for which the function is zero,

$$f(a_1) = f(a_2) = f(a_3) = \cdots = f(a_n) = 0$$

112

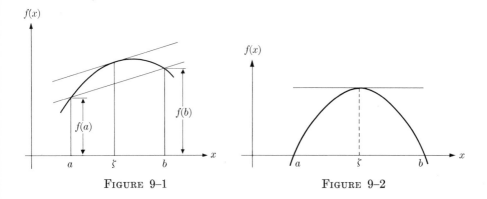

FIGURE 9–1   FIGURE 9–2

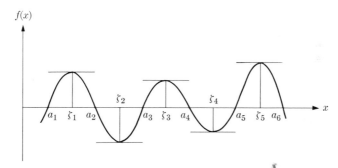

FIGURE 9–3

then there are $n - 1$ intermediate values at which the derivative vanishes:

$$f'(\varsigma_1) = f'(\varsigma_2) = \cdots = f(\varsigma_{n-1}) = 0$$

(see Fig. 9–3).

2. The integral mean-value theorem. If the functions $f(x)$ and $p(x)$ are continuous in $a \leq x \leq b$ and $p(x)$ is nonnegative in the interval, then

$$\int_a^b f(x)p(x)\,dx = f(\varsigma)\int_a^b p(x)\,dx$$

where $a \leq \varsigma \leq b$.

The graphical version of this theorem for the special case $p(x) = 1$ is shown in Fig. 9–4, where M is the maximum value of $f(x)$ in $a \leq x \leq b$, and m is the minimum value in the interval. Certainly

$$m\int_a^b dx = m(b - a) \leq \int_a^b f(x)\,dx \leq M\int_a^b dx = M(b - a)$$

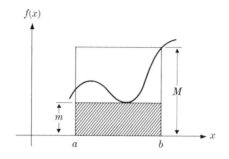

FIGURE 9–4

and since $f(x)$ takes all the values between m and M,

$$\int_a^b f(x) \, dx = f(\zeta)(b - a)$$

where $a \le \zeta \le b$. In the same way, so long as $\int_a^b p(x) \, dx$ is known to be positive or zero,

$$m \int_a^b p(x) \, dx \le \int_a^b f(x)p(x) \, dx \le M \int_a^b p(x) \, dx$$

or

$$\int_a^b f(x)p(x) \, dx = f(\zeta) \int_a^b p(x) \, dx, \qquad a \le \zeta \le b$$

3. A mean-value theorem. If the function $f(x)$ is continuous in $a \le x \le b$ and c and d are nonnegative constants, then

$$cf(a) + df(b) = (c + d)f(\zeta)$$

where $a \le \zeta \le b$. That this result is true can be seen by rewriting it:

$$cf(a) + df(b) = (c + d) \left[\frac{c}{c + d} f(a) + \frac{d}{c + d} f(b) \right]$$

The sum of the two fractions is unity so that

$$f(a) \le \frac{c}{c + d} f(a) + \frac{d}{c + d} f(b) \le f(b)$$

or

$$f(b) \le \frac{c}{c + d} f(a) + \frac{d}{c + d} f(b) \le f(a)$$

Since the function is continuous, there is some intermediate abscissa at which the function is equal to this sum.

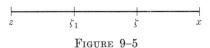

FIGURE 9–5

The result of the first of these three theorems can be rewritten to show its application to approximating functions:

$$f(b) = f(a) + (b - a)f'(\zeta), \qquad a \le \zeta \le b$$

In the further development it is useful to label the end points of the interval (z, x) instead of (a, b) and, with this change, one obtains

$$f(x) = f(z) + (x - z)f'(\zeta), \qquad z \le \zeta \le x$$

The rightmost term above is an error term in the sense that its value gives the amount of error introduced when the function $f(x)$ is approximated by the single value $f(z)$. This error is reduced as z approaches x. When $f(x)$ is constant, there is no error since $f'(x) = 0$ for any x, but for more elaborate functions this does not seem to be a particularly useful approach since z must usually be quite close to x to keep the error small. A more usable approximation can be constructed by using Theorem 1 to introduce a second derivative:

$$f(x) = f(z) + (x - z)[f'(z) + f'(\zeta) - f'(z)]$$

$$= f(z) + (x - z)f'(z) + (x - z)(\zeta - z)\left[\frac{f'(\zeta) - f'(z)}{\zeta - z}\right]$$

$$= f(z) + (x - z)f'(z) + (x - z)(\zeta - z)f''(\zeta_1)$$

where $z \le \zeta_1 \le \zeta \le x$. If the interval is pictured as a line segment, these four abscissas are spaced as shown in Fig. 9–5. The intermediate points ζ_1 and ζ are not constants but will vary as x or z is varied. If x is regarded as fixed and z is varied, there is no effect on $f(x)$. In symbols,

$$\frac{d}{dz} f(x) = \frac{d}{dz} [f(z) + (x - z)f'(z) + (x - z)(\zeta - z)f''(\zeta_1)] = 0$$

or

$$\frac{d}{dz} f(x) = f'(z) - f'(z) + (x - z)f''(z)$$

$$+ \frac{d}{dz} [(x - z)(\zeta - z)f''(\zeta_1)] = 0$$

From this last result it is seen that

$$\frac{d}{dz}[(\zeta - z)(x - z)f''(\zeta_1)] = -(x - z)f''(z)$$

Now, if both sides are integrated, with the lower limit of integration, z, treated as a variable, the correspondence between these two forms becomes clearer:

$$\int_z^x \left\{ \frac{d}{dt}\left((\zeta - t)(x - t)f''(\zeta_1) \right) \right\} dt = \int_z^x - (x - t)f''(t) \, dt$$

Theorem 2 can be applied to the right-hand side of the expression above:

$$-(\zeta - z)(x - z)f''(\zeta_1) = -f''(\zeta_2) \int_z^x (x - t) \, dt$$

$$= \left[f''(\zeta_2) \frac{(x - t)^2}{2} \right]_z^x$$

$$(\zeta - z)(x - z)f''(\zeta_1) = \frac{(x - z)^2}{2} f''(\zeta_2), \qquad z \le \zeta_2 \le x$$

Using this result in the improved approximation yields

$$f(x) = f(z) + (x - z)f'(z) + \frac{(x - z)^2}{2} f''(\zeta_2)$$

In this case, if $f(x)$ were a straight line, for example, $f(x) = ax + b$, the rightmost error term would be zero, since the second derivative would be zero, and the first two terms would not be approximate. It is possible to add higher derivatives to this approximation, which is an elaboration of the differential mean-value theorem, but it is simpler to start with the general form.

TAYLOR'S SERIES

In the preceding section an approximation for $f(x)$ was obtained which contained terms involving $(x - z)$ and $(x - z)^2$. Extending this approach to include higher powers of $x - z$, let us suppose that an arbitrary function $f(x)$ can be represented by the $n + 1$ terms of a polynomial,

$$f(x) = a_0 + a_1(x - z) + a_2(x - z)^2 + \cdots + a_n(x - z)^n + R_{n+1}$$

where the sum of the terms dropped from this presumably infinite series is represented by a remainder term R_{n+1}. To determine the values of the coefficients $a_0, a_1, \ldots, a_n$, the series is first differentiated n times:

$$f'(x) = 1 \cdot a_1 + 2 \cdot a_2(x - z) + \cdots + na_n(x - z)^{n-1} + R'_{n+1}$$

$$f''(x) = 2 \cdot a_2 + 3 \cdot 2a_3(x - z) + \cdots$$
$$+ n(n - 1)a_n(x - z)^{n-2} + R''_{n+1}$$

$$f'''(x) = 3 \cdot 2 \cdot a_3 + 4 \cdot 3 \cdot 2 \cdot a_4(x - z) + \cdots$$
$$+ n(n - 1)(n - 2)a_n(x - z)^{n-3} + R'''_{n+1}$$

$$\vdots$$

$$f^{(n)}(x) = n!a_n + R^{(n)}_{n+1}$$

By taking advantage of the fact that evaluating the expressions above at $x = z$ causes all terms on the right except the first to vanish, the coefficients can be simply determined. Even the $R^{(k)}_{n+1}$-terms vanish, since terms of this kind represent an indefinite sum of terms of the same form, i.e., each having as a factor a power of $(x - z)$. Making the substitution $x = z$, one then has

$$f(z) = a_0, \qquad a_0 = f(z)$$

$$f'(z) = a_1, \qquad a_1 = f'(z)$$

$$f''(z) = 2 \cdot a_2, \qquad a_2 = \frac{f''(z)}{2}$$

$$f'''(z) = 3 \cdot 2 \cdot a_3, \qquad a_3 = \frac{f'''(z)}{3 \cdot 2}$$

$$\vdots \qquad\qquad \vdots$$

$$f^{(n)}(z) = n! \, a_n, \qquad a_n = \frac{f^{(n)}(z)}{n!}$$

Making these substitutions for the coefficients in the original form leads to the Taylor series,

$$f(x) = f(z) + f'(z)(x - z) + \frac{f''(z)}{2!} (x - z)^2$$
$$+ \frac{f'''(z)}{3!} (x - z)^3 + \cdots + \frac{f^{(n)}(z)}{n!} (x - z)^n + R_{n+1}$$
$$= \sum_{i=0}^{n} \frac{f^{(i)}(z)}{i!} (x - z)^i + R_{n+1}$$

If one chooses

$$x = z + h$$

then another common representation of Taylor's series is obtained:

$$f(z + h) = f(z) + f'(z)h + \frac{f''(z)}{2!} h^2 + \cdots + \frac{f^{(n)}(z)}{n!} h^n + R_{n+1}$$

$$= \sum_{i=0}^{n} \frac{f^{(i)}(z)}{i!} h^i + R_{n+1}$$

When $z = 0$, the resultant series is called Maclaurin's series:

$$f(h) = f(0) + f'(0)h + f''(0)h^2 + \cdots + \frac{f^{(n)}(0)}{n!} h_n + R_{n+1}$$

$$= \sum_{i=0}^{n} \frac{f^{(i)}(0)}{i!} h^i + R_{n+1}$$

The first representation may be regarded as a method of determining $f(x)$ from information known about the function at a point z [that is, $f(z)$, $f'(z)$, $f''(z)$, . . .]. The second form is, of course, the same; only the point of view has shifted. The series provides a way of determining the functional value at some point $(z + h)$ near the central point z, again using the known information at z. Both expressions are "expansions about z," but the second one gives z the position of central importance and the question, always present when series are considered, of how far from the known values at z values of the function may be evaluated can be expressed in terms of h. The range of h for which a series converges, $-r < h < r$, must be determined for each series and, although it is not always conclusive, the Cauchy ratio test is useful in the determination of the "circle of convergence." To make this test, the ratio of the absolute values of the $(n + 1)$ and the nth terms is formed. If the limit of this ratio as $n \to \infty$ is less than unity, the series converges; if it is greater, it diverges. The situation when the ratio is unity is left undetermined.

The remainder term R_{n+1} is an infinite series, but to estimate the truncation error introduced by dropping the remainder, a method is needed which permits one to estimate the magnitude of R_{n+1} without adding terms of the series it represents. Proceeding as before, one can produce such an estimate by differentiating the first form of Taylor's series:

$$f(x) = f(z) + f'(z)(x - z) + \frac{f''(z)}{2!} (x - z)^2$$

$$+ \cdots + \frac{f^{(n)}(z)}{n!} (x - z)^n + R_{n+1}$$

Differentiating with respect to z yields

$$0 = \underbrace{f'(z) - f'(z)}_{= \, 0} + \underbrace{(x - z)f''(z) + \frac{2f''(z)(x - z)}{2!}}_{= \, 0}$$

$$+ \underbrace{(x - z)^2 \frac{f'''(z)}{2!} + \cdots + n \frac{f^{(n)}(z)}{n!} (x - z)^{n-1}}_{= \, 0}$$

$$+ (x - z)^n \frac{f^{(n+1)}(z)}{n!} + R'_{n+1}$$

and hence

$$R'_{n+1} = - \frac{(x - z)^n f^{(n+1)}(z)}{n!}$$

To obtain an expression for R_{n+1}, both sides of the equation above are integrated. As in the earlier error-term determination, integrating the derivative with respect to z of R_{n+1} (with the lower limit of integration taken to be z) gives

$$\int_z^x R'_{n+1} \, dt = -R_{n+1}$$

This is a function of z, and the constant obtained from the evaluation at the upper limit x is zero since R'_{n+1} has a factor of $(x - z)^n$. Accordingly,

$$-R_{n+1} = -\int_z^x \frac{(x - t)^n}{n!} f^{(n+1)}(t) \, dt = \left[f^{(n+1)}(\varsigma) \frac{(x - t)^{n+1}}{(n + 1)!} \right]_z^x$$

$$= -f^{(n+1)}(\varsigma) \frac{(x - z)^{n+1}}{(n + 1)!}$$

where $z \leq \varsigma \leq x$. If the substitution $x = z + h$ is made, then

$$R_{n+1} = f^{(n+1)}(\varsigma) \frac{h^{n+1}}{(n + 1)!}$$

where $z \leq \varsigma \leq z + h$. The integration above is justified by the integral mean-value theorem. For the case of $x < z$ some additional argument is required since $p(x) = (x - z)^n$ is not necessarily nonnegative in the interval.

It is apparent that if $n + 1$ terms of a Taylor series are retained (this count includes the constant term), the truncation error is proportional to the $(n + 1)$-derivative and the $(n + 1)$-power of the interval h. If the function $f(x)$ were an nth-degree polynomial, there would be no error in a Taylor series representation of it, since the $(n + 1)$-derivative of an nth-degree polynomial is zero. For example, the Taylor series representation of a second-degree polynomial terminates with the third term:

$$f(x) = a_0 + a_1 x + a_2 x^2$$

$$f(x + h) = (a_0 + a_1 x + a_2 x^2) + (a_1 + 2a_2 x)h + \frac{(2a_2)h^2}{2}$$

$$= a_0 + a_1(x + h) + a_2(x + h)^2$$

As an example, consider the approximation of $f(x) = \cos (x)$ by the first three terms of Taylor's series. The necessary derivatives are

$$f'(x) = -\sin (x)$$

$$f''(x) = -\cos (x)$$

$$f'''(x) = \sin (x)$$

Therefore,

$$\cos (x + h) = \cos (x) - h \sin (x) - \frac{h^2}{2} \cos (x) + \frac{h^3}{6} \sin (\varsigma)$$

where $x \leq \varsigma \leq x + h$.

To numerically illustrate the application of this formula, compute $\cos (\pi/4) = \cos (\pi/6 + \pi/12)$:

$$x = \frac{\pi}{6} = 0.5236 \text{ rad}$$

$$h = \frac{\pi}{12} = 0.2618 \text{ rad}$$

$$\cos \left(\frac{\pi}{4}\right) \approx \cos (0.5236) - 0.2618 \sin (0.5236) - (0.5)(0.2618)^2 \cos (0.5236)$$

$$\approx 0.8660 - (0.2618)(0.5) - (0.5)(0.2618)^2(0.8660)$$

$$\approx 0.7054$$

$$|R_3| \leq \left| \frac{(0.2618)^3}{6} \max \sin (\varsigma) \right|, \qquad 0.5236 \leq \varsigma \leq 0.5236 + 0.2618$$

where

$$\max \sin (\varsigma) = \sin (0.7854) = 0.7071$$

$$|R_3| \leq \frac{(0.2618)^3}{6} 0.7071 = 0.0021$$

To four decimal places the correct result is $\cos (\pi/4) = 0.7071$ so that the actual error is $(0.7071 - 0.7054) = 0.0017$. The error bound, 0.0021, is larger than the actual error, as one would expect.

DIVIDED-DIFFERENCE POLYNOMIALS

The Taylor expansion utilized known values of the approximated function and its derivatives at a specific point. Very often such information is not available for the function of interest, but there exists only a set of tabulated values such as would be obtained from an experiment or from mathematical tables. The question then is: given a set of tabulated values,

$$
\begin{array}{ll}
x_0 & f(x_0) \\
x_1 & f(x_1) \\
x_2 & f(x_2) \\
\vdots & \vdots \\
x_n & f(x_n)
\end{array}
$$

can some expression analogous to the Taylor series be developed? From the definition of a derivative,

$$
f'(x) = \lim_{h \to 0} \frac{f(x + h) - f(x)}{h} \quad \text{and} \quad f'(x_0) = \lim_{x_1 \to x_0} \frac{f(x_1) - f(x_0)}{x_1 - x_0}
$$

it appears that the quotient formed from the *finite differences* $f(x_1) - f(x_0)$ and $x_1 - x_0$ would provide an approximation to the first derivative which could replace the first derivative in Taylor's series. Similarly, the second derivative can be approximated by such *finite divided differences:*

$$
\lim_{\substack{x_1 \to x_0 \\ x_2 \to x_0}} \frac{[f(x_2) - f(x_1)]/(x_2 - x_1) - [f(x_1) - f(x_0)]/(x_1 - x_0)}{x_2 - x_0} = \frac{f''(x_0)}{2}
$$

Hower, the substitution of the divided differences is not sufficient in itself, because one has no longer a single interval $(x - z)$ but many: $(x - x_0)$, $(x - x_1)$, $(x - x_2)$, ... A more revealing approach to the divided-difference polynomial is to proceed in a fashion analogous to the Taylor series development.

It is probably appropriate at this point to make a short digression on the subject of getting something for nothing. To produce an estimate of the truncation error it was necessary in the case of Taylor's series to use some information that was not used in the truncated series, i.e., knowledge about the $(n + 1)$-derivative. Without this information, no statements about the accuracy of the approximation could be made. Similarly, in the finite-difference case, additional information, not used in producing the rational approximation, will be required to say something about error. If one is given only two points, $(x_0, f(x_0))$ and $(x_1, f(x_1))$, and a straight line is made to pass through these points, nothing can be said about how closely this line approximates the "true" function $f(x)$. However, if a third

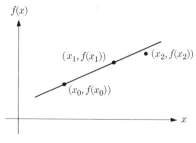

FIGURE 9–6

point, $(x_2, f(x_2))$, is also known, then the proximity of this "unused" point to the line is some measure of the degree of approximation of the line (Fig. 9–6).

The differential mean-value theorem can be used to replace derivatives by divided differences. As an illustration, let us replace the first derivative in the three-term Taylor series. (The symbol x_0 is substituted for z to achieve consistency with the tabular notation.)

$$f(x) = f(x_0) + (x - x_0)f'(x_0) + \frac{(x - x_0)^2}{2} f''(\zeta), \qquad x_0 \leq \zeta \leq x$$

For an arbitrary $x_1 < x_0$,

$$\frac{f(x_1) - f(x_0)}{x_1 - x_0} = f'(\zeta_1), \qquad x_1 \leq \zeta_1 \leq x_0$$

and therefore

$$f(x) = f(x_0) + (x - x_0)\left[\frac{f(x_1) - f(x_0)}{x_1 - x_0} - (f'(\zeta_1) - f'(x_0))\right]$$
$$+ \frac{(x - x_0)^2}{2} f''(\zeta)$$

Applying Theorem 2 again, one obtains

$$\frac{f'(\zeta_1) - f'(x_0)}{\zeta_1 - x_0} = f''(\zeta_2), \qquad \zeta_1 \leq \zeta_2 \leq x_0$$

Making this substitution and writing $-(\zeta_1 - x_0)$ as $(x_0 - \zeta_1)$ yields

$$f(x) = f(x_0) + (x - x_0)\frac{f(x_1) - f(x_0)}{x_1 - x_0}$$
$$+ (x - x_0)(x_0 - \zeta_1)f''(\zeta_2) + \frac{(x - x_0)^2}{2} f''(\zeta)$$

Since the multipliers of the derivatives in the two right-hand terms are nonnegative, Theorem 3 can be used to simplify the above result, and one obtains

$$f(x) = f(x_0) + (x - x_0)\frac{f(x_1) - f(x_0)}{x_1 - x_0}$$

$$+ \left[(x - x_0)(x_0 - \zeta_1) + \frac{(x - x_0)^2}{2}\right]f''(\zeta_3)$$

where $\zeta_2 \leq \zeta_3 \leq \zeta$.

The derivative has now been replaced at the cost of considerable complication of the error term, but some further simplification can be made if it is required that this term must be zero when $x = x_1$. At $x = x_1$,

$$\left[(x_1 - x_0)(x_0 - \zeta_1) + \frac{(x_1 - x_0)^2}{2}\right]f''(\zeta_3) = 0$$

from which

$$(x_0 - \zeta_1) + \frac{x_1 - x_0}{2} = 0$$

or

$$\zeta_1 = \frac{x_0 + x_1}{2}$$

and

$$f(x) = f(x_0) + (x - x_0)\frac{f(x_1) - f(x_0)}{x_1 - x_0} + (x - x_0)(x - x_1)\frac{f''(\zeta_3)}{2}$$

The intermediate point ζ_3 is in the interval containing x, x_0, and x_1.

Now that this form for the sum of products is established, the next step is to postulate that the function can be represented by n terms of this form. Assume that an arbitrary function, $f(x)$, for which there are $n + 1$ values, $f(x_0), f(x_1), \ldots, f(x_n)$, can be represented by the polynomial

$$\begin{aligned}f(x) = a_0 &+ a_1(x - x_0) + a_2(x - x_0)(x - x_1)\\ &+ a_3(x - x_0)(x - x_1) \times (x - x_2) + \cdots\\ &+ a_n(x - x_0)(x - x_1) \cdots (x - x_{n-1})\\ &+ (x - x_0)(x - x_1) \cdots (x - x_n)R_{n+1}\end{aligned}$$

The complete error term is composed of two factors: the product, $\prod_{i=0}^{n}(x - x_i)$, and R_{n+1}, whose specific form is yet to be determined. The coefficients may be determined by evaluating the polynomial at the given points.

At $x = x_0$:

$$f(x_0) = a_0, \qquad a_0 = f(x_0)$$

At $x = x_1$:

$$f(x_1) = a_0 + a_1(x_1 - x_0), \qquad a_1 = \frac{f(x_1) - f(x_0)}{x_1 - x_0}$$

At $x = x_2$:

$$f(x_2) = a_0 + a_1(x_2 - x_0) + a_2(x_2 - x_0)(x_2 - x_1),$$

$$a_2 = \frac{[f(x_2) - f(x_1)]/(x_2 - x_1) - [f(x_1) - f(x_0)]/(x_1 - x_0)}{x_2 - x_0}$$

The values of the a's become more complicated at each evaluation, but each is systematically formed. The general form is

$$a_k = \frac{(a_{k-1} \text{ with subscripts increased by 1}) - a_{k-1}}{x_k - x_0}$$

The coefficient a_k depends upon all the x's and functional values with subscripts k and less, that is, $a_k = f(x_k, x_{k-1}, \ldots, x_0)$. This notation is a convenient means of designating the coefficients since the f denotes the function involved and the x's enclosed in parentheses label the abscissas and functional values upon which the coefficient depends. To distinguish it from ordinary function notation, square brackets will be used instead of parentheses. Thus

$$a_0 = f[x_0]$$
$$a_1 = f[x_1, x_0]$$
$$a_2 = f[x_2, x_1, x_0]$$
$$\vdots$$
$$a_n = f[x_n, x_{n-1}, \ldots, x_0]$$

With this notation, it is a simple matter to express the recursive relation between successive coefficients:

$$a_0 = f[x_0]$$

$$a_1 = \frac{f[x_1] - f[x_0]}{x_1 - x_0} = f[x_1, x_0]$$

$$a_2 = \frac{f[x_2, x_1] - f[x_1, x_0]}{x_2 - x_0} = f[x_2, x_1, x_0]$$

$$a_3 = \frac{f[x_3, x_2, x_1] - f[x_2, x_1, x_0]}{x_3 - x_0}$$

$$\vdots$$

$$a_n = \frac{f[x_n, \ldots, x_1] - f[x_{n-1}, \ldots, x_0]}{x_n - x_0} = f[x_n, x_{n-1}, \ldots, x_0]$$

The coefficients are called *divided differences*, and $a_k = f[x_k, x_{k-1}, \ldots, x_0]$ is the kth divided difference. Note that the x's in the denominators are those which are not common to the two numerator terms. With this notation, the original polynomial is written

$$f(x) = f[x_0] + f[x_1, x_0](x - x_0) + f[x_2, x_1, x_0](x - x_0)(x - x_1)$$

$$+ \cdots + f[x_n, x_{n-1}, \ldots, x_0](x - x_0)(x - x_1) \cdots (x - x_{n-1})$$

$$+ \prod_{i=0}^{n} (x - x_i) R_{n+1}$$

Differentiation is not available as a tool for determining a value for R_{n+1}, as it was in the Taylor series case. But the expression for R_{n+1} can be recursively simplified into a single term:

$$\prod_{i=0}^{n} (x - x_i) R_{n+1} = \underbrace{f(x) - f(x_0)} - f[x_1, x_0](x - x_0)$$

$$- f[x_2, x_1, x_0](x - x_0)(x - x_1) - \cdots$$

$$= \underbrace{(x - x_0)f[x, x_0] - f[x_1, x_0](x - x_0)} - f(x_2, x_1, x_0)(x - x_0)(x - x_1) - \cdots$$

$$= \underbrace{(x - x_0)(x - x_1)f[x, x_1, x_0] - f(x_2, x_1, x_0)(x - x_0)(x - x_1)} - \cdots$$

$$= (x - x_0)(x - x_1)(x - x_2)f[x, x_2, x_1, x_0] - \cdots$$

Continuing in this way, one obtains

$$\prod_{i=0}^{n} (x - x_i) R_{n+1} = (x - x_0)(x - x_1) \cdots (x - x_n)f[x, x_n, x_{n-1}, \ldots, x_0]$$

and

$$R_{n+1} = f[x, x_n, \ldots, x_0]$$

Here the variable x appears as one of the arguments of a divided difference, that is, x is not one of the given abscissas. Since x is just "some point" in the interval containing $x_0, \ldots, x_n$, this formula is not an effective means of estimating R_{n+1}. It is worth noting at this time, however, that if x is replaced by x_{n+1}, the right-hand side of the expression above would be the first term dropped from the divided-difference polynomial for $f(x)$. As a practical procedure, then, evaluating this first neglected term (provided the necessary additional $(n + 1)$-point is available) yields an *estimate* of the magnitude of the error. However, a little analysis produces an expression for the error which is closer to the Taylor series form.

If the nth-degree divided-difference polynomial is designated $p_n(x)$, then

$$f(x) = p_n(x) + R_{n+1} \prod_{i=0}^{n} (x - x_i)$$

At the given points, both $f(x) - p_n(x)$ and $\prod_{i=0}^{n}(x - x_i)$ are zero. The first expression is zero at these points because $p_n(x)$ was constructed to equal $f(x_0)$ at $x = x_0$, $f(x_1)$ at $x = x_1$, etc., and the second expression has a zero factor at each of the given points. However, if the equality above is to hold at some other value of x, there must be some value for R_{n+1} which makes the equality possible. Consider

$$F(x) = f(x) - p_n(x) - R_{n+1} \prod_{i=0}^{n}(x - x_i)$$

In this case, $F(x)$ is zero at the $n + 1$ points $x_0, x_1, \ldots, x_n$, and for a given value of x, it is also zero at at least one other abscissa. Applying Rolle's theorem, one finds that the derivative $F'(x)$ is zero at $n + 1$ points included in the interval containing the given points. By the same reasoning, $F''(x)$ has n zeros, $F'''(x)$ has $n - 1$ zeros, etc.:

$$F'(x) = f'(x) - p_n'(x) - R_{n+1} \frac{d}{dx}\left(\prod_{i=0}^{n}(x - x_i)\right)$$

$$F''(x) = f''(x) - p_n''(x) - R_{n+1} \frac{d^2}{dx^2}\left(\prod_{i=0}^{n}(x - x_i)\right)$$

Since $p_n(x)$ is an nth-degree polynomial, its $(n + 1)$-derivative is zero. The product $\prod_{i=0}^{n}(x - x_i)$ is an $(n + 1)$-degree polynomial,

$$x^{n+1} + b_{n-1}x^n + \cdots + b_0,$$

and its $(n + 1)$-derivative is a constant,

$$(n + 1)(n)(n - 1) \cdots (1) = (n + 1)!$$

From these observations, it follows that

$$F^{(n+1)}(x) = f^{(n+1)}(x) - R_{n+1}(n + 1)!$$

Since $F^{(1)}$ has $n + 1$ zeros, $F^{(2)}$ has n zeros, $F^{(3)}$ has $n - 1$ zeros, etc., $F^{(n+1)}$ has 1 zero. Assume that this zero is at the point $x = \zeta$, that is, $F^{(n+1)}(\zeta) = 0$. Then

$$0 = f^{(n+1)}(\zeta) - R_{n+1}(n + 1)!$$

and

$$R_{n+1} = \frac{f^{(n+1)}(\zeta)}{(n + 1)!}$$

where ζ is in the interval containing $x_0, x_1, \ldots, x_n$. Using this result, one obtains the complete error term,

$$E_{n+1}(x) = \prod_{i=0}^{n} (x - x_i) \frac{f^{(n+1)}(\zeta)}{(n+1)!}$$

which is the Taylor series result except for the replacement of h^{n+1} by the $n+1$ factors which are the intervals from x to the given points. For computational purposes, this form of the remainder has even less utility than in the Taylor series since, in general, no information on the magnitude of derivatives is available. However, this form is useful in the analytic expression of truncation errors. For example, it shows very clearly that if $f(x)$ is a polynomial of degree n or less, the divided-difference polynomial $p_n(x)$ is exact, that is, the error is zero since $f^{(n+1)}(x)$ is zero.

The systematic rules for computing divided differences suggest a tabular arrangement.

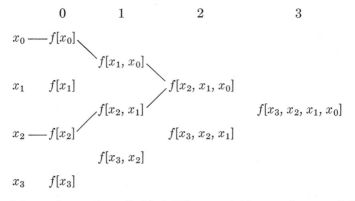

The first two columns in a divided-difference table are given, and the remaining entries are formed according to a very simple rule: To compute an entry in the kth column, subtract the adjacent entries in the $(k-1)$-column and divide that difference by the difference of the abscissas intercepted by proceeding diagonally upward and diagonally downward to the left. For example,

$$f[x_2, x_1, x_0] = \frac{f[x_2, x_1] - f[x_1, x_0]}{x_2 - x_0}$$

The coefficients entering into the divided-difference polynomial which has been derived are those on the downward diagonal of the table:

$$f(x) \approx f[x_0] + f[x_1, x_0](x - x_0) + f[x_2, x_1, x_0](x - x_0)(x - x_1)$$
$$\approx f[x_0] + (x - x_0)\{f[x_1, x_0] + (x - x_1)f[x_2, x_1, x_0]\}$$

Note that no restrictions have been placed on the order or even the spacing between points, so that it is possible (by rearranging the three points used) to use the same formula with different divided differences and increments. The result would be the same, however, since only one second-degree polynomial can pass through the three points. If there is no rearrangement, then any zigzag "path" through the table which terminates on the same divided difference can be used to determine the coefficients of the polynomial.

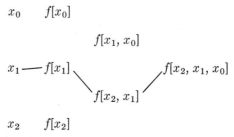

$$x_0 \qquad f[x_0]$$
$$f[x_1, x_0]$$
$$x_1 \text{———} f[x_1] \qquad\qquad f[x_2, x_1, x_0]$$
$$f[x_2, x_1]$$
$$x_2 \qquad f[x_2]$$

For this table, there are four possible paths. If, for example, the path shown above is chosen, then the approximating polynomial for $f(x)$ is written:

$$f(x) \approx f[x_1] + f[x_2, x_1](x - x_1) + f[x_2, x_1, x_0](x - x_1)(x - x_2)$$

To illustrate some of these properties, a simple example is included at this point. Suppose that

$$f(x) = x^3 - 12x + 2$$

Some values of $f(x)$ are listed below, and the divided-difference table is appended to the right of these columns.

II	I	x	$f[x]$	1	2	3	4
x_3	x_0	-1	13				
				-11			
x_2	x_1	0	2		1		
				-8		1	
x_0	x_2	2	-14		6		0
				16		1	
x_1	x_3	4	18		11		
				49			
x_4	x_4	5	67				

The fact that the fourth divided difference is zero verifies that all the given points are evaluations of a third-degree polynomial. Writing

$$f(x) \approx f[x_0] + f[x_1, x_0](x - x_0) + f[x_2, x_1, x_0](x - x_0)(x - x_1)$$
$$+ f[x_3, x_2, x_1, x_0](x - x_0)(x - x_1)(x - x_2),$$

and considering the points to be labeled as in column I, one obtains the numerical form:

$$f(x) = 13 + (-11)(x + 1) + (1)(x + 1)(x) + (1)(x + 1)(x)(x - 2)$$
$$= 13 - 11x - 11 + x^2 + x + x^3 - x^2 - 2x$$
$$= x^3 - 12x + 2$$

Relabeling the points as in column II leads to the illustrated zigzag path, and

$$f(x) = -14 + (16)(x - 2) + (6)(x - 2)(x - 4) + 1(x - 2)(x - 4)(x)$$
$$= -14 + 16x - 32 + 6x^2 - 36x + 48 + x^3 - 6x^2 + 8x$$
$$= x^3 - 12x + 2$$

The representation of a function which is not a polynomial is illustrated by the following table listing values for $f(x) = \cos[(\pi/1.8)x]$. To keep the divided differences from being very small, and hence difficult to represent in tabular form, the argument x is expressed in hundreds of degrees.

	x	$\cos[(\pi/1.8)x]$	1	2	3
x_0	0.00	1.0000000			
			-0.44658201		
x_1	0.30	0.8660254		-1.2891711	
			-1.2200847		0.60540858
x_2	0.60	0.5000000		-0.74430335	
			-1.6666667		
x_3	0.90	0.0000000			

$$\cos\left(\frac{\pi}{1.8}x\right) \approx 1.0000000 - 0.44658201x - 1.2891711(x)(x - 0.30)$$

$$E_3(x) \approx (x)(x - 0.30)(x - 0.60)0.60540858$$

As a specific numerical example, let $x = 0.45$. Then

$$\cos\left(\frac{0.45}{1.8}\pi\right) \approx 0.712019$$

$$E_3(0.45) \approx 0.006130$$

In this case, since the function is known, a bound for the derivative part of the error can be computed. The relevant derivatives are:

$$f(x) = \cos\left(\frac{\pi}{1.8} x\right)$$

$$f'(x) = -\frac{\pi}{1.8} \sin\left(\frac{\pi}{1.8} x\right)$$

$$f''(x) = -\left(\frac{\pi}{1.8}\right)^2 \cos\left(\frac{\pi}{1.8} x\right)$$

$$f'''(x) = \left(\frac{\pi}{1.8}\right)^3 \sin\left(\frac{\pi}{1.8} x\right)$$

The derivative part of the error term, $R_3 = f'''(\zeta)/3!$, where $0.0 \leq \zeta \leq 0.9$, will have its greatest value when $\zeta = 0.9$. Accordingly,

$$R_3 \leq \left(\frac{\pi}{1.8}\right)^3 \frac{\sin(0.9\pi/1.8)}{6} = \left(\frac{\pi}{1.8}\right)^3 \frac{1}{6} = 0.886090$$

When this factor is multiplied by $0.45(0.45 - 0.30)(0.45 - 0.60) = -0.010125$, an error bound for the case $x = 0.45$ is determined:

$$|E_3(0.45)| \leq 0.010125(0.866090) = 0.00897166$$

To four decimal places, $\cos[(\pi/1.8)0.45] = 0.7071$, and hence the error is $(0.7120 - 0.7071) = 0.0049$. The value of $E_3(0.45) = 0.0061$ provides only an estimate of the magnitude of error and is not a bound. The derivative form, however, did provide a bound, $|E_3(0.45)| \leq 0.0090$.

The Solution of Equations

CHAPTER

TEN

The Taylor series and divided-difference approximations can be used as tools in a familiar context, the solution of equations. Finding the zeros of a function, which is synonymous with solving an equation, is an inverse application of these forms since the value of $f(x)$ is known and what is desired is the value of x that produces the known value $f(x) = 0$. Since the value of x so obtained is only approximate, the methods are iterative, that is, successively applied until the truncation error is acceptably small. (Or, perhaps, until it becomes apparent that the error will not become small!)

NEWTON'S METHOD

The first form of Taylor's series, using only two terms, is the basis for Newton's method (or Newton-Raphson method) of solving equations:

$$f(x) = f(z) + f'(z)(x - z) + \frac{f''(\xi)}{2}(x - z)^2$$

Assuming that $f(x) = 0$, one obtains

$$x = z - \frac{f(z)}{f'(z)} + \frac{f''(\xi)}{2f'(z)}(x - z)^2$$

By dropping the error term $R_2 = [f''(\xi)/2f'(z)](x - z)^2$, an approximate root, x_{k+1}, is determined from an estimate, z, which will now be named x_k:

$$x_{k+1} = x_k - \frac{f(x_k)}{f'(x_k)}$$

For the results obtained by repeated evaluation of this formula (starting with the initial trial value x_0) to converge to the root x, the sequence of remainders

$$R_2^{(0)}, R_2^{(1)}, \ldots, R_2^{(k)} = \frac{f''(\xi_k)}{2f'(x_k)}(x - x_k)^2$$

131

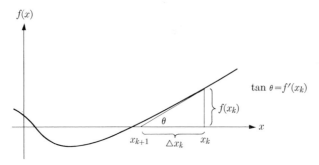

FIGURE 10–1

must become small. Note that if $(x - x_k)$ does become small, the decrease of these remainders accelerates because this small quantity is squared. Such convergence is called a *second-order* process, or *quadratic* convergence.

The geometrical interpretation of this process is often used to introduce it. The function $f(x)$ and its first derivative are evaluated at $x = x_k$. The derivative can be regarded as the tangent of the angle which the slope at the point x_k makes with the x-axis. The base of the triangle, Δx_k, can then be determined and subtracted from x_k to produce the new trial value x_{k+1} (Fig. 10–1):

$$f'(x_k) = \frac{f(x_k)}{\Delta x_k}$$

$$\Delta x_k = \frac{f(x_k)}{f'(x_k)}$$

$$x_{k+1} = x_k - \Delta x_k = x_k - \frac{f(x_k)}{f'(x_k)}$$

As intimated earlier, Newton's method does not necessarily lead to convergence. Moreover, unless the initial trial root was close to the root sought, the process may actually yield some other root. Figure 10–2 illustrates these two cases, whose possible occurrence requires that computer programs include some upper bound on the number of iterations to be carried out. Another refinement which is often useful is to limit the minimum magnitude of $f'(x_k)$. If $f'(x_k)$ is zero, division by zero is attempted, and if it is nonzero but very small, Δx_k becomes large and may very well introduce values of x_k that are outside the range of interest. As with all digital algorithms whose operands are real numbers, or more accurately, machine approximations of real numbers, it is rarely possible to compare values for equality since the propagation of round-off error causes variations in what should otherwise be algebraically identical

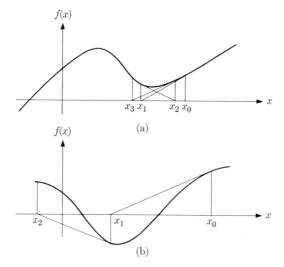

FIG. 10–2 (a) Oscillation about a minimum. (b) Jump to another root.

values. One cannot ask, Is $f(x) = 0$?, but only, Is $|f(x)| \le \epsilon$? where ϵ is small and positive. Occasionally it is difficult to make a good choice of ϵ, and sometimes experimentation is required. The kind of rough reasoning useful for initial choices of ϵ is: A floating-point number is approximately eight decimal digits; hence, if the terms of the expression are fractions in the neighborhood of unity, it would be reasonable to expect that all but the rightmost two digits of two equal numbers would correspond. A first-choice ϵ might then be 1×10^{-6}. The concept of relative (rather than absolute) error is useful in this connection since it avoids the necessity of estimating the magnitudes of the expressions involved. If a and b are to be compared for equality, the question,

$$\left| \frac{a - b}{a + b} \right| < \epsilon?$$

asks whether the error $a - b$ is a negligibly small fraction of the sum. Phrased in this manner, the error relative to the magnitude of the operands and $a - b$ could, for instance, be of the order of 10^2 and still be acceptably small, provided that a and b were of the order 10^8.

Before illustrating a complete computer problem utilizing Newton's method, we wish to present an example in which the technique is used to produce an iterative formula for solving the equation $f(x) = x^2 - a = 0$. If this equation can be readily solved by iteration, an effective way of

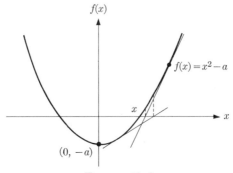

FIGURE 10–3

computing square roots ($x = \pm\sqrt{a}$) can be obtained. Applying the iteration formula

$$x_{k+1} = x_k - \frac{f(x_k)}{f'(x_k)}$$

one obtains

$$x_{k+1} = x_k - \frac{x_k^2 - a}{2x_k} = \frac{1}{2}\left(x_k + \frac{a}{x_k}\right)$$

For a simple initial trial, choose $x_0 = a$ so that $x_1 = \frac{1}{2}(a + 1)$. Obviously, this initial choice cannot be made if $a = 0$, since $a/x_0 = 0/0$ cannot be computed; however, for $a = 0$, the root is known to be $x = 0$, and no iteration is required. When the zero case is excluded, the iteration will always converge. Since $f''(x) = 2$, the error term becomes

$$R_2^{(k)} = \frac{(x - x_k)^2}{2x_k}$$

From the graph of the function $f(x) = x^2 - a$ (Fig. 10–3), it is apparent that after one interative step the differences

$$(x - x_1),\ (x - x_2),\ (x - x_3),\ \ldots$$

will become steadily smaller. For $a \geq 1$, the initial value is to the right of the positive root (that is, $x_0 = a$), and the tangential projection to the x-axis will always produce a value of x_k that is closer to the root but is still somewhat large. For $a < 1$, the first approximation to x will be to the left of x, but the first iteration will produce a value on the right, and the case described above will apply.

Example. Write a computer program to solve the transcendental equation $\cos x - ax^3 = 0$, using Newton's method. Consider only cases where $a \geq 0.04$.

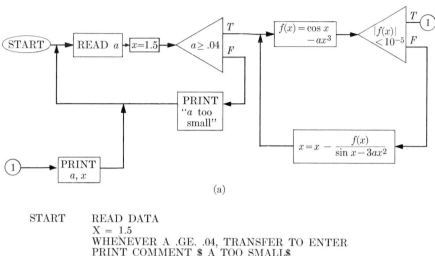

(a)

```
START        READ DATA
             X = 1.5
             WHENEVER A .GE. .04, TRANSFER TO ENTER
             PRINT COMMENT $ A TOO SMALL$
             TRANSFER TO START
REPEAT       X = X + F/(SIN.(X) + 3.0*A*X .P. 2)
ENTER        F = COS. (X) − A*X .P. 3
             WHENEVER .ABS. F .G. 1E − 5, TRANSFER TO REPEAT
             PRINT RESULTS A, X
             TRANSFER TO START
             END OF PROGRAM

Data
A =   .04*
A =   .02*
A =   .5 *
A = 1.0 *
A = 2.0 *
```

(b)

Fig. 10–4 (a) Flow chart. (b) Program.

The function is the cosine superimposed on a negative cubic. The restriction on a guarantees that there is only one real root. The method could be applied without this restriction, but a more detailed analysis and a greater number of trials would be required if all roots were to be obtained. Since $\cos x$ has a zero at $\pi/2$, a value between 0 and $\pi/2$, $x_0 = 1.5$, is chosen as an initial approximation to x. The flow chart and the program for the problem are presented in Fig. 10–4. Note that an array of approximations $x_0, x_1, \ldots, x_k$ is not developed in spite of the fact that the iteration formula suggests such a procedure. Only the previous value is needed to obtain the next, and hence one variable, x, is all that is required. The results for these values of a are:

$$X = 1.44884, \quad \text{A TOO SMALL}, \quad X = 1.01699$$

$$X = .86547, \quad \text{and} \quad X = .72141, \quad \text{respectively}$$

DIFFERENCE METHODS

One would expect that the first two terms of the divided-difference polynomial could be similarly used to find roots of equations and, indeed, this is the case:

$$f(x) = f[x_0] + (x - x_0)f[x_1, x_0] + (x - x_0)(x - x_1)\frac{f''(\xi)}{2}$$

By writing the divided differences in their expanded form and assuming that $f(x) = 0$, one can derive an expression for the root x:

$$0 = f(x_0) + (x - x_0)\frac{f(x_1) - f(x_0)}{x_1 - x_0} + (x - x_0)(x - x_1)\frac{f''(\xi)}{2}$$

$$x = \frac{-(x_1 - x_0)f(x_0) + x_0(f(x_1) - f(x_0))}{f(x_1) - f(x_0)}$$

$$+ \frac{(x - x_0)(x - x_1)}{f(x_1) - f(x_0)}\frac{f''(\xi)}{2}(x_1 - x_0)$$

Dropping the error term and simplifying, one obtains

$$x \approx \frac{x_0 f(x_1) - x_1 f(x_0)}{f(x_1) - f(x_0)}$$

Writing this result as an iterative formula yields

$$x_{k+1} = \frac{x_{k-1}f(x_k) - x_k f(x_{k-1})}{f(x_k) - f(x_{k-1})}$$

The situation is not quite so clear as it was before, since the new value obtained depends on two previous values, and some rule is needed to determine which of the previous abscissas is to be replaced before the next iteration. Before deriving a rule from geometric considerations, one can extend this observation to the error term. The factors $(x - x_0)(x - x_1)$, which, perhaps, should now be written $(x - x_k)(x - x_{k-1})$, will not both become small as the iteration converges. Therefore, since only one of these two factors goes to zero, the process is called *first-order* or *linearly* convergent. The geometrical procedure is illustrated in Fig. 10–5. The new approximation to the root x_{k+1} is the abscissa of the intersection of the x-axis and the secant passing through the two given points. One possible replacement rule would be to retain the two abscissas corresponding to the smaller magnitudes of $f(x_{k+1})$, $f(x_k)$, $f(x_{k-1})$.

As outlined, this procedure, called Lin's method, is fraught with all the convergence difficulties of Newton's method and is only a first-order process. A specialization which makes the method much more useful is to require that $f(x_k)$ and $f(x_{k-1})$ be selected so that they are of opposite sign.

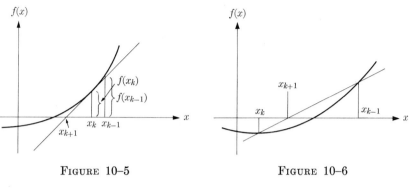

FIGURE 10–5   FIGURE 10–6

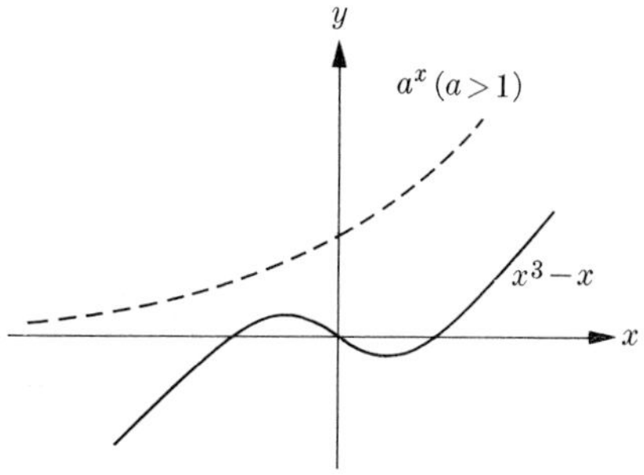

FIGURE 10–7

In this form the process is called the *method of false position* (*Regula Falsi*)
and is guaranteed to converge. Note, however, that the convergence is
still linear. In Fig. 10–6, x_{k+1} would replace x_k to preserve the sign change
before the procedure was repeated. The confusion arising from the change
in subscript names is reduced if only two abscissas are considered, x_l for
the left end point, and x_r for the right end point. The iteration formula
can then be expressed as follows:

$$x \approx \frac{x_r f(x_l) - x_l f(x_r)}{f(x_l) - f(x_r)}$$

if $f(x)f(x_l) > 0$, $x_l \leftarrow x$; otherwise $x_r \leftarrow x$.

Examining the sign of the product of two numbers is a convenient means
of determining whether or not the two are of like sign.

Example. Write a computer program to find one root of the equation
$f(x) = a^x + x^3 - x = 0$, using the method of false position.

To determine an interval in which the function undergoes a sign change,
one sketches two separate graphs for a^x and $x^3 - x$ (Fig. 10–7). Con-

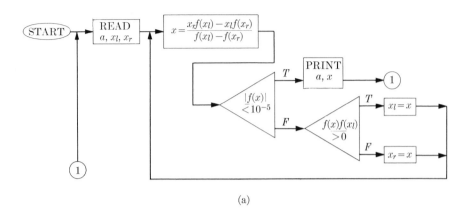

(a)

```
START    READ DATA
COMP     X = (XL*F.(XR) − XR*F.(XL))/(F.(XL) − F.(XR))
         WHENEVER .ABS. F.(X). L. 1E − 5
         PRINT RESULTS A, X
         TRANSFER TO START
         OR WHENEVER F.(X)*F.(XL) .G.0.
         XL = X
         OTHERWISE
         XR = X
         END OF CONDITIONAL
         TRANSFER TO COMP
         INTERNAL FUNCTION F.(ARG) = A.P.ARG + ARG*(ARG*ARG − 1.0)
         END OF PROGRAM
Data
XL = −2.0, XR = 0.0, A = 1.0*
XL = −2.0, XR = 0.0, A = 2.0*
XL = −2.0, XR = 0.0, A = 4.0*
XL = −2.0, XR = 0.0, A = 8.0*
```

(b)

Fig. 10–8. (a) Flow chart. (b) Program.

sidering only $a \geq 1$, one finds that $f(0) = 1$ and $f(-2) < -5$; so there is a root in the interval $(-2, 0)$. Figure 10–8 shows the flow chart and the program for this example.

HALF-INTERVAL METHOD

Instead of determining the next approximation to the root by linearly interpolating between the end points of the interval in which the sign change occurs, one may proceed by a method called the *bisection* or *Bolzano* algorithm, i.e., the interval is simply divided in half, then the half-interval containing the sign change is *halved*, etc. The iteration formula is more logical than computational but, given that $f(x_l)$ and $f(x_r)$ are of different sign, one step may be described as follows.

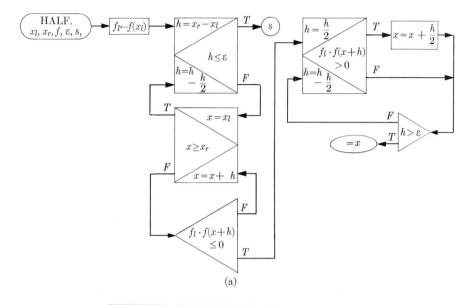

(a)

```
            EXTERNAL FUNCTION (XL, XR, F., EPS, S)
            STATEMENT LABEL S
START       FL = F.(XL)
            THROUGH ST1, FOR H = XR − XL, −H/2.0, H .L. EPS
            THROUGH ST1, FOR X = XL, H, X .GE. XR
ST1         WHENEVER FL*F.(X + H) .LE. O., TRANSFER TO ROOT
            TRANSFER TO S
ROOT        THROUGH ST2, FOR H=H/2.0, −H/2.0, FL*F.(X + H).G.0.
ST2         WHENEVER H .L. EPS, FUNCTION RETURN X
            X = X + H/2.0
            TRANSFER TO ST2
            END OF FUNCTION
```

(b)

FIG. 10–9. (a) Flow chart. (b) Program.

If $f\left(\dfrac{x_l + x_r}{2}\right) f(x_l) > 0,$ then $x_l \leftarrow \dfrac{x_l + x_r}{2}$; otherwise, $x_r \leftarrow \dfrac{x_l + x_r}{2}$

Another useful way of viewing these steps is to consider the interval delimited by the abscissas x and $x + h$; then

$$\text{if } f\left(x + \frac{n}{2}\right) f(x) > 0, \quad x \leftarrow x + \frac{h}{2}, \quad \text{then} \quad h \leftarrow \frac{h}{2}$$

The interval-halving step is always performed whether or not the conditional step preceding it is executed.

To illustrate the use of this root-finding method a specific function will not be considered, but rather the task outlined will be one of writing a function using this process.

Example. Write an external function (a subroutine) for which the
following specifications are given: (1) the end points of an interval, (2) the
name of a function to be examined for roots in the interval, (3) the permissible error in the sought-for root, and (4) the label of a statement which
is to be executed if no root is found. If a root is determined, it is to be
directly returned to the calling program. The function is to be named
HALF.

These specifications do not guarantee that there is a sign change in the
interval given. If the original interval did not indicate a sign change, the
function must search for a subinterval containing a sign change. This
search may be carried out by bisection, that is, the two intervals formed
are examined by evaluating the function at the mid-point of the given
interval. If no sign change is observed, halve each of these intervals, test
for sign change in the four intervals, etc. When the intervals being examined are less than the root error tolerance, there is no point in proceeding
further. This technique has obvious difficulties if there are roots of even
multiplicity and, moreover, it could be extremely time consuming if, in
fact, no roots were present in the interval specified. Nonetheless, the
inclusion of the interval-search procedure does not seriously reduce the
effectiveness of the function in the usual case where the interval designated was known to contain a root. This function illustrates the utility
of iteration statements which are not of the repeated product or summation
type. The corresponding flow chart and program are presented in Fig. 10–9.

SOLVING POLYNOMIAL EQUATIONS

Polynomial equations are of such frequent occurrence that their solution
deserves special attention. These equations are of the form $\sum_{i=0}^{n} a_i x^i = 0$
and the n roots, assuming for the moment that they are real, can be obtained by the methods already described. In particular, Newton's method
may be used since the derivatives of polynomials are readily obtained.
However, the problems of convergence and root separation will be present.
For polynomials, one can handle the latter problem by factoring out a root
once it is known (thus reducing the degree of the polynomial). It turns out
that in applying Newton's method to polynomial equations these tasks of
evaluating the polynomial, evaluating the first derivative, and determining
the coefficients of the depressed equation (i.e., with determined roots
factored out) can be performed quite simply by means of synthetic division.

Synthetic division is merely the division of a polynomial by a linear
factor where, for convenience, the variable names are not written and the
sign of the divisor is reversed so that the "division" may be carried out by
addition instead of subtraction. An example of ordinary division by a

linear factor is given below.

$$
x - x_0 \overline{\left) \begin{array}{l} a_n x^{n-1} + (a_n x_0 + a_{n-1})x^{n-2} + \cdots \\ a_n x^n + a_{n-1}x^{n-1} + \cdots + a_0 \end{array} \right.}
$$

$$a_n x^n - a_n x_0 x^{n-1}$$

$$(a_n x_0 + a_{n-1})x^{n-1} + a_{n-2}x^{n-2}$$

$$(a_n x_0 + a_{n-1})x^{n-1} - (a_n x_0 + a_{n-1})x_0 x^{n-2}$$

$$((a_n x_0 + a_{n-1})x_0 + a_{n-2})x^{n-2}$$

$$\vdots$$

Continuing in this manner would produce a last line (a remainder) of

$$(\cdots ((a_n x_0 + a_{n-1})x_0 + a_{n-2})x_0 + \cdots + a_0) = p(x_0)$$

where $p(x) = \sum_{i=0}^{n} a_i x^i$. Deleting the x's and reversing the sign of x_0 turns the problem into synthetic division:

$$
\begin{array}{l}
\quad\quad a_n \quad (a_n x_0 + a_{n-1}) \\
\overline{x_0 \,\big|\, a_n \quad a_{n-1} \quad a_{n-2} \ldots a_0} \\
\quad\quad + a_n x_0 \\
\overline{\quad\quad a_n x_0 + a_{n-1}} \\
\quad\quad\quad\quad + (a_n x_0 + a_{n-1})x_0 \\
\quad\quad\quad\quad \overline{(a_n x_0 + a_{n-1})x_0 + a_{n-2}}
\end{array}
$$

These expressions are formed according to the following rule: Obtain the expression under the kth coefficient by multiplying the $(k + 1)$-expression by x_0 and adding a_k. Using $b_n, b_{n-1}, \ldots, b_0$ to indicate the expressions, we have

$$
\begin{array}{c|ccccc}
x_0 & a_n & a_{n-1} & a_{n-2} & \cdots & a_0 \\
    & & b_n x_0 & b_{n-1}x_0 & \cdots & b_1 x_0 \\
\hline
    & b_n & b_{n-1} & b_{n-2} & \cdots & b_0
\end{array}
$$

and

$$b_n = a_n$$

$$b_j = b_{j+1}x_0 + a_j \quad \text{for} \quad j < n$$

The remainder is $b_0 = p(x_0)$.

Once it is clear that synthetic division is simply a convenient way of dividing by a linear factor $(x - x_0)$, the fact that the remainder equals $p(x_0)$ can be demonstrated in a simpler way:

$$p(x) = a_n x^n + a_{n-1}x^{n-1} + \cdots + a_0$$

The division produces a quotient,

$$q(x) = b_{n-1}x^{n-1} + b_{n-2}x^{n-2} + \cdots + b_0$$

and a remainder,

$$\frac{R}{x - x_0}$$

that is,

$$\frac{p(x)}{x - x_0} = q(x) + \frac{R}{x - x_0}$$

This result can be written

$$p(x) = q(x)(x - x_0) + R$$

and evaluation at $x = x_0$ produces $R = p(x_0)$.

Repeating the process by dividing $q(x)$ by $(x - x_0)$ reveals that the value of the first derivative at $x = x_0$ can be obtained by evaluating $q(x)$:

$$\frac{q(x)}{x - x_0} = q_2(x) + \frac{R_2}{x - x_0}$$

$$q(x) = (x - x_0)q_2(x) + R_2$$

$$\frac{p(x)}{x - x_0} = (x - x_0)q_2(x) + R_2 + \frac{R}{x - x_0}$$

$$p(x) = (x - x_0)^2 q_2(x) + (x - x_0)R_2 + R$$

$$p'(x) = (x - x_0)^2 q_2'(x) + 2(x - x_0)q_2(x) + R_2$$

For $x = x_0$, $p'(x_0) = R_2$. Therefore division by $(x - x_0)$ evaluates the polynomial $p(x)$ at $x = x_0$, and division of $q(x)$, the quotient thus produced, gives the value of the first derivative $p'(x)$ at x_0. These two values are the necessary constituents of Newton's iteration formula, and a value x_1 to be used in the next division cycle is obtained from $x_1 = x_0 - p(x_0)/p'(x_0)$. Clearly, when x_0 is a root, the remainder R is zero ($R = f(x_0) = 0$), and the quotient is the polynomial with $(x - x_0)$ factored out.

Before proceeding to a program, we wish to illustrate the steps by a numerical example. Suppose that

$$p(x) = x^4 - 10x^3 + 37x^2 - 60x + 36$$

and that $x = 1$ is chosen as a first approximation to a root. The polynomial is first evaluated by synthetic division, and then the quotient is similarly evaluated:

$$
\begin{array}{r|rrrrr}
1 & 1 & -10 & 37 & -60 & 36 \\
  &   & 1 & -9 & 28 & -32 \\
\hline
\text{Coefficients of } q(x): & 1 & -9 & 28 & -32 & \;4 = R = p(1) \\
  &   & 1 & -8 & 20 & \\
\hline
  & 1 & -8 & 20 & -12 = R_2 = p'(1) \\
\end{array}
$$

$$
x_1 = x_0 - \frac{p(x_0)}{p'(x_0)} = 1 - \left(\frac{4}{-12}\right) = 1.33
$$

The new approximation to the root is then used as the divisor in the synthetic division:

$$
\begin{array}{r|rrrrr}
1.33 & 1 & -10 & 37 & -60 & 36 \\
  &   & 1.33 & -11.5 & 34 & -34.6 \\
\hline
  & 1 & -8.67 & 25.5 & -26 & \;1.4 \quad R = p(1.33) \\
  &   & 1.33 & -9.76 & 21.0 & \\
\hline
  & 1 & -7.34 & 15.74 & -5 = R_2 = p'(1.33) \\
\end{array}
$$

$$
x_2 = 1.33 - \left(\frac{1.4}{-5}\right) = 1.61
$$

One more cycle brings the approximate value still closer to one of the roots, $x = 2$:

$$
\begin{array}{r|rrrrr}
1.61 & 1 & -10 & 37 & -60 & 36 \\
  &   & 1.61 & -13.5 & 37.8 & -35.7 \\
\hline
  & 1 & -8.39 & 23.5 & -22.2 & \;0.3 = R = p(1.61) \\
  &   & 1.61 & -10.9 & 20.3 & \\
\hline
  & 1 & -6.78 & 12.6 & -1.9 = R_2 = p'(1.61) \\
\end{array}
$$

$$
x_3 = 1.61 - \left(\frac{0.3}{-1.9}\right) = 1.77
$$

This process is iterative on several levels. The most often repeated, or "inner," cycle is the evaluation of the two polynomials; these evaluations are repeated until a root is found (or until a specified number of trials have been made); the root-improvement cycle must be repeated for each root of the n or less real roots of an nth-degree polynomial.

Example. Write a program which reads values for n and for the coefficients of an nth-degree polynomial and then finds the real roots of the polynomial until n roots are obtained or more than 100 trials of finding a root have been made.

In the absence of any other information, the initial trial value x_0 is chosen to be $-a_0/a_1$, the ratio of the constant and first-order coefficients of the polynomial. This choice is good if the polynomial has a root near zero since in that case the higher powers of x are small and the linear approximation $a_1x + a_0 = 0$ from which the ratio was determined would be reasonably close.

Although the synthetic-division procedure has already been illustrated, it is presented once more to show that the division of the two polynomials $p(x)$ and $q(x)$ can be performed in a single iterative cycle.

$$
\begin{array}{c|ccccccc}
x_0 & a_n & a_{n-1} & a_{n-2} & \ldots & a_j & \ldots & a_0 \\
\hline
& b_n & b_{n-1} & b_{n-2} & \ldots & b_j & \ldots & b_0 = R = p(x_0) \\
& 0 & c_n & c_{n-1} & \ldots & c_{j+1} & \ldots & c_1 = R_2 = p'(x_0)
\end{array}
$$

The displacement of the bottom row is intentional, for it allows the iteration to be described as follows (a single step is considered to be the computation of one column going from left to right):

$$
\begin{aligned}
b_n &= a_n \\
c_{n+1} &= 0 \\
b_j &= b_{j+1}x_0 + a_j \\
c_{j+1} &= c_{j+2}x_0 + b_{j+1}
\end{aligned} \Bigg\} \quad j = n - 1, \, n - 2, \ldots, 0
$$

Actually the c's need not be preserved as individual array elements since only the value of c_1 is needed. Because a c-element depends only upon its immediately preceding value, the procedure can be carried out without an array for the c-coefficients:

$$
\begin{aligned}
b_n &= a_n \\
c &= 0 \\
b_j &= b_{j+1}x_0 + a_j \\
c &= cx_0 + b_{j+1}
\end{aligned} \Bigg\} \quad j = n - 1, \ldots, 0
$$

The flow chart and the program for this example are presented in Fig. 10–10. The block indicating the substitutions $a_{k-1} = b_k$, $a_{k-2} = b_{k-1}, \ldots, a_0 = b_1$ is actually implemented by an iteration statement, and its purpose is to transfer the coefficients of the depressed equation to the a-array. As indicated, if 100 iterative trials are ever taken, the coefficients of the current polynomial and its degree k are printed before termination of the program.

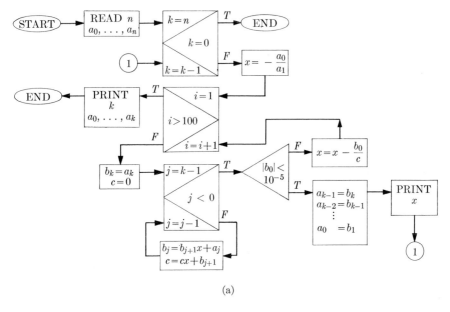

(a)

```
            DIMENSION  A(10),  B(10)
            INTEGER  I,  J,  K,  N
START       READ  DATA
            THROUGH  S1,  FOR  K = N,  −1,  K.E.1
            X  =  −A(0)/A(1)
            THROUGH  S2,  FOR  I = 1,  1,  I.G.  100
            B(K)  =  A(K)
            C  =  0.
            THROUGH  S3,  FOR  J = K − 1,  −1,  J.L.0
            B(J)  =  B(J + 1)∗X + A(J)
S3          C  =  C∗X + B(J + 1)
            WHENEVER  .ABS.  B(0)  .L.  1E − 5,  TRANSFER  TO  S4
S2          X  =  X − B(0)/C
            PRINT  RESULTS  K,  A(0) . . . A(K)
            TRANSFER  TO  S6
S4          THROUGH  S5,  FOR  J = K,  −1,  K.L.1
S5          A( J − 1)  =  B( J )
S1          PRINT  RESULTS  X
S6          END  OF  PROGRAM
Data
N = 4,  A(0) = 36,  −60,  37,  −10,  1∗
```

(b)

FIG. 10–10. (a) Flow chart. (b) Program.

The discussion of Newton's method has been limited to finding real roots. Actually the method is more general in the sense that if complex arithmetic operations are used, complex roots may be determined by means of this iterative technique. However, a little experience with this method of complex-root determination for equations with real coefficients convinces one that a better technique must be possible. This conviction arises from the fact that the complex roots of a polynomial with real coefficients, if any, occur in conjugate pairs and hence, once one root is known, its conjugate is also known and need not be determined by iteration. The additional complexities of complex arithmetic can be eliminated if the quadratic factor, the product of the linear factors representing the conjugate roots, can be factored from the polynomial by iteration. The division technique can again be applied, but the trial divisor will be of the form $x^2 + px + q$:

$$p(x) = (x^2 + px + q)(b_n x^{n-2} + b_{n-1} x^{n-3} + \cdots + b_2) + (b_1 x + b_0)$$

The parenthesized expressions on the right are the divisor, quotient and remainder, respectively. By deleting the variable names and changing the signs of the divisor to substitute addition for subtraction, one may write these components in synthetic-division form:

$$
\begin{array}{ccccccccc}
p & q & a_n & a_{n-1} & a_{n-2} & a_{n-3} & \cdots & a_2 & a_1 & a_0 \\
& & & pb_n & qb_n & & & & & \\
& & & & pb_{n-1} & qb_{n-1} & & & & \\
& & & & & pb_{n-2} & \cdots & qb & & \\
& & & & & & & pb_3 & qb_3 & \\
& & & & & & & & pb_2 & qb_2 \\
\hline
& & b_n & b_{n-1} & b_{n-2} & & \cdots & b_2 & b_1 & b_0
\end{array}
$$

The rules for obtaining the quotient coefficients can be written from this diagram:

$$
\begin{aligned}
b_n &= a_n \\
b_{n-1} &= a_{n-1} + pb_n \\
b_j &= a_j + pb_{j+1} + qb_{j+2}, \qquad \text{for } j = n-2, n-3, \ldots, 1 \\
b_0 &= a_0 + qb_2
\end{aligned}
$$

The divisor is a factor when the coefficients of the remainder, b_1 and b_0, are zero. The basis of the iteration is to select values of p and q that make these coefficients zero:

$$
\begin{aligned}
b_0 &= a_0 + qb_2 \\
b_1 &= a_1 + pb_2 + qb_3
\end{aligned}
$$

The next trial values, p' and q', are therefore

$$q' = -\frac{a_0}{b_2}$$

$$p' = -\left(\frac{a_1 + qb_3}{b_2}\right)$$

Once the process converges, the two roots of the factor can, of course, be computed from $x = (-p \pm \sqrt{p^2 - 4q})/2$. With the factor removed, the depressed equation can again be subjected to iteration or, if it is now of degree 2 or 1, simply solved.

By way of review and as an indication of procedures available for the isolation of quadratic factors, recall that Newton's method was obtained from Taylor's series and Lin's method from the finite-difference approximation. The former was a second-order process and required the evaluation of the derivative, while the latter was of first order and involved only values of the function. Similarly, for polynomials the two approaches are possible with the same qualifications. Specifically, the iterative isolation of quadratic factors, which is not completely described here although it is the most popular approach to polynomial-root finding, is called Lin's method if the finite-difference approach above is used, and Bairstowe's method when the scheme involves the evaluation of the derivative.

Additional Programming Topics

The description of the numerical methods to be considered next will be facilitated by the use of two-dimensional array notation. Hence it is appropriate now to digress from numerical methods to consider array notation in general, as well as several other diverse programming topics.

HIGHER-DIMENSIONAL ARRAYS

As mentioned before, a matrix or higher-dimensional array element is identified by more than one coordinate. For instance, to obtain the value of a specific element, a_{ij}, one must have values for both of the subscript variables i and j. A point of great relevance in programming is the range of subscript variables. Conventionally, such variables may have integer values, with the smallest value being 0 or 1, that is, $0 \leq i < m$ and $0 \leq j < n$.

Since computer storage elements are designated by a single number (or coordinate), it is apparent that the storage can be regarded as being *built* as one large linear array. Therefore, multicoordinate references to storage, e.g., a matrix element, must be converted to an equivalent single coordinate reference before a particular value can be located. Carrying this notion of equivalence a little further, one finds that there can be several levels of identification for a particular storage location. This storage cell has a built-in numerical address, say 1207; it may also be an element of a linear array, say a_4; and it may also be convenient to identify that particular linear array element with a two-coordinate designation, say $a_{0,0}$. This multiple naming is more apparent perhaps from the diagram below.

1202	1203	1204	1205	1206	1207	1208	1209	1210	1211	...
	a_0	a_1	a_2	a_3	a_4	a_5	a_6	a_7	a_8	...
					$a_{0,0}$	$a_{0,1}$	$a_{0,2}$	$a_{1,0}$	$a_{1,1}$	...
Conventional matrix notation →					$a_{1,1}$	$a_{1,2}$	$a_{1,3}$	$a_{2,1}$	$a_{2,2}$	...

148

Note that the identification described imposes others: a_3 must correspond to 1206, a_5 to 1208, etc. Some convention is needed to identify other two-dimensional elements; the one most often adopted is illustrated in the diagram, that is, the rightmost subscript is increased by one (going from left to right) until it reaches the highest value in its range when the next subscript to the left is increased by one, and so on. With this order established, it is possible to write a simple formula which, given the two-dimensional subscripts, describes a technique of finding the equivalent linear subscript. Once the linear subscript is found, the actual machine address is readily determined. Simply add the linear subscript to the machine address of a_0, a task that index registers were built to perform. The problem is then:

Given $a_{i,j}$, $0 \leq i < m$, $0 \leq j < n$, and given that $a_{0,0}$ corresponds to a_b, determine k so that $a_{i,j}$ corresponds to a_k.

Just from observation one can see that

$$k = b + in + j$$

Matters are a little more complicated than this, since the subscripts of the first element in matrices (the upper left corner) are usually unity, although it is very common for linear arrays to have a zeroth element. With this modification, the matrix indicated by the appended row,

$$
\begin{array}{ccc}
a_{1,1} & a_{1,2} & a_{1,3} \\
a_{2,1} & a_{2,2} & a_{2,3} \\
a_{3,1} & a_{3,2} & a_{3,3}
\end{array}
$$

would be composed of the linear array elements

$$
\begin{array}{ccc}
a_4 & a_5 & a_6 \\
a_7 & a_8 & a_9 \\
a_{10} & a_{11} & a_{12}
\end{array}
$$

The formula with the subscript ranges adjusted to be $1 \leq i \leq m$, $1 \leq j \leq n$ is

$$k = b + (i - 1)n + (j - 1)$$

Checking the specific case $a_{2,3}$, one finds that

$$k = 4 + (2 - 1)3 + (3 - 1) = 9$$

or $a_{2,3} \sim a_9$ as shown by the two square arrays.

Multiple subscripts are, in fact, similar to the digits of a positional number where the understood multipliers for each digit are not integral powers of a base. The British pounds-shillings-pence price of 2/16/18 is such an example and may be expanded as $2(240) + 16(12) + 8 = 680$ or

$(2 \cdot \overline{20} + 16)\overline{12} + 8 = 680$. The overlined numbers give the number of values in the ranges, e.g., 20 shillings in one pound, 12 pence in a shilling. The linear subscript corresponding to an array element $a_{i,j,k,l}$, whose base correspondence is $a_{1,1,1,1} \sim a_b$, and whose subscripts have the ranges $m_1 \leq i \leq m_2$, $n_1 \leq j \leq n_2$, $p_1 \leq k \leq p_2$, $q_1 \leq l \leq q_2$ is similarly given by

$$r = b + (((i - 1)\overline{n_2 - n_1 + 1} + (j - 1))\overline{p_2 - p_1 + 1} + (k - 1))$$
$$\times \overline{q_2 - q_1 + 1} + (l - 1)$$

Note that m_1 and m_2, which give the range of i, are not needed in the formula. In summary, to convert an element with N subscripts to an equivalent linear subscript, the following information is required:

(1) N, the number of subscripts;
(2) b, the linear subscript which corresponds to the first array element;
(3) the ranges of the subscripts except for the upper bound of the leftmost subscript.

Matters are a little simpler if the smallest values of the subscripts are assumed to be 1; that is, $m_1 = n_1 = p_1 = q_1 = 1$. The required information is then

$$N, \quad b, \quad \underbrace{n_2, \quad p_2, \quad \dots}_{N - 1 \text{ upper bounds}}$$

The format above suggests that this information be conveyed as a linear array which might be called a *dimension vector*. In the MAD language the simplification mentioned above is adopted and, when it is desirable to refer to elements of an array with the multiple subscript notation, it is necessary to associate with the array a dimension vector. This association is made explicit in the DIMENSION statement. Thus a linear array A for which 100 locations are to be reserved, and for which, in addition, elements of A are to be selected by references such as A(I, J) or A(I, J, K), is associated with a dimension vector, named ADIM, as follows:

DIMENSION A(99, ADIM)

The name ADIM is, more accurately, the name of a vector element whose value is N. Pursuing this example, the content of ADIM(0) (which is the same as ADIM) is N, that of ADIM(1) is b, that of ADIM(2) is n_2, etc.

Very often dimension vectors are constant, i.e., they are not changed during the course of a computation. It would be useful to be able to preset such vectors to their constant values before execution of the program, thus eliminating the need to read these vector values or set them by means of substitution statements. The VECTOR VALUES statement accomplishes this task and hence is a declaration statement since it causes no action during the execution of the program but merely causes the constants named to become a part of the translated program. The form of the statement is

$$\text{VECTOR VALUES } \alpha_k = \mathcal{L}$$

where α_k is the name of a linear array element and $\mathcal{L}$ is a list of constants usually separated by commas. Note that α_k is given the value of the first element on the list, α_{k+1} the value of the second, etc. As a specific example, VECTOR VALUES ADIM(4) = 2, 1, 8 would cause the elements ADIM(4), ADIM(5), ADIM(6) to initially have the integer values 2, 1, and 8, respectively. In all contexts, a vector element written without a subscript corresponds to the zeroth element.

As a complete illustration, suppose that a problem requires three two-dimensional matrices A, B, C which are 10 × 10, 3 × 20, and 8 × 12, respectively. The designation used, for example, 8 × 12, indicates that the matrix has 8 rows and 12 columns; such an array would, of course, require a total of 96 locations. As additional specifications, the A(1, 1) is to correspond to A(11), B(1, 1) to B(1), C(1, 1) to C(1), and the B- and C-arrays are associated with the same dimension vector DIM. The statements are:

> DIMENSION A(110, DA), B(60, DIM), C(96, DIM(3))
> VECTOR VALUES DA = 2, 11, 10
> VECTOR VALUES DIM = 2, 1, 20
> VECTOR VALUES DIM(3) = 2, 1, 12

The last two statements could be combined into

$$\text{VECTOR VALUES DIM} = 2, 1, 20, 2, 1, 12$$

The vectors DA and DIM, except for their identification as containing dimension information, are ordinary linear arrays, and hence their elements may be changed by substitution statements at any point in the program. The implication of this last remark is that the basis for locating multiple-subscripted elements may be changed during the course of a computation.

The subscript bounds m_2, n_2, etc., are truly bounds in that if a matrix is designated to have 6 elements in a row, that is, $m_2 = 6$, then the algorithm will work properly even if the highest column index is in fact 3. The storage pattern makes this clear:

$$A_0 \quad A_1 \quad A_2 \quad A_3 \quad A_4 \quad A_5 \quad A_6 \quad A_7 \quad A_8 \quad A_9 \quad A_{10} \quad \cdots$$
$$\quad\;\; A_{1,1} \quad A_{1,2} \quad A_{1,3} \qquad\qquad\qquad A_{2,1} \quad A_{2,2} \quad A_{2,3} \qquad \cdots$$

The result of a bound which is larger than necessity demands is simply that storage is not used compactly, i.e., some unused spaces precede the initial elements of each row. Although such excessive bounds do not cause any computational difficulty, they may cause excessive printing when the block notation for arrays is used. The reason for this extra printing is apparent from the mechanism for handling such blocks. According to the storage diagram above, the block designation $A(1, 1) \ldots A(2, 3)$ is converted to the linear designation $A(1) \ldots A(9)$ before the block is located. Thus, since the maximum column index used (3) was less than the maximum designated (6), nine locations were referred to instead of six as was probably intended. To avoid this minor difficulty it is good practice, though not necessary, to make the maximum subscript in the dimension vector correspond to the actual maximum used in a particular execution of a problem. It often occurs that a matrix is used whose size is a variable, that is, it is $m \times n$, where m and n are variables. The maximum size of the linear array which is to contain this two-dimensional array must be specified as a numerical constant. Thus, if the program was designed for $m \leq 20$ and $n \leq 30$, then the size of the linear array reserved must be $20 \times 30 = 600$. But since the particular value of m may vary, the following sequence is advisable:

> DIMENSION MTX (600, D)
> VECTOR VALUES D = 2, 1, 0
> READ DATA   (causes a value for N to be read)
> D(2) = N
> $\vdots$

Now, since the upper range of the column index is exact, block notation does not present any problems.

It should be emphasized that the VECTOR VALUES statement is not limited to uses in this context; it is used simply to initially set the elements of a linear array to given constant values. Thus, for example,

> VECTOR VALUES CON = 3.1416, 2.1892, 88.92

causes the floating-point constants shown on the right to become the initial values of CON(0), CON(1), and CON(2).

The dimension vector could be arranged in another way which reduces the amount of computation required to determine the equivalent linear subscript. However, this alternative is cumbersome when dimensions greater than two are considered. The technique, "trading space for time," is a familiar one in computer programming. The number of elements in the dimension vector is increased so that the equivalent linear subscript can be computed without multiplication. Using the same notation as before, but limiting the discussion to two-dimensional arrays, one could set up the dimension vector as follows:

$$
\begin{aligned}
&d_1 \qquad b - 1\\
&d_2 \qquad b + n_2 - 1\\
&d_3 \qquad b + 2n_2 - 1\\
&d_4 \qquad b + 3n_2 - 1\\
&d_5 \qquad b + 4n_2 - 1\\
&\ \vdots \qquad\ \ \vdots\\
&d_{m_2} \quad\ b + (m_2 - 1)n_2 - 1
\end{aligned}
$$

For an element $a_{i,j}$, it is assumed here that $1 \le i \le m_2$, $1 \le j \le n_2$ and that the initial element is $a_{1,1}$. With this arrangement, the equivalent linear subscript, k, which corresponds to the double subscript (i, j) is obtained as

$$k = d_i + j$$

The dimension vector for the specific example used earlier would then be

$$
\begin{array}{ccc}
d_1, & d_2, & d_3\\
3, & 6, & 9
\end{array}
$$

and for $(i, j) = (2, 3)$,

$$k = d_i + j = 6 + 3 = 9$$

This implementation is not used in the language described herein; rather the dimension vector is constructed as described earlier. However, the approach just discussed is a more expeditious way of converting double subscripts to the equivalent linear form.

ITERATION SCOPES

A repetitive sequence which is described by the iteration statement

$$\text{S1} \qquad \text{THROUGH S2, FOR I} = 1, 1, \text{I .G. N}$$

is represented by the flow chart shown in Fig. 11–1. The final box in the

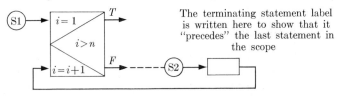

FIGURE 11–1

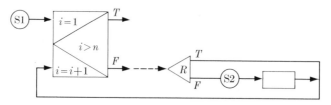

FIGURE 11-2

scope of the iteration is often a simple substitution statement although it may be any executable statement, even one preceded by a conditional prefix. Occasionally, there is a conditional expression in the scope of an iteration which, if true, should result in skipping the entire scope. The flow chart describing this situation is given in Fig. 11-2. Note that

$$\text{WHENEVER } \mathcal{R}, \text{ TRANSFER TO S1}$$

will not accomplish the desired result since i would again be set to 1 instead of continuing the cycle as desired. What is needed in this case is a label which follows, not precedes, the final box to indicate the end of the sequence being repeated. This terminal designation may be accomplished by making the final block a statement which does not produce any useful computation, such as

$$\text{S2} \quad \text{X} = \text{X}$$

and then, when $\mathcal{R}$ is true, a transfer is made to S2. This occasional need for a statement whose purpose is merely to provide a label is met by the CONTINUE statement. If

$$\text{S2} \quad \text{CONTINUE}$$

is used as the terminal statement of the iteration, transfers to this statement will cause the iteration variable to be properly incremented. The previously encountered END OF CONDITIONAL statement is similar in that it is not computational but serves to designate the terminus of a statement group. When labeled, this statement can be used to designate the end of an iteration.

INPUT-OUTPUT OPTIONS

For most scientific problems the input and output procedures which have been described are adequate. The important thing is to produce correct results correctly identified. However, it is convenient, particularly when a great many input and output numbers are involved, to read and print information in a more compact form. For instance, with a large volume of data it would be convenient to dispense with variable names on the input list and to permit more flexibility in the form of the numbers. If a number is always written with two decimal places, it could be *described* in this form, and then the space-consuming decimal point need not appear explicitly. The elimination of names may be accomplished by accompanying the READ statement with a list of variables which are to be quantified from an input list of numbers, the understanding being that the input values are in the same order as the list of names. Similarly, output values could be *described* as to their printing form and identifying names could be included or omitted, as desired. However, this more flexible scheme raises the problem of how to write these *format descriptions* as well as identify, by a list, the variables involved in the input or output procedure. In developing a language for the purpose of describing the form of numbers, there is no precedent to fall back on; moreover, it cannot be universal since the descriptions are closely tied to the particular input-output media used.

One approach might be to augment the variable list with the format descriptions discussed above. The statement might be written:

READ DATA   K(INTEGER, 2 POSITIONS), X
        (EXPONENTIAL FORM, 4 POSITIONS, 2 DECIMAL
        PLACES)

Quite obviously, a lot can be gained in the way of concise expression if the parenthesized descriptions are encoded in shorter form. Also (but perhaps not so obviously) greater flexibility can be achieved if the list of descriptions can be separated from the list of variables because then the same format description list can apply to more than one variable list or, conversely, different format descriptions may be associated with the same variable list. However, even if these two descriptive functions are made distinct in separate lists, the format descriptions and the variable names must be in the same order to permit one to identify one with the other.

As an example of an encoding scheme that has evolved, the form of the value of a variable to be read or printed is described with the code $Lm.n$, where L is a letter designating the type of variable, m is an integer specifying the number of positions (e.g., columns on a card, printing positions on paper) occupied by the quantity, and n is the number of decimal places which are assumed, if relevant (counting from the right of the number). Some code letters and their meanings are listed in Table 11–1. The C-group deserves some amplification. Each character in the 709 computer is represented in binary-coded decimal (BCD) form as six bits. The letter A, for example, is represented by 010001 and the number 9 by

TABLE 11–1

Code letter (L)	External representation (on card or paper)	Internal representation (in storage)
I	Integer—simple number without a decimal point Ex 12, 21, —3	Integer
F	Number—printed with a decimal point or a decimal point understood Ex 4.2, —684.3, .005	Floating point
E	Number—printed with an exponent (with or without decimal point) Ex 2 E—4, 14 E2, 1.673E3	Floating point
C	Character—printed as an alphabetic, numerical, or special character Ex AB, +23, A + C	Integer

001001. One can see, then, that these characters can be treated as binary integers. The scheme becomes a little confusing, however, when numbers are treated as BCD characters. The number $(86)_{10}$ is equal to $(1010110)_2$ but, treated as two BCD characters, it is 001000 000110. However, these twelve bits may still be treated as a binary integer, stored, and compared so that character manipulation is possible.

With this code, then, four numbers could be described by the following format description list:

$$I4, \quad I4, \quad F8.2, \quad E9.2$$

The first two are integers occupying four digit positions. For convenience in handling such repeated field descriptions, as these code groups are called, the number of repetitions may precede the descriptions, that is, 2I4. The complete description format then is $kLm.n$, where k is the multiplicity. The next number is an eight-position floating-point number (external form, without an exponent) with two decimal places, and the last field description applies to a nine-position number in exponential form, with two decimal places in the fractional part.

When a format description does not vary during the execution of a program, the VECTOR VALUES statement may be used to initially set a linear array so that it contains the BCD form of a format description. To indicate that a sequence of characters is to be interpreted as characters, instead of, for instance, being converted to binary numbers, dollar signs ($) are used to enclose the sequence which is to be understood in this fashion.

Here the dollar signs are analogous to quotation marks in everyday English; their use for this purpose has been encountered before in the PRINT COMMENT statement. For the example above, the VECTOR VALUES statement would be

$$\text{VECTOR VALUES F1} = \$2I4, \text{ F8.2, E9.2*}\$$$

and the characters enclosed by dollar signs on the right would become, in BCD form, the initial values of F1(0), F1(1), and F1(2). The asterisk indicates the end of a format description. Three array elements are used because one 36-bit word can contain six 6-bit characters and there are 16 characters included between the dollar signs. (Blanks are counted as characters.)

With this format description language briefly described, one can then introduce alternative input-output statements that require such descriptions. For example, there is an input statement of the form

$$\text{READ FORMAT } \upsilon, \text{ } \pounds$$

where υ is an element of a linear array and $\pounds$ is a list of variable names. Some additional words make the statement more understandable. READ [according to the] FORMAT [whose first word is stored in vector element] υ, [values for the variables] $\pounds$.

As an illustration,

$$\text{READ FORMAT F1, J, K, X, EPSLON}$$
$$\text{VECTOR VALUES F1} = \$ \text{ } 2I4, \text{ F8.2, E9.2*}\$$$

There is a similar output statement,

$$\text{PRINT FORMAT } \upsilon, \text{ } \pounds$$

which differs only in that the list, $\pounds$, may contain expressions as well as variable names, and the format description, in addition to describing a printed line, must somehow convey information about the spacing of the line. The first group of characters in a line description gives such spacing information by the following code:

1H☐	(blank)		space one line
1H0			space two lines
1H1		Before printing	skip to top of next page
1H2			skip to next half page
1H4			skip to next fourth page

For the example above, the statement,

PRINT FORMAT F1 = I, I + J, X, Z*4.0 − Y
VECTOR VALUES F1 = $1H1, 2I4, F8.2, E9.2*$

would indicate that the four numbers in the line described would print at the top of a page.

This account is by no means a complete description of the specification of formats. Some of the items not discussed and best left to programming manuals are: (1) The repetition of format descriptions for lists of variable length. (2) The inclusion of labels among printed numbers. (3) Multiple-line descriptions. (4) Line and card space limitations—only 72 positions can be described in a single punched card (8 positions, or columns, of a card are used for identification purposes) and, for many printers, there are 131 printing positions per line.

Although the examples above have shown the format specification written as a constant, it should be clear that, since characters can be read and the format vector is just an ordinary linear array, its value (the format description) could be read as datum during the execution of a program. Setting the value of a format vector in this manner means that the format description itself can be variable and take different "values" from one computing run to another.

RELOCATABLE PROGRAMS

With some background now as to what constitutes a machine program, the idea of a relocatable program should be understandable. A machine program occupies a particular region of storage. Part of the region is filled with instructions, part with necessary constants, and part is reserved for data and working storage. For the most part the address parts of the instructions in this region refer either to instructions (transfer instructions) or to constants, data, and working storage in the same regions (arithmetic operations). The exception to these self-contained references are transfers to other routines, or subroutines, which are not contained in the region. Pictorially, such a machine program can be represented as a block within a larger block which is the main storage of the computer (Fig. 11–3). The external references are shown in this diagram as transfers to a routine which computes the sine of a number transmitted to the routine and a transfer to a square-root routine. Such a machine program could be moved, or relocated, in storage if the amount of the relocation, i.e., the number of storage cells by which the routine is to be displaced, is added to every address in the region. With three precautions, this relocation process can be carried out. (1) The identity of the routine itself and the location

STORAGE

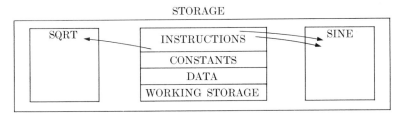

FIGURE 11-3

of its first instruction must be preserved since other routines may transfer to it. (2) The transfers to other routines cannot be obtained by simply adding a constant to the address since such an address is not in the region being moved. (3) Constants must not be altered in such a move. Therefore constants must be identified and left unchanged. Only the locations of the constants will be altered by the fixed amount, not the values of the constants themselves. Indeed, some of the addresses of instructions must be regarded as constants also. Thus AXT 3, 1 (address to index true—in octal, 0774001 00003) must not have its address part, 00003, altered in a move. To identify what is constant and what is relocatable, additional information must be included in the program.

Item (2) above is, in a sense, the converse of (1). According to (1), a routine and its initial instruction must be identified, and (2) sets forth the need for identifying routines called on, i.e., transferred to, by the routine identified under (1). If the identification is assumed to be an alphabetic name, transfers to other routines could be designated by substituting the alphabetic name for the address and assuming that the name would be replaced by the initial address when the routine called on had been located in storage. Since a routine may be called on many times, the address-replacement procedure mentioned above can be simplified if only one reference to another routine is included in a program, regardless of how many times the routine is, in fact, called on. This single reference can be effected by transferring to another transfer instruction *within* the program's own region. The instruction transferred to is then the only reference to the other routine. Perhaps an illustration will help at this point. Suppose that there is a routine called HAR, for *har*monic analysis, which makes many references to the sine (SIN) and cosine (COS) routines. Incorporating now the identifying name, initial location, and the relocation information, one can see that both diagrams in Fig. 11-4 describe the routine. Diagram (b) shows that only one replacement of SIN and COS by transfers to the proper initial location was sufficient to link this routine (HAR) with the sine and cosine. The list of names of routines called on is called a *transfer vector*.

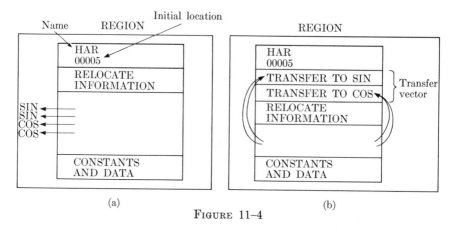

FIGURE 11-4

In summary, then, machine programs, or routines, are generally written in standardized, relocatable form so that they may be easily used, without change, with other programs in the same form. The various relocatable routines which make up an entire program are relocated so that they are compactly stored in storage and linked together (the symbolic transfer vectors are replaced by appropriate transfers) by a loading routine. Since all such programs are moved in storage before they are actually executed, they are uniformly written in a region whose initial location is 00000. The necessary constituents of a relocatable program are:

(1) Identifying information; the symbolic name(s) of the routine and the addresses of matching initial instruction or entry point; also the number of locations in the region, as well as the size of the transfer vector.

(2) Connecting information or transfer vector; a list of the names of routines called on. These names are replaced by transfers by the loading routine.

(3) Relocation information; a code associated with every word of the routine indicating whether or not the address portion(s) of the word are to be altered in the relocation process.

(4) The instructions and constants.

It should be apparent from this description that an external function is a separate relocatable routine and, once it is translated to the machine language form, it need not be retranslated for incorporation with any other relocatable routine. An internal function, however, is merely a part of a larger relocatable routine.

Interpolation

It is probably difficult to identify interpolation, in the context in which one is first introduced to the word, as a special case of rational approximation. The table-scanning problem of finding an intermediate value between two tabulated values is simply one of approximating the tabulated function by a straight line near the point of interest and then evaluating the straight line by means of the given argument. This process lends itself readily to symbolic description. Suppose that one is given the table,

$$
\begin{array}{ll}
x_0 & f(x_0) \\
x_1 & f(x_1) \\
x_2 & f(x_2) \\
x_3 & f(x_3)
\end{array}
$$

and it is desired to find the approximate functional value which corresponds to an argument x, where $x_1 < x < x_2$. The usual formula is

$$
f(x) \approx f(x_1) + \frac{x - x_1}{x_2 - x_1} \left(f(x_2) - f(x_1) \right)
$$

With a little algebraic rearrangement this formula can be written $f(x) \approx Ax + B$, where A and B are constants; hence the approximation is a straight line (or first-degree polynomial). For our purposes, however, it is more interesting to write

$$
f(x) \approx f[x_1] + f[x_2, x_1](x - x_1)
$$

or to eliminate the "approximately equal":

$$
p(x) = f[x_1] + f[x_2, x_1](x - x_1)
$$

The familiar linear interpolation, then, is simply representing the function by the first two terms of the divided-difference polynomial $p(x)$. This identification suggests that more generalized interpolation procedures can be produced by simply including more terms of the divided-difference polynomial. If, in addition, the development of the divided-difference polynomial is recalled, a complete definition of "interpolation" can be formulated. The divided-difference polynomial was constructed from tabular values in such a way that it equaled the given functional values at the given arguments; that is, $f(x_0) = p(x_0), f(x_1) = p(x_1), f(x_2) = p(x_2)$, etc. With this additional qualification, interpolation is defined as follows:

> Given $n + 1$ noncoincident points (abscissas and ordinates) and an argument x, then in the interval containing the given abscissas, nth-degree *interpolation* is accomplished by constructing the nth-degree polynomial which passes through the given points and by evaluating it for the given argument.

If x is outside the interval containing the abscissas, the process is *extrapolation*. The divided-difference polynomial provides a way of constructing the nth-degree polynomial, but whatever scheme is employed, there is only one nth-degree polynomial which will pass through the given $n + 1$ points. This last statement is true because the assumption that there is more than one such polynomial leads to a contradiction. Suppose that $p(x)$ and $q(x)$ are nth-degree polynomials which are equal for $x = x_0$, $x_1, \ldots, x_n$; that is,

$$p(x_0) = q(x_0), \quad p(x_1) = q(x_1), \ldots, \quad p(x_n) = q(x_n)$$

Then the difference, $p(x) - q(x)$, which is at most an nth-degree polynomial, is zero at $n + 1$ points; this is a contradiction, since an nth-degree polynomial can have only n zeros (or roots).

The subject of interpolation seems to have been quickly dispatched since for a given set of points only one approximating polynomial can be produced and the divided-difference interpolation polynomial provides an effective method of producing it. There are some alternative procedures which, of course, produce the same polynomial, but nonetheless deserve attention; either they are obvious, they have computational advantages, or they are useful specializations.

SIMULTANEOUS-EQUATION APPROACH

Under the obvious category is the straightforward approach described below. As before, the given data are the tabular values.

$$
\begin{array}{cc}
x_0 & f(x_0) \\
x_1 & f(x_1) \\
x_2 & f(x_2) \\
\vdots & \vdots \\
x_n & f(x_n)
\end{array}
$$

What is sought are the coefficients of an nth-degree polynomial, a_0, $a_1, \ldots, a_n$, which passes through these given points; that is,

$$a_0 + a_1 x_0 + a_2 x_0^2 + \cdots + a_n x_0^n = f(x_0)$$
$$a_0 + a_1 x_1 + a_2 x_1^2 + \cdots + a_n x_1^n = f(x_1)$$
$$a_0 + a_1 x_2 + a_2 x_2^2 + \cdots + a_n x_2^n = f(x_2)$$
$$\vdots \qquad\qquad\qquad \vdots$$
$$a_0 + a_1 x_n + a_2 x_n^2 + \cdots + a_n x_n^n = f(x_n)$$

There are $n + 1$ linear equations in this set, and there are $n + 1$ unknowns (the a's, not the x's). Hence, solving this set of equations determines the interpolation polynomial. To illustrate the equivalence of this approach to the one using the divided-difference polynomial, consider the two-point case:

$$a_0 + a_1 x_0 = f(x_0)$$
$$a_0 + a_1 x_1 = f(x_1)$$

Subtracting the first equation from the second determines a_1:

$$a_1(x_1 - x_0) = f(x_1) - f(x_0)$$

$$a_1 = \frac{f(x_1) - f(x_0)}{x_1 - x_0} = f[x_1, x_0]$$

and substituting this result in the first equation determines a_0:

$$a_0 = f(x_0) - a_1 x_0 = f(x_0) - f[x_1, x_0] x_0$$

so that

$$f(x) = f[x_1, x_0] x + (-f[x_1, x_0] x_0 + f(x_0))$$

This result is the form $Ax + B$ alluded to earlier, but it is easily recognized as the first two terms of the divided-difference interpolation polynomial.

At this point, the question can be raised, why, since this method is so straightforward, is it not used as the basis for interpolation rather than the notationally more complex divided-difference approach? There are three answers: (1) Solving simultaneous linear equations is computationally (if not conceptually) more complex than forming difference tables and interpolating polynomials from these tables. (2) The difference tables are useful in the estimation of error. (3) The divided differences can be readily specialized to the commonly occurring equal-interval tables.

LAGRANGIAN INTERPOLATION

For computational reasons it would be of advantage to have an interpolation method that did not require the computation of a divided-difference table or the solution of simultaneous equations. Such a method would be particularly useful when only one or two interpolations are computed in a given range of tabular values. One way of deriving such a method is to take the divided-difference polynomial and, by algebraic manipulation, write it so that the given ordinates $f(x_0), f(x_1), \ldots, f(x_n)$ do not appear in differences but explicitly. The first step is to rewrite the divided differences in this form:

$$f[x_0] = f(x_0)$$

$$f[x_1, x_0] = \frac{f(x_1) - f(x_0)}{x_1 - x_0} = \frac{f(x_1)}{x_1 - x_0} + \frac{f(x_0)}{x_0 - x_1}$$

$$f[x_2, x_1, x_0] = \frac{\begin{aligned}[t] [f(x_2)/(x_2 - x_1) + f(x_1)/(x_1 - x_2)] \\ - [f(x_1)/(x_1 - x_0) + f(x_0)/(x_0 - x_1)] \end{aligned}}{x_2 - x_0}$$

$$= \frac{f(x_2)}{(x_2 - x_1)(x_2 - x_0)} + \frac{f(x_1)}{(x_1 - x_2)(x_1 - x_0)}$$

$$+ \frac{f(x_0)}{(x_0 - x_2)(x_0 - x_1)}$$

The algebra becomes involved beyond this point but a pattern is apparent:

$$f[x_n, x_{n-1}, \ldots, x_0] = \frac{f(x_n)}{(x_n - x_{n-1}) \cdots (x_n - x_0)}$$

$$+ \frac{f(x_{n-1})}{(x_{n-1} - x_n)(x_{n-1} - x_{n-2}) \cdots (x_{n-1} - x_0)} + \cdots$$

$$+ \frac{f(x_0)}{(x_0 - x_n) \cdots (x_0 - x_1)} = \sum_{i=0}^{n} \frac{f(x_i)(x_i - x_i)}{\prod_{j=0}^{n} (x_i - x_j)}$$

The (seemingly) zero factor in the numerator $(x_i - x_i)$ is included to cancel the factor $(x_i - x_j)$, where $i = j$ in the denominator. A more satisfying form of expressing this deletion of a term in the denominator is

$$f[x_n, x_{n-1}, \ldots, x_0] = \sum_{i=0}^{n} \frac{f(x_i)}{\prod_{j=0, j \neq i}^{n} (x_i - x_j)}$$

It is apparent from writing the divided differences in this form that they are symmetric. For instance, reversing the values of x_1 and x_0 in the first divided difference does not change its value since the terms are additive and x_1 and x_0 appear symmetrically in every term. In fact, permutations of the x's in divided differences of any order do not result in a change in value. This result can be stated differently: In computing an nth-order divided difference, one can introduce the $n + 1$ values in any order without affecting the result.

Returning to the original task, one now uses these symmetric forms to replace the divided difference in, say, a second-degree polynomial:

$$p(x) = f[x_0] + (x - x_0)f[x_1, x_0] + (x - x_0)(x - x_1)f[x_2, x_1, x_0]$$

$$= f(x_0) + (x - x_0)\left\{\frac{f(x_1)}{x_1 - x_0} + \frac{f(x_0)}{x_0 - x_1}\right\} + (x - x_0)(x - x_1)$$

$$\times \left\{\frac{f(x_2)}{(x_2 - x_0)(x_2 - x_1)} + \frac{f(x_1)}{(x_1 - x_2)(x_1 - x_0)} + \frac{f(x_0)}{(x_0 - x_2)(x_0 - x_1)}\right\}$$

which, after some algebraic labor, reduces to the *Lagrangian* form:

$$p(x) = \frac{(x - x_1)(x - x_2)}{(x_0 - x_1)(x_0 - x_2)}\,f(x_0) + \frac{(x - x_0)(x - x_2)}{(x_1 - x_0)(x_1 - x_2)}\,f(x_1)$$

$$+ \frac{(x - x_0)(x - x_1)}{(x_2 - x_0)(x_2 - x_1)}\,f(x_2)$$

$$= \sum_{i=0}^{2} \prod_{\substack{j=0 \\ j \neq i}}^{2} \left[\frac{x - x_j}{x_i - x_j}\right] f(x_i)$$

Observe that no difference table is required to evaluate this second-degree polynomial. To be sure, the coefficients of the given ordinates are fairly complex, but their systematic form means that their computation can be simply described by a computer program. The generalization to an nth-degree polynomial is obtained by inserting n, instead of 2, for the terminal values of the indices i and j.

Relating the Lagrangian form to the divided-difference polynomial, as was done here, has the advantage that the error term need not be examined again since it is the same as it was before. However, an alternative development similar to the divided-difference case is perhaps easier to understand. Assume that an nth-degree polynomial has the form

$$p(x) = a_0(x - x_1)(x - x_2) \cdots (x - x_n)$$

$$+ a_1(x - x_0)(x - x_2) \cdots (x - x_n) + \cdots$$

$$+ a_n(x - x_0)(x - x_1) \cdots (x - x_{n-1})$$

This form, i.e., the sum of factored polynomials, guarantees that all terms but one will be zero when $x = x_0, x_1, x_2, \ldots, x_n$. Thus a_0 may be determined when $x = x_0$:

$$f(x_0) = p(x_0) = a_0(x_0 - x_1)(x_0 - x_2) \cdots (x_0 - x_n)$$

$$a_0 = \frac{f(x_0)}{(x_0 - x_1)(x_0 - x_2) \cdots (x_0 - x_n)}$$

In general, a_k can be determined by letting $x = x_k$, where $k = 0, 1, 2, \ldots, n$:

$$a_k = \frac{f(x_k)}{(x_k - x_1) \cdots (x_k - x_{k-1})(x_k - x_{k+1}) \cdots (x_k - x_n)}$$

If these coefficients are substituted into the original polynomial, it is identifiable as the Lagrangian form just described. The computation of this interpolation polynomial provides an interesting programming example since it involves a nested iteration having a conditional computation in its scope. To numerically illustrate Lagrangian interpolation before proceeding to such an example, let us suppose that second-degree interpolation is to be used to find an approximate value for $f(3.5)$ from the following table.

	x	$f(x)$
x_0	2	10
x_1	3	30
x_2	4	68
x_3	5	130

We write

$$f(3.5) \approx \frac{(x - x_1)(x - x_2)}{(x_0 - x_1)(x_0 - x_2)} f(x_0) + \frac{(x - x_0)(x - x_2)}{(x_1 - x_0)(x_1 - x_2)} f(x_1)$$

$$+ \frac{(x - x_0)(x - x_1)}{(x_2 - x_0)(x_2 - x_1)} f(x_2)$$

$$\approx \frac{(3.5 - 3)(3.5 - 4)}{(2 - 3)(2 - 4)} 10 + \frac{(3.5 - 2)(3.5 - 4)}{(3 - 2)(3 - 4)} 30$$

$$\approx 46.75 \qquad + \frac{(3.5 - 2)(3.5 - 3)}{(4 - 2)(4 - 3)} 68$$

Using linear interpolation, we obtain

$$f(3.5) \approx \frac{(3.5 - 4)}{(3 - 4)} 30 + \frac{(3.5 - 3)}{(4 - 3)} 68 = 49$$

The tabulated function happens to be $f(x) = x^3 + x$ for which $f(3.5) = 46.375$.

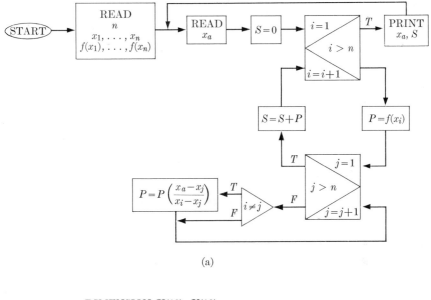

(a)

```
              DIMENSION X(10), Y(10)
              INTEGER I, J, N
READ          READ DATA
              SUM = 0.
              THROUGH OUTER, FOR I = 1, 1, I.G. N
              PROD = Y(I)
              THROUGH INNER, FOR J = 1, 1, J .G. N
INNER         WHENEVER I .NE. J, PROD = PROD * (ARG − X(J))/(X(I) − X(J))
OUTER         SUM = SUM + PROD
              PRINT RESULTS ARG, SUM
              TRANSFER TO READ
              END OF PROGRAM
```

Data

N = 7, X(1) = −.45, −.15, .15, .45, .75, .90, 1.35
Y(1) = 1.0, .86602540, .5, 0., −.5, −.70710678, −1.0

ARG = −.3∗
ARG = 0∗
ARG = .15∗
ARG = .45∗
ARG = 1.05∗
ARG = 1.20∗   (b)

FIG. 12–1.   (a) Flow chart.   (b) Program.

Example. Write a computer program which reads a value for $n \leq 10$ and then n abscissas with the corresponding functional values. After these tabular values have been read, the program should read an argument and, using $(n - 1)$-degree Lagrangian interpolation, compute the corresponding functional value. After this approximate value and the argument are printed, another argument is to be read and the interpolation repeated until the input list of arguments has been exhausted.

If the points are numbered from 1 to n, the formula is

$$p(x) = \sum_{i=1}^{n} \left(\prod_{\substack{j=1 \\ j \neq i}}^{n} \frac{x - x_j}{x_i - x_j} \right) f(x_i)$$

Note that both a repeated product and a repeated sum are to be calculated. The sum must initially be set to zero, but the partial product variable, instead of being initially set to 1, can in this case, be set to $f(x_i)$. The flow chart and program are presented in Fig. 12–1. The results for the arguments shown here are

$$0.96578302$$
$$0.70714495$$
$$0.50000000$$
$$0.0$$
$$-0.86590460$$
$$-0.96560140$$

listed in the same order as the arguments above.

EQUAL-INTERVAL INTERPOLATION

Neither the divided difference nor the Lagrangian polynomials imposed any restrictions on the spacing of the given abscissas. In fact, even the order of the points was unimportant. However, it is very often convenient to tabulate a function for equal intervals of the argument, since this technique considerably simplifies both notation and computation.

Forward differences. The problem is to rewrite the divided-difference polynomial, which, together with the divided difference remainder, is called *Newton's fundamental formula*, in a form that takes advantage of the fact that

$$x_1 - x_0 = x_2 - x_1 = x_3 - x_2 = \cdots = x_n - x_{n-1} = h.$$

All the denominators of the divided differences are differences of tabulated x's and hence can be represented as multiples of h, i.e.,

$$f[x_1, x_0] = \frac{f(x_1) - f(x_0)}{x_1 - x_0} = \frac{f(x_1) - f(x_0)}{h}$$

$$f[x_2, x_1, x_0] = \frac{[f(x_2) - f(x_1)]/h - [f(x_1) - f(x_0)]/h}{x_2 - x_0}$$

$$= \frac{[f(x_2) - f(x_1)] - [f(x_1) - f(x_0)]}{2h^2}$$

In fact, the powers of h can be separated and the differences formed from the ordinates only. To express these differences (there is no longer any division involved), one can use the forward-difference notation which is defined in tabular form, called a forward-difference table, as follows:

x_0 $f(x_0)$

$$\Delta f(x_0) = f(x_1) - f(x_0)$$

x_1 $f(x_1)$ $\Delta^2 f(x_0) = \Delta f(x_1) - \Delta f(x_0)$

$$\Delta f(x_1) = f(x_2) - f(x_1) \qquad \Delta^3 f(x_0) = \Delta^2 f(x_1) - \Delta^2 f(x_0)$$

x_2 $f(x_2)$ $\Delta^2 f(x_1) = \Delta f(x_2) - \Delta f(x_1)$

$$\Delta f(x_2) = f(x_3) - f(x_2)$$

x_3 $f(x_3)$

In general, $\Delta^n f(x_k) = \Delta^{n-1} f(x_{k+1}) - \Delta^{n-1} f(x_k)$. The relationship of this notation to the divided difference follows from our previous remarks.

$$f[x_1, x_0] = \frac{\Delta f(x_0)}{h}$$

$$f[x_2, x_1, x_0] = \frac{\Delta^2 f(x_0)}{2h^2}$$

$$f[x_n, \ldots, x_0] = \frac{\Delta^n f(x_0)}{n! h^n}$$

Making these substitutions yields Newton's fundamental formula in forward-difference notation:

$$f(x) = f(x_0) + (x - x_0)\frac{\Delta f(x_0)}{h} + (x - x_0)(x - x_1)\frac{\Delta^2 f(x_0)}{2! h^2}$$
$$+ (x - x_0)(x - x_1)(x - x_2)\frac{\Delta^3 f(x_0)}{3! h_3} + \cdots$$

The error term is still

$$(x - x_0) \cdots (x - x_n)\frac{f^{(n+1)}(\xi)}{(n + 1)!}$$

There is a simple change in variable which produces a further simplification because it cancels out the powers of the increment, h, in the denominator. Due to the equal spacing, all the given abscissas can be written with reference to x_0,

$$x_0 = x_0$$
$$x_1 = x_0 + h$$
$$x_2 = x_0 + 2h$$
$$x_3 = x_0 + 3h$$
$$\vdots$$

and any x can be represented as $x = x_0 + sh$, where s is now a new variable and may be thought of as being expressed in "units of h." Since $x - x_0 = sh$, $x - x_1 = (s - 1)h$, $x - x_2 = (s - 2)h$, etc., this change of variable simplifies the forward-difference form to

$$f(x_0 + sh) = f(x_0) + s\,\Delta f(x_0) + s(s - 1)\frac{\Delta^2 f(x_0)}{2!}$$

$$+ s(s - 1)(s - 2)\frac{\Delta^3 f(x_0)}{3!} + \cdots$$

As a quick illustration, the Lagrangian example is used again.

x	f	Δ	Δ^2	Δ^3
2	10			
		20		
3	30		18	
		38		6
4	68		24	
		62		
5	130			

The required differences are obtained from the forward-difference table above. For $x = 3.5$ and $h = 1$, the value of s is determined as follows:

$$s = \frac{x - x_0}{h} = \frac{3.5 - 2}{1} = 1.5$$

$$f(3.5) \approx 10 + 1.5(20) + 1.5(0.5)\tfrac{18}{2} = 46.75$$

The computation was much less involved in this instance; however, equal intervals were, of course, required and some computation was necessary to compute the differences.

As with the divided-differences polynomial, the first neglected term provides an estimate of the magnitude of error. In this example,

$$s(s - 1)(s - 2)\frac{\Delta^3 f(x_0)}{3!} = 1.5(0.5)(-0.5)\frac{6}{3!} = -0.375$$

which happens to be the exact error since the function was tabulated from the third-degree polynomial $x^3 + x$.

Operator notation. The primary difficulty with interpolation is notational. The basic idea of finding a polynomial that will pass through a given set of points is straightforward, but the notation required to express these polynomials tends to become cumbersome and does, at times, obscure certain useful relationships. Part of this difficulty can be overcome in the equal-interval case by defining linear operators. The relationships can then be deduced by the algebraic manipulation of the operators. For example, a forward-difference operator, Δ, which can operate on any function, say $f(x)$, can be defined as follows:

$$\Delta f(x) = f(x + h) - f(x)$$

This corresponds to the use of the symbol Δ in the preceding section, where

$$\Delta f(x_0) = f(x_1) - f(x_0)$$

since $x_1 - x_0 = h$. That this operator is linear can be seen by applying the operator to a function which is the sum of two other functions:

$$
\begin{aligned}
\Delta[af(x) + bg(x)] &= [af(x + h) + bg(x + h)] - [af(x) + bg(x)] \\
&= a[f(x + h) - f(x)] + b[g(x + h) - g(x)] \\
&= a\,\Delta f(x) + b\,\Delta g(x)
\end{aligned}
$$

The application of the operator to a sum of functions is the same as the sum of operators applied to each function individually. This property is the basis for much of the algebraic manipulation of operators.

In interpolation, the emphasis is on tabulated values rather than on functions in symbolic form. The interest is, of necessity, focused on $\Delta f(x_0)$, which is the value of a difference at a specific point, x_0, rather than on $\Delta f(x)$, where x is still not bound to a specific value. It is important to note that the operator Δ is certainly applicable in the latter sense. For instance, if

$$f(x) = ax^2 + bx + c$$

then

$$
\begin{aligned}
\Delta f(x) = \Delta(ax^2 + bx + c) &= a(x + h)^2 + b(x + h) + c - ax^2 - bx - c \\
&= 2ahx + ah^2 + bh
\end{aligned}
$$

This expression begins to look like a derivative, and dividing by h and letting $h \to 0$ do produce the derivative:

$$\frac{\Delta f(x)}{h} = 2ax + ah + b$$

$$\lim_{h \to 0} \frac{\Delta f(x)}{h} = 2ax + b = f'(x)$$

The calculus of finite differences is a subject in its own right, quite independent of the specific problem of interpolation.

TABLE 12–1

r k	0	1	2	3	4
0	1				
1	1	−1			
2	1	−2	1		
3	1	−3	3	−1	
4	1	−4	6	−4	1

As an illustration of the utility of operators, note from the preceding section that

$$\Delta^2 f(x_0) = \Delta f(x_1) - \Delta f(x_0)$$
$$= [f(x_2) - f(x_1)] - [f(x_1) - f(x_0)]$$
$$= f(x_2) - 2f(x_1) + f(x_0)$$

The appearance of the coefficients, 1, −2, 1, suggests that they may have been obtained by raising a binomial expression to the second power, that is, $(a - b)^2 = 1 \cdot a^2 - 2ab + 1 \cdot b^2$; or, stated in another way, the coefficients might have come from the row labeled 2 of Pascal's triangle (Table 12–1). This table contains the binomial coefficients

$$C_{k,r} = (-1)^{k-r} \left(\frac{k!}{r!(k - r)!} \right)$$

If the suspicion stated above is correct, then

$$\Delta^3 f(x_0) = 1 \cdot f(x_3) - 3f(x_2) + 3f(x_1) - 1 \cdot f(x_0)$$

That this result is true can be easily verified by using operators. First it is convenient to introduce another operator, E, called a shift operator because it simply shifts the argument x by the incremental amount h:

$$Ef(x) = f(x + h)$$

The difference operator may be applied repeatedly:

$$\Delta^2 f(x) = \Delta \, \Delta f(x) = \Delta(f(x + h) - f(x)) = f(x + 2h) - 2f(x + h) + f(x)$$

The repeated application of the shift operator results in a further shift of the argument:

$$E^2 f(x) = EEf(x) = Ef(x + h) = f(x + 2h)$$

The original goal was to determine the coefficients of the ordinates in a high-order difference, say $\Delta^k f(x_0)$:

$$\Delta = E - 1$$

since

$$(E - 1)f(x) = f(x + h) - f(x)$$

and therefore $\Delta^k = (E - 1)^k$, which essentially demonstrates the desired result since $E - 1$ is a binomial. To give a specific instance,

$$\begin{aligned}
\Delta^3 f(x_0) &= (E - 1)^3 f(x_0) = (E^3 - 3E^2 + 3E - 1)f(x_0) \\
&= f(x_0 + 3h) - 3f(x_0 + 2h) + 3f(x_0 + h) - f(x_0) \\
&= f(x_3) - 3f(x_2) + 3f(x_1) - f(x_0)
\end{aligned}$$

This result is much more easily proved by means of operators than by manipulation of the differences themselves.

As a last illustration of the concise expression which operators permit, a Taylor's series expansion is presented in the very compact form made possible by the use of the well-known expansion of e^x:

$$e^x = 1 + x + \frac{x^2}{2!} + \frac{x^3}{3!} + \frac{x^4}{4!} + \cdots$$

Now, if x is formally replaced by $h(d/dx)$ and the entire expansion is treated as an operator, one has

$$\begin{aligned}
f(x + h) &= \{e^{h(d/dx)}\}f(x) \\
&= \left\{1 + h\frac{d}{dx} + \frac{h^2}{2!}\frac{d^2}{dx^2} + \frac{h^3}{3!}\frac{d^3}{dx^3} + \frac{h^4}{4!}\frac{d^4}{dx^4} + \cdots\right\}f(x) \\
&= f(x) + hf'(x) + \frac{h^2}{2!}f''(x) + \frac{h^3}{3!}f'''(x) + \cdots
\end{aligned}$$

Just the reduction in the amount of writing would be useful, but here again certain manipulations with the operator itself are permissible.

Backward-differences. The forward-difference notation is constructed with reference to the first of a given set of points. As before, paths through the difference table other than the upper diagonal can be used to form an interpolating polynomial, but it is convenient to identify all the differences as "starting from" the initial point x_0. In some problems, particularly the solution of ordinary differential equations, it is convenient to identify differences with respect to the last point included. The symbol for such *backward differences* is the inverted delta (∇), and the relationship to divided differences is completely analogous to the forward-difference

LIBRARY

TABLE 12–2

---

x_{k-3} $f(x_{k-3})$

$\quad \nabla f(x_{k-2}) = f(x_{k-2}) - f(x_{k-3})$

x_{k-2} $f(x_{k-2})$ $\qquad\qquad\qquad\qquad \nabla^2 f(x_{k-1}) = \nabla f(x_{k-1}) - \nabla f(x_{k-2})$

$\quad \nabla f(x_{k-1}) = f(x_{k-1}) - f(x_{k-2})$ $\qquad \nabla^3 f(x_k) = \nabla^2 f(x_k) - \nabla^2 f(x_{k-1})$

x_{k-1} $f(x_{k-1})$ $\qquad\qquad\qquad\qquad \nabla^2 f(x_k) = \nabla f(x_k) - \nabla f(x_{k-1})$

$\quad \nabla f(x_k) = f(x_k) - f(x_{k-1})$

x_k $\quad f(x_k)$

---

case. The x's are at equal intervals,

$$x_k - x_{k-1} = x_{k-1} - x_{k-2} = x_{k-2} - x_{k-3} = \cdots = x_1 - x_0 = h$$

and the differences are defined in Table 12–2. One can now define a backward-difference operator which is consistent with this table:

$$\nabla f(x) = f(x) - f(x - h)$$

With a backward-shift operator,

$$E^{-1}f(x) = f(x - h)$$

one can make a similar analysis of the form of the high-order differences, starting from the relation

$$\nabla = (1 - E^{-1})$$

Since the notation is with respect to x_k, the logical change of variable is $x = x_k + sh$, and the fundamental formula in backward-difference notation is

$$f(x_k + sh)$$
$$= f(x_k) + s\nabla f(x_k) + s(s+1)\frac{\nabla^2 f(x_k)}{2!} + s(s+1)(s+2)\frac{\nabla^3 f(x_k)}{3!} + \cdots$$

If the last three of the four points of the numerical example are used, one should not expect the same result. The difference table is the same, but the names have changed:

x	f	∇	∇^2	∇^3
2	10			
		20		
3	30		18	
		38		6
4	68		24	
		62		
5	130			

$$s = \frac{x - x_k}{h} = \frac{3.5 - 5}{1} = -1.5$$

$$f(3.5) \approx 130 - 1.5(62) + 1.5(0.5)\tfrac{24}{2} = 46$$

For the same reasoning as before, the error estimate should give the exact error in this case:

$$s(s + 1)(s + 2)\frac{\nabla^3 f(x_k)}{3!} = -1.5(-0.5)(0.5)\frac{6}{3!} = 0.375$$

Central differences. Neither of the equal-interval difference notations thus far introduced are really well suited for straightforward interpolation. Ideally, in forming an interpolating polynomial, it is desirable to include points symmetrically about some central point (or interval) as terms are added to the polynomial. That is, as additional ordinates are needed for higher-order differences, they should be taken from both sides of the central point rather than consistently forward (as in forward differences) or consistently backward (as in backward differences). The troublesome part of such efforts for notational symmetry is that every other column of a difference table is nonsymmetrical with respect to a point; i.e., if x_0 is a central point, the first difference to be added is either $f(x_1) - f(x_0)$ or $f(x_0) - f(x_1)$, that is, a point is being added unsymmetrically from either one side or the other. One can force symmetry in the notation, however, by referring to "fictional" (i.e., nontabulated) points for all differences that are obtained from an even number of ordinates. For instance, the first difference will include points symmetrically about x_0 if it is defined to be

$$\delta f(x_0) = f\left(x_0 + \frac{h}{2}\right) - f\left(x_0 - \frac{h}{2}\right)$$

TABLE 12–3

x	f	δ	δ^2	δ^3
x_{-2}	$f(x_{-2})$			
		$\delta f\left(x_{-1} - \dfrac{h}{2}\right) = f(x_{-1}) - f(x_{-2})$		
x_{-1}	$f(x_{-1})$		$\delta^2 f(x_{-1}) = \delta f\left(x_0 - \dfrac{h}{2}\right) - \delta f\left(x_{-1} - \dfrac{h}{2}\right)$	
		$\delta f\left(x_0 - \dfrac{h}{2}\right) = f(x_0) - f(x_{-1})$		$\delta^3 f\left(x_0 - \dfrac{h}{2}\right) = \delta^2 f(x_0) - \delta^2 f(x_{-1})$
x_0	$f(x_0)$		$\delta^2 f(x_0) = \delta f\left(x_0 + \dfrac{h}{2}\right) - \delta f\left(x_0 - \dfrac{h}{2}\right)$	
		$\delta f\left(x_0 + \dfrac{h}{2}\right) = f(x_1) - f(x_0)$		$\delta^3 f\left(x_0 + \dfrac{h}{2}\right) = \delta^2 f(x_1) - \delta^2 f(x_2)$
x_1	$f(x_1)$		$\delta^2 f(x_1) = \delta f\left(x_1 + \dfrac{h}{2}\right) - \delta f\left(x_0 + \dfrac{h}{2}\right)$	
		$\delta f\left(x_1 + \dfrac{h}{2}\right) = f(x_2) - f(x_1)$		
x_2	$f(x_2)$			

but these designated functional values are not tabulated. However,

$$\delta f\left(x_0 + \frac{h}{2}\right) = f(x_0 + h) - f(x_0) = f(x_1) - f(x_0)$$

which are tabulated values. The second difference, involving three points, is symmetric and is determined from given values:

$$\delta^2 f(x_0) = \delta f\left(x_0 + \frac{h}{2}\right) - \delta f\left(x_0 - \frac{h}{2}\right)$$
$$= (f(x_1) - f(x_0)) - (f(x_0) - f(x_{-1}))$$

The central-difference table then has mid-interval arguments for every other column, as shown in Table 12–3. The equivalence to divided differences has to be written separately for the central differences of even and odd order. This separation of even and odd is often indicated by considering an index $n = 0, 1, 2, \ldots$; then $2n$ represents the even numbers and $2n + 1$ the odd ones:

$$\frac{\delta^{2n} f(x_0)}{(2n)!h^{2n}} = f[x_{2n}, x_{2n-1}, \ldots, x_0]$$

$$\frac{\delta^{2n+1} f\left(x_0 + h/2\right)}{(2n + 1)!h^{2n+1}} = f[x_{2n+1}, x_{2n}, \ldots, x_0]$$

It is not possible to select a path through the table which will involve only differences with the x_0-argument. The closest one can come to symmetry about x_0 is to select

$$f(x_0), \quad \delta f\left(x_0 + \frac{h}{2}\right), \quad \delta^2 f(x_0), \quad \delta^3\left(x_0 + \frac{h}{2}\right), \quad \text{etc.}$$

which is a path that zigzags *forward* from the central point x_0. Making the change of variable $x = x_0 + sh$ and writing an interpolation polynomial with the path selected above produce *Gauss' forward formula.*

$$f(x_0 + sh) = f(x_0) + s\,\delta f\left(x_0 + \frac{h}{2}\right) + s(s - 1)\frac{\delta^2 f(x_0)}{2!}$$
$$+ s(s - 1)(s + 1)\frac{\delta^3 f\left(x_0 + \frac{h}{2}\right)}{3!} + \cdots$$

This zigzag path suggests how the desired symmetry can be attained. Add to it a *backward* zigzag-path polynomial (*Gauss' backward formula*) and take one-half of the resulting sum. The resulting interpolating polynomial, called *Sterling's formula*, is symmetric about x_0, and its terms are the same as above when the paths coincide, and are the average of the adjacent differences when they do not:

$$f(x_0 + sh) = f(x_0)$$

$$+ \frac{s}{2}\left(\delta f\left(x_0 + \frac{h}{2}\right) + \delta f\left(x_0 - \frac{h}{2}\right)\right) + s(s-1)\frac{\delta^2 f(x_0)}{2!}$$

$$+ \frac{s(s-1)(s+1)}{2}\left(\delta^3 f\left(x_0 + \frac{h}{2}\right) + \delta^3 f\left(x_0 - \frac{h}{2}\right)\right) + \cdots$$

Similar addition of appropriate zigzag paths can produce a formula, which is symmetric about an interval, called *Bessel's formula*.

Even the operator formulation is a little more involved in this case:

$$\delta f(x) = f\left(x + \frac{h}{2}\right) - f\left(x - \frac{h}{2}\right)$$

Half-shift operators are needed to write an equivalent form for δ:

$$E^{1/2}f(x) = f\left(x + \frac{h}{2}\right), \qquad E^{-1/2}f(x) = f\left(x - \frac{h}{2}\right)$$

Therefore, $\delta = E^{1/2} - E^{-1/2}$. To see that the high-order differences have the same binomial form, observe that

$$\delta^k = (E^{1/2} - E^{-1/2})^k = [E^{-k/2}(E-1)^k]$$

The same binomial is obtained as in the forward-difference case, but a "halfway" shift of the point of reference of $-k/2$ is also applied.

As an illustration of Sterling's formula, we present the same simple example.

	x	f	$\delta^3_{1/2}$	δ^2	$\delta^3_{1/2}$
x_{-1}	2	10			
			20		
x_0	3	30		18	
			38		6
x_1	4	68		24	
			62		
x_2	5	130			

$$s = \frac{x - x_0}{h} = \frac{3.5 - 3}{1} = 0.5$$

$$f(3.5) \approx 30 + \frac{0.5}{2}(38 + 20) + (0.5)(-0.5)\frac{18}{2} = 46.75$$

This result is the same as in the forward-difference case, as it must be since the same three points were used to construct a second-degree polynomial. Note, however, that the first two terms of this approximation add up to 44.5, while the first two terms of the previous forward-difference example are 40. This is an expected result since the central approach means that the first terms will be closer to the final result. If the number of points to be used for an approximation is a variable, it is common sense to adopt the central approach and include first those points which are closest to the given argument.

Instead of writing a program using one of these equal-interval formulas, we shall illustrate the more general divided-difference procedure.

Example. Write a program which reads a set of $n + 1$ points with abscissas in ascending order and then computes the divided differences up to order m. After the difference table has been formed, the program reads an argument a and the degree of the interpolation polynomial to be computed, d. Using a, the program searches the list of abscissas to find the appropriate $d + 1$ points from which to construct the polynomial. The interpolation is central in that, as far as possible, the points to be used will be taken equally from either side of the argument. Compute and print the first term neglected as an estimate of the magnitude of the truncation error. If the argument is outside the given tabular values, either the first or last $d + 1$ points are used for extrapolation. The reading of arguments is continued until the input list is exhausted. The program should accommodate a table of 100 entries and divided differences up to sixth order. Due to the complexity of the problem statement, it is probably worthwhile to give some description of the procedure before writing a flow chart.

Step 1. Read M, N and

$$x_0 \quad x_1 \quad x_2 \quad x_3 \quad x_4 \quad \ldots \quad x_N$$
$$y_0 \quad y_1 \quad y_2 \quad y_3 \quad y_4 \quad \ldots \quad y_N$$

Step 2. Compute the divided differences. For this purpose the y's can be regarded as the zeroth divided differences and are the zeroth row of a matrix. The first row to be computed is the first divided difference, the second, the divided difference of order two, etc.:

$$
\begin{array}{cccccc}
y_{0,0} & y_{0,1} & y_{0,2} & y_{0,3} & y_{0,4} & \cdots & y_{0,N} \\
& y_{1,1} & y_{1,2} & y_{1,3} & y_{1,4} & \cdots & y_{1,N} \\
& & y_{2,2} & y_{2,3} & y_{2,4} & \cdots & y_{2,N} \\
& & & & y_{M,M} & \cdots & y_{M,N}
\end{array}
$$

The formula for computing a specific divided difference, $y_{i,j}$, is, in these terms,

$$y_{i,j} = \frac{y_{i-1,j} - y_{i-1,j-1}}{x_j - x_{j-i}}$$

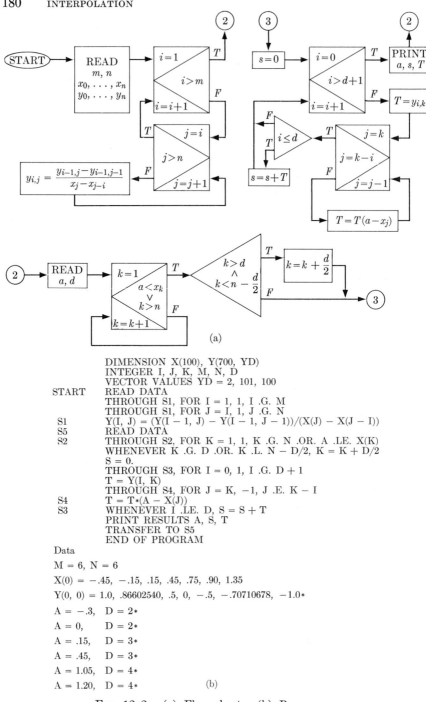

FIG. 12–2.   (a) Flow chart.   (b) Program.

where $1 \le i \le M$ and $i \le j \le N$. To compute the Mth-order differences, a sufficient number of tabulated points must be available; that is, $N \ge M + 1$.

Step 3. Read the argument a and the degree of interpolation, d, and search the x's to find the first x, say x_k, for which $a \le x_k$. If $d < k < N - d/2$, add $d/2$ to k so that the $d + 1$ points ending with x_k are on both sides of a:

$$d + 1 \text{ values}$$

$$x_0 \quad x_1 \quad \overbrace{x_2 \quad x_3 \quad x_4 \quad x_5 \quad x_6} \quad \cdots$$

$$\uparrow$$
$$a$$

(For this case, $k = 4$, $d = 3$)

It is important to understand here that the result of integer division is truncated to an integer quotient; e.g., $[\frac{1}{2}] = 0$, $[\frac{3}{2}] = 1$.

Step 4. Evaluate the divided-difference polynomial. The relevant divided differences will all be in the kth column so that

$$P(A) = y_{0,k} + (a - x_k)y_{1,k} + (a - x_k)(a - x_{k-1})y_{2,k} + \cdots$$

Step 5. Compute, but do not add into the sum of terms, the $(d + 2)$-term; its value is the estimate of the truncation-error magnitude. With this requirement, it is convenient to compute the polynomial starting from the constant term, rather than using the nested evaluation.

The flow chart and program for this example are presented in Fig. 12–2. The results from these trial values are:

A	S	T
-0.3	0.998798	-0.030649
0	0.699760	0.006130
0.15	0.5	0
0.45	0	0
1.05	-0.866828	0.000911
1.20	-0.967624	0.001993

The two dimensional y-array is unusual in that the initial element is $y_{0,0}$ instead of $y_{1,1}$. This notation is accommodated by including in the dimension vector for the y-array an appropriate base linear subscript. To allow for an additional row of 100 elements preceding the first row, the linear-subscript equivalent to $y_{1,1}$ is selected to be 101. Since the y-array can have at most 7 rows of 100 elements, the amount to be reserved is 700.

Numerical Integration

One of the reasons for the preeminence of polynomials in numerical methods is that they are readily differentiated and integrated; moreover, the result obtained by differentiating or integrating a polynomial is also a polynomial. Since interpolation polynomials permit one to represent a set of points in functional form, an approximation to the derivative or integral of such a tabular function can be obtained by differentiating or integrating the interpolation polynomial. This procedure is much more effective for integration, since it is a "smoothing" process, than for differentiation which tends to amplify small variations. This rather vague description may be made somewhat more understandable by the diagram in Fig. 13–1. It is certainly possible that $\int_{x_0}^{x_4} p(x)\,dx$ could be a good approximation to $\int_{x_0}^{x_4} f(x)\,dx$. It looks as if the deviations of $p(x)$ above and below $f(x)$ would about cancel out in the integration. On the other hand, the derivatives of the interpolating polynomial $p(x)$ would differ markedly from those of $f(x)$ since it has much more variation than the relatively smooth $f(x)$. This difference in the degree of approximation of the two processes can be recognized in the corresponding error terms, but since integration has the greater utility it will be emphasized in what follows.

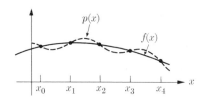

FIGURE 13–1

The most frequently used integration formulas are obtained from the equal-interval interpolation polynomials. The simplest example is that of two points where the first-degree forward-difference polynomial is integrated from x_0 to x_1, or by making the substitution $x = x_0 + sh$, where the variable s is varied from 0 to 1. The function, expressed as a poly-

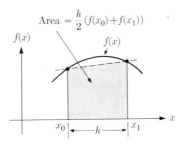

Area $= \dfrac{h}{2}(f(x_0)+f(x_1))$

$f(x)$

$f(x)$

x

x_0 x_1

h

FIGURE 13–2

nomial with error term, is

$$f(x) = f(x_0) + s\,\Delta f(x_0) + s(s - 1)h^2\frac{f''(\zeta)}{2}, \qquad x_0 \le \zeta \le x_0 + h$$

From the substitution, $dx = h\,ds$, and the integral becomes

$$\int_{x_0}^{x_1} f(x)\,dx = h \int_0^1 f(x_0 + sh)\,ds$$

$$= h \int_0^1 \left[f(x_0) + s\,\Delta f(x_0) + (s^2 - s)\,h^2\frac{f''(\zeta)}{2} \right] ds$$

$$= h \left[sf(x_0) + \frac{s^2}{2}\Delta f(x_0) + \left(\frac{s^3}{3} - \frac{s^2}{2}\right) h^2\frac{f''(\zeta)}{2} \right]_0^1$$

When evaluated at the lower limit, all the terms are zero so that the result, with the substitution $f(x_1) - f(x_0) = \Delta f(x_0)$ made, is

$$\int_{x_0}^{x_1} f(x)\,dx = \frac{h}{2}\left[f(x_0) + f(x_1) \right] - \frac{h^3}{12}f''(\zeta)$$

Dropping the error term on the right leads to the familiar *trapezoidal rule* which, as the interpolation polynomial required, is simply the area under the straight-line segment connecting the two adjacent points on the function (Fig. 13–2). The next formula, and by far the most popular for numerical integration, is obtained by integrating over two equal intervals. On the assumption that integration over even more intervals will be of interest, a labor-saving method is to obtain the indefinite integral

$$\int_{x_0}^{x} f(x)\,dx = h \int_0^s f(x_0 + hs)\,ds$$

and then truncate the resulting series to the appropriate term:

$$h \int_0^s f(x_0 + hs)\, ds = h \int_0^s \left[f(x_0) + s\, \Delta f(x_0) + s(s-1) \frac{\Delta^2 f(x_0)}{2!} \right.$$

$$+ s(s-1)(s-2) \frac{\Delta^3 f(x_0)}{3!} + \cdots$$

$$+ s(s-1)(s-2)(s-3)$$

$$\left. \times \frac{\Delta^4 f(x_0)}{4!} + \cdots \right] ds$$

$$= h \left[s f(x_0) + \frac{s^2}{2} \Delta f(x_0) + \left(\frac{s^3}{3} - \frac{s^2}{2} \right) \Delta^2 \frac{f(x_0)}{2} \right.$$

$$+ \left(\frac{s^4}{4} - s^3 + s^2 \right) \frac{\Delta^3 f(x_0)}{6}$$

$$+ \left(\frac{s^5}{5} - \frac{6s^4}{4} + \frac{11s^3}{3} - \frac{6s^2}{2} \right)$$

$$\left. \times \frac{\Delta^4 f(x_0)}{24} + \cdots \right]_0^s$$

As before, all the terms are zero when this expression is evaluated at the lower limit $s = 0$. Now to obtain a formula for the two-interval (or three-point) case, substitute $s = 2$ and truncate to the number of terms desired. It would not seem reasonable to include terms beyond the second difference since the higher-order differences depend upon more than three points. Actually there is nothing wrong with using many points to obtain the interpolating polynomial and then integrating this approximation to the function over a smaller interval. In the two-interval case under consideration, including the third difference yields an unexpected dividend:

$$h \int_0^2 f(x_0 + hs)\, ds = h \left[2f(x_0) + 2\, \Delta f(x_0) + \frac{2}{3} \frac{\Delta^2 f(x_0)}{2} \right.$$

$$\left. + 0 \frac{\Delta^3 f(x_0)}{6} - \frac{4}{15} \frac{h^4 f^{(4)}(\zeta)}{24} \right]$$

Again, the rightmost term is the remainder obtained by substituting

$$\frac{h^4 f^{(4)}}{4!} \quad \text{for} \quad \frac{\Delta^4 f(x_0)}{4!}$$

Note that since the coefficient of the third difference is zero, a fourth-order remainder term is applicable although only three points are required to

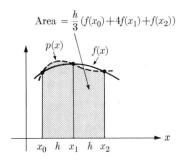

FIGURE 13–3

compute the nonzero terms. By substituting

$$f(x_1) - f(x_0) = \Delta f(x_0) \text{ and } f(x_2) - 2f(x_1) + f(x_0) = \Delta^2 f(x_0)$$

for the differences, one obtains the usual form of *Simpson's rule:*

$$\int_{x_0}^{x_2} f(x)\, dx = \frac{h}{3}\left[f(x_0) + 4f(x_1) + f(x_2) \right] - \frac{h^5 f^{(4)}(\zeta)}{90}$$

Without the error term, evaluation of this formula amounts to computing the area under a third-degree polynomial passing through three points with equally spaced abscissas (Fig. 13–3). Comparison of the error terms for the trapezoidal and Simpson's rules shows why the latter is so popular. In the two-interval case, the computation of the formula is only slightly more complicated than in the one-interval case, and yet the error term is proportional to the fourth derivative instead of, as might be expected, the third.

A similar jump in the order of the error term is encountered for all even-interval (or odd-point) formulas and hence they are preferred to the others. The next two formulas are:

$$\int_{x_0}^{x_3} f(x)\, dx = \frac{3h}{8}\left[f(x_0) + 3f(x_1) + 3f(x_2) + f(x_3) \right] - \frac{3h^5}{80} f^{(4)}(\zeta)$$

$$\int_{x_0}^{x_4} f(x)\, dx = \frac{2h}{45}\left[7f(x_0) + 32f(x_1) + 12f(x_2) + 32f(x_3) + 7f(x_4) \right]$$

$$- \frac{8h^7}{945} f^{(6)}(\zeta)$$

When these formulas are repeatedly applied they can be written in a combined form over the entire interval of application. Thus, if the trapezoidal rule is used in the intervals (x_0, x_1) and (x_1, x_2), then

$$\int_{x_1}^{x_2} f(x)\, dx \approx \frac{h}{2}[f(x_0) + f(x_1)] + \frac{h}{2}[f(x_1) + f(x_2)]$$

$$\approx \frac{h}{2}[f(x_0) + 2f(x_1) + f(x_2)]$$

And in general, for $x_0, x_1, \ldots, x_n$,

$$\int_{x_0}^{x_n} f(x)\, dx \approx \frac{h}{2}[f(x_0) + 2f(x_1) + 2f(x_2) + \cdots + 2f(x_{n-1}) + f(x_n)]$$

The repeated application of Simpson's rule for the total interval (x_0, x_{2n}) is expressed in the same manner:

$$\int_{x_0}^{x_{2n}} f(x)\, dx \approx \frac{h}{3}[f(x_0) + 4f(x_1) + 2f(x_2) + 4f(x_3) + 2f(x_4) + \cdots$$
$$+ 2f(x_{2n-2}) + 4f(x_{2n-1}) + f(x_{2n})]$$

The terminal subscript is expressed as $2n$ to indicate that the subscript must be even. This requirement makes the total number of points odd since there is a zeroth point.

To illustrate the relative effectiveness of the two methods developed, a familiar definite integral, $\int_0^\pi \sin\theta\, d\theta = 2$, is approximated by numerical integration in several ways   The given values are:

x	$f(x) = \sin x$
0	0
$\pi/4$	0.7071
$\pi/2$	1.0
$3\pi/4$	0.7071
π	0

(1) Trapezoidal rule applied twice ($h = \pi/2$):

$$\int_0^\pi \sin x\, dx \approx \frac{\pi}{4}\left[\sin 0 + 2\sin\frac{\pi}{2} + \sin\pi\right] = 1.5708$$

$$\left|\frac{h^3}{12}\sin(\zeta)\right| \leq \frac{h^3}{12}\max\sin\zeta, \qquad 0 \leq \zeta \leq \frac{\pi}{2},$$

$$\leq \frac{(1.5708)^3}{12}\, 1 = 0.32$$

Since there are two similar intervals involved, the error bound is $2 \times 0.32 = 0.64$.

(2) Trapezoidal rule applied four times ($h = \pi/4$):

$$\int_0^\pi \sin x \, dx \approx \frac{\pi}{8}\left[\sin 0 + 2 \sin \frac{\pi}{4} + 2 \sin \frac{\pi}{2} + 2 \sin \frac{3\pi}{4} + \sin \pi\right] = 1.895$$

It is necessary to obtain the sum of the maximum error from two different intervals, $(0, \pi/4)$ and $(\pi/4, \pi/2)$, and, due to the symmetry, double this sum to obtain the error bound.

$$\left|\frac{h^3}{12} \sin (\zeta)\right| \leq \left(\frac{\pi}{4}\right)^3 \frac{1}{12} \max \sin \zeta = 0.0287, \qquad 0 \leq \zeta \leq \frac{\pi}{4}$$
$$= 0.0405, \qquad \frac{\pi}{4} < \zeta \leq \frac{\pi}{2}$$

The error bound is $2(0.287 + 0.0405) = 0.1384$.

(3) Simpson's rule applied once ($h = \pi/2$).

$$\int_0^\pi \sin x \, dx \approx \frac{\pi}{6}\left[\sin 0 + 4 \sin \frac{\pi}{2} + \sin \pi\right] = 2.0943$$

$$\left|\frac{h^5}{90} \cos \zeta\right| \leq \left(\frac{\pi}{2}\right)^5 \times \frac{1}{90} \max \cos (\zeta) = 0.1006$$

(4) Simpson's rule applied twice ($h = \pi/4$).

$$\int_0^\pi \sin x \, dx \approx \frac{\pi}{12}\left[\sin 0 + 4 \sin \frac{\pi}{4} + 2 \sin \frac{\pi}{2} + 4 \sin \frac{3\pi}{4} + \sin \pi\right] = 2.0043$$

As before, the error bound can be determined from one interval and, due to symmetry, simply doubled,

$$\left|\frac{h^5}{90} \cos \zeta\right| \leq \left(\frac{\pi}{4}\right)^5 \frac{1}{90} \max \cos \zeta = .00331$$

so that the error bound is $2(0.00331) = 0.00662$.

GAUSSIAN QUADRATURE

Several observations can be made at this point to motivate an alternative approach to numerical integration, or *quadrature* as it is often called. (1) Applying Simpson's rule, one is able to integrate a third-degree polynomial *exactly*, using only three points. One would at first glance expect four to be necessary. (2) The formulas for integration are of the form $\sum_{i=0}^n a_i f(x_i)$. Since $n + 1$ constants, as well as $n + 1$ ordinates, are given in this formula, the total of $2n + 2$ parameters suggests that sufficient information is available to permit specification of a polynomial of degree $2n + 1$. (3) In the equal-interval formulas derived the ordinates could not be freely chosen in the range of interest but were limited by the equal-interval requirement. It might be possible, then, to realize in greater measure the benefits of Simpson's rule, i.e., integrate exactly a $(2n + 1)$-degree polynomial using only an nth-degree polynomial approximation, by appropriately selecting the abscissas as well as the constant coefficients.

The Lagrangian interpolation polynomial is a logical starting point in determining the constants and abscissas since the ordinates appear explicitly and there is no restriction on the selection of x's:

$$f(x) = \sum_{i=0}^{n} \overline{c_i}(x) f(x_i) + \prod_{i=0}^{n} (x - x_i) \frac{f^{(n+1)}(\zeta)}{(n + 1)!}, \quad a \leq \zeta \leq b$$

where

$$\overline{c_i} = \prod_{\substack{j=0 \\ j \neq i}}^{n} \left(\frac{x - x_j}{x_i - x_j} \right)$$

It will be convenient to make a change of variable so that the interval containing the abscissas, $a \leq x_0, x_1, \ldots, x_n \leq b$, is transformed to the interval $(-1, 1)$:

$$t = \frac{2x - (a + b)}{b - a}$$

Then

$$f(x) = f\left(\frac{(b - a)t + a + b}{2} \right) = F(t)$$

and

$$F(t) = \sum_{i=0}^{n} c_i(t) F(t_i) + \prod_{i=0}^{n} (t - t_i) \frac{F^{(n+1)}(\bar{\zeta})}{(n + 1)!}$$

$$c_i = \prod_{\substack{j=0 \\ j \neq i}}^{n} \left(\frac{t - t_j}{t_i - t_j} \right), \quad -1 \leq \bar{\zeta} \leq 1$$

Now if $F(t)$ is assumed to be a polynomial of degree $2n + 1$, the derivative term can be replaced by a polynomial of degree n, $p_n(t)$:

$$F(t) = \sum_{i=0}^{n} c_i(t) F(t_i) + \prod_{i=i}^{n} (t - t_i) p_n(t)$$

The rationale for this replacement is simply that there is a $(2n + 1)$-degree polynomial on the left, and hence the right must represent the same polynomial. The first expression on the right, $\sum_{i=0}^{n} c_i(t)F(t_i)$, is an nth-degree polynomial, and therefore the remaining term on the right must be of degree $2n + 1$. But the product, $\prod_{i=0}^{n}(t - t_i)$, is a polynomial in factored form of degree $n + 1$, and hence the remaining polynomial factor $p_n(t)$ must be of nth degree.

Integrating both sides, one obtains

$$\int_{-1}^{1} F(t)\, dt = \int_{-1}^{1} \left[\sum_{i=0}^{n} c_i(t)F(t_i) \right] dt + \int_{-1}^{1} \prod_{i=0}^{n}(t - t_i)p_n(t)\, dt$$

$$= \sum_{i=0}^{n} \left(\int_{-1}^{1} c_i(t)\, dt \right) F(t_i) + \int_{-1}^{1} \prod_{i=0}^{n}(t - t_i)p_n(t)\, dt$$

$$= \sum_{i=0}^{n} a_i F(t_i) + \int_{-1}^{1} \prod_{i=0}^{n}(t - t_i)p_n(t)\, dt$$

To achieve the desired goal the remainder term, the integral on the right, must be zero. The question now is: Are there values t_i such that the integral of the polynomial product $\prod_{i=0}^{n}(t - t_i)p_n(t)$ in the interval $(-1, 1)$ is zero? The factor $p_n(x)$ is arbitrary but one degree less than the other factor. Two polynomials meeting this integration requirement are said to be *orthogonal*. There are families of polynomials $p_0(x)$, $p_1(x)$, $p_2(x)$, ..., $p_n(x)$ which have this property; i.e.,

$$\int_{-1}^{1} p_i(x)p_j(x)\, dx = 0 \qquad \text{for} \quad i \neq j$$

But the most common set of polynomials,

$$P_0(x) = 1$$
$$P_1(x) = x$$
$$P_2(x) = x^2$$
$$\vdots$$
$$P_n(x) = x^n$$

does not. There is a set of polynomials, called *Legendre* polynomials, which do have this orthogonal property:

$$L_0(x) = 1$$
$$L_1(x) = x$$
$$L_2(x) = \tfrac{1}{2}(3x^2 - 1)$$
$$L_3(x) = \tfrac{1}{2}(5x^3 - 3x)$$
$$\vdots$$

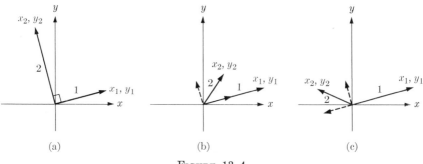

(a)   (b)   (c)

FIGURE 13–4

It is worth a short digression at this point to present a geometrical meaning for the term "orthogonality" which is, in fact, a generalization of "perpendicularity." Two directed line segments (vectors) which have no collinear tendency are perpendicular (Fig. 13–4a). Segment 2 has no component which is collinear with 1. When the segments are not perpendicular (Fig. 13–4b and c), then segment 2 can be decomposed into two components (the dashed lines), one of which is collinear with, and the other perpendicular to, segment 1. Note that the condition for perpendicularity is that the slope of one line is the negative reciprocal of the other, i.e.,

$$\frac{y_1}{x_1} = -\frac{x_2}{y_2}$$

or, as the condition is more often stated,

$$x_1 x_2 + y_1 y_2 = 0$$

When the coordinates are regarded as end points of a vector, this sum of products is called the *scalar product*. The condition is readily extended to three-dimensional vectors whose termini are (x_1, y_1, z_1) and (x_2, y_2, z_2):

$$x_1 x_2 + y_1 y_2 + z_1 z_2 = 0$$

It is difficult to picture how this condition is extended beyond three dimensions, but formally it is simply a matter of including more coordinate values. If n values are named, that is, $x_1, x_2, x_3, \ldots, x_n$, instead of $(x_1, y_1, z_1, \ldots)$, and $y_1, y_2, \ldots, y_n$, instead of $(x_2, y_2, z_2, \ldots)$, the condition for orthogonality is

$$x_1 y_1 + x_2 y_2 + x_3 y_3 + \cdots + x_n y_n = \sum_{i=1}^{n} x_i y_i = 0$$

As n becomes large, and presuming that the x- and y-values can be repre-

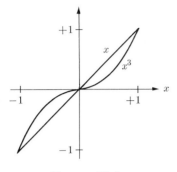

FIGURE 13–5

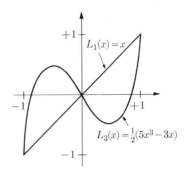

FIGURE 13–6

sented as a function of an independent variable t, one sees that this sum tends to approach the integral

$$\int_a^b x(t)y(t)\, dt = 0$$

This is the definition for orthogonality over the interval (a, b) when functions are involved. Although "orthogonal" is a two-valued term (lines are perpendicular or they are not), the value of the integral and sums of products above are measures of the "similar tendency" of two line segments or functions; or, from a slightly different point of view, it is a measure of how much of a function can be represented by another function. In other contexts this measure is called *correlation*.

An example from each of the families of polynomials shown serves to illustrate this idea.

$$\int_{-1}^1 P_1(x)P_3(x)\, dx = \int_{-1}^1 x \cdot x^3\, dx = \tfrac{2}{5}$$

Plotting these functions on the same graph (Fig. 13–5) shows that they do indeed have a similar tendency in $(-1, 1)$. Both functions continually increase as x goes from -1 to 1. As a matter of fact, the best lower-degree approximation for x^3 is $\tfrac{3}{4}x$. On the other hand,

$$\int_{-1}^1 L_1(x)L_3(x)\, dx = \int_{-1}^1 x \cdot \tfrac{1}{2}(5x^3 - 3x)\, dx = \tfrac{1}{2}[x^5 - x^3]_{-1}^1 = 0$$

In this case the graph (Fig. 13–6) shows that in the center portion of the interval the functions have a tendency opposite to that of the remaining portion of the interval. The resultant orthogonality implies that $L_3(x)$ has no part that is representable by $L_1(x)$. Just as it is possible to represent arbitrary functions by weighted sums of $P_0(x)$, $P_1(x)$, $P_2(x)$, for example,

$$q(x) = a_0 + a_1 x + a_2 x^2 + \cdots + a_n x^n$$
$$= a_0 P_0(x) + a_1 P_1(x) + \cdots + a_n P_n(x)$$

it is also possible to represent the function in terms of the orthogonal family. This ability to write

$$q(x) = a_0 L_0(x) + a_1 L_1(x) + a_2 L_2(x) + \cdots + a_n L_n(x)$$

permits a solution to the problem of finding the Gaussian integration formulas.

Returning now to the problem of eliminating the integral term, one finds that the expansion of the two polynomial factors in terms of Legendre polynomials provides a method of determining the t_i's which will make this error term zero:

$$p_n(t) = a_0 L_0(t) + a_1 L_1(t) + \cdots + a_n L_n(t) = \sum_{i=0}^{n} a_i L_i(t)$$

$$\prod_{i=0}^{n} (t - t_i) = b_0 L_0(t) + b_1 L_1(t) + \cdots + b_{n+1} L_{n+1}(t) = \sum_{j=0}^{n+1} b_j L_j(t)$$

The product of these two expanded polynomials will be a sum of terms of the form $a_i b_j L_i(t) L_j(t)$. Integrating this sum from -1 to 1 causes all the terms where $i \neq j$ to become zero since $\int_{-1}^{1} L_i(t) L_j(t)\, dt = 0$ when $i \neq j$. The remaining terms are now

$$\int_{-1}^{1} \prod_{i=0}^{n} (t - t_i) p_n(t)\, dt = \int_{-1}^{1} a_0 b_0 (L_0(t))^2\, dt + \int_{-1}^{1} a_1 b_1 (L_1(t))^2\, dt +$$

$$\cdots + \int_{-1}^{1} a_n b_n (L_n(t))^2\, dt = \int_{-1}^{1} \left[\sum_{i=0}^{n} a_i b_i (L_i(t))^2 \right] dt$$

These terms can be made zero by choosing $b_0 = b_1 = b_2 = \cdots = b_n = 0$ and $b_{n+1} = 1$. With this choice the error term will be zero if $\prod_{i=0}^{n} (t - t_i) = L_{n+1}(t)$. This means that the abscissas to be used in forming the interpolation polynomial, which in turn is the basis of the integration formula, are the roots of the $(n + 1)$-Legendre polynomial. Once these roots, $t_0, t_1, t_2, \ldots, t_n$, are determined, then the coefficients of the ordinates, a_i, in the integration approximation can be obtained by integration:

$$a_i = \int_{-1}^{1} c_i(t)\, dt = \int_{-1}^{1} \prod_{\substack{j=0 \\ i \neq j}}^{n} \frac{t - t_j}{t_i - t_j}\, dt$$

The roots and coefficients for $n = 0, 1, 2$ are:

n	t_0	t_1	t_2	a_0	a_1	a_2
0	0			2		
1	$-1/\sqrt{3}$	$1/\sqrt{3}$		1	1	
2	$-\sqrt{\frac{3}{5}}$	0	$\sqrt{\frac{3}{5}}$	$\frac{5}{9}$	$\frac{8}{9}$	$\frac{5}{9}$

Thus in the interval $(-1, 1)$ the integral of a first-degree polynomial $p_1(x)$ is, without error, $2p_1(0)$. Similarly,

$$\int_{-1}^{1} p_3(x)\, dx = p_3\left(-\frac{1}{\sqrt{3}}\right) + p_3\left(\frac{1}{\sqrt{3}}\right)$$

and

$$\int_{-1}^{1} p_5(x)\, dx = \frac{5}{9} p_5\left(-\sqrt{\frac{3}{5}}\right) + \frac{8}{9} p_5(0) + \frac{5}{9} p_5\left(\sqrt{\frac{3}{5}}\right)$$

For comparison, the two- and three-point Gaussian formulas are applied to the problem used as an equal-interval example:

x	$\sin x$
0	0
$\pi/2$	1.0
π	0

(1) Double application of two-point Gaussian formula. From the symmetry one sees that

$$\int_0^{\pi} \sin x\, dx = 2\int_0^{\pi/2} \sin x\, dx$$

For $a = 0$ and $b = \pi/2$, the transformations

$$x = \frac{(b-a)t + a + b}{2}, \qquad dx = \frac{b-a}{2} dt$$

become

$$x = \frac{\pi}{4}(t+1), \qquad dx = \frac{\pi}{4} dt$$

and

$$\int_0^{\pi} \sin x\, dx = 2\left(\frac{\pi}{4}\right) \int_{-1}^{1} \sin\left[\frac{\pi}{4}(t+1)\right] dt$$

$$\approx \frac{\pi}{2}\left[\sin\frac{\pi}{4}\left(-\frac{1}{\sqrt{3}}+1\right) + \sin\frac{\pi}{4}\left(\frac{1}{\sqrt{3}}+1\right)\right] = 1.9968$$

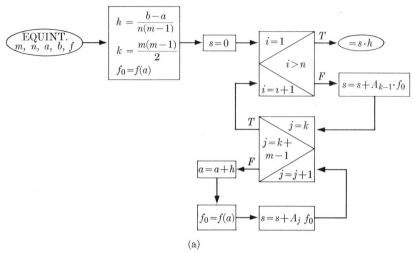

(a)

```
EXTERNAL FUNCTION (M, N, A, B, F.)
INTEGER M, N, I, J, K
ENTRY TO EQUINT.
H = (B − A)/(N*(M − 1))
K = (M*(M − 1))/2
FO = F.(A)
S = 0.
THROUGH L1, FOR I = 1, 1, I .G. N
S = S + ARRAY(K − 1)*FO
THROUGH L1, FOR J = K, 1, J .E. K + M
A = A + H
FO = F. (A)
L1    S = S + A(J)*FO
FUNCTION RETURN S*H
VECTOR VALUES ARRAY = .5, .5, .33333333, 1.3333333, .33333333,
1 .375, 1.125, 1.125, .375, .31111111, 1.4222222, .53333333, 1.4222222, .31111111
END OF FUNCTION
```
(b)

FIG. 13–7.   (a) Flow chart.   (b) Program.

(2) Single application of three-point Gaussian formula:

$$x = \frac{\pi}{2}(t + 1), \qquad dx = \frac{\pi}{2} dt$$

$$\int_0^\pi \sin x \, dx = \frac{\pi}{2} \int_{-1}^1 \sin \frac{\pi}{2}(t + 1) \, dt$$

$$\approx \frac{\pi}{2}\left[\frac{5}{9} \sin \frac{\pi}{2}\left(-\sqrt{\frac{3}{5}} + 1\right) + \frac{8}{9} \sin \frac{\pi}{2}(0 + 1)\right.$$

$$\left. + \frac{5}{9} \sin\left(\sqrt{\frac{3}{5}} + 1\right)\right] = 2.0014$$

Both approximations are better than the best equal-interval result, and yet fewer evaluations of the function were required. Gaussian integration should be used when there is freedom to select the abscissas.

There are other families of orthogonal polynomials which are used when the interval of interest cannot be transformed to $(1, -1)$. Using the roots of these polynomials produces Gaussian formulas which are similar to the ones developed here.

To illustrate the programming of numerical integration, two external functions are included. Both functions are fairly general in that the calling program specifies (a, b), the total interval, n, the number of subintervals n to be integrated separately (i.e., the number of applications of the formula selected), m, the number of points to be used in the integration over one subinterval, and f, the name of the function to be integrated. In both instances it is assumed that the function can be evaluated; it is not tabulated. Equal-interval formulas are used for the first routine, and the Gaussian formula is used for the second.

Example. Write an external function, called EQUINT., which has dummy variables a, b, f, m, n defined as above. The numerical integration of f over the interval (a, b) is to be accomplished by n applications of an equal-interval m-point formula $(2 \leq m \leq 5)$.

The flow chart (Fig. 13–7a) is simple enough to be readily followed if the following two points are understood.

(1) The ordinate which corresponds to the division between subintervals is used twice, once as the last ordinate in a formula and again as the first ordinate in the next application of the formula. The algorithm is constructed so that this ordinate is computed only once.

(2) The constants which are multipliers of the ordinates are arranged in a linear array. Moreover, the constants are arranged so that h is always a multiplier of the entire sum of weighted ordinates.

Number of points	Formula	Constants
2	$(h/2)\big(f(x_0) + f(x_1)\big)$	$\frac{1}{2}, \ \frac{1}{2}$
3	$(h/3)\big(f(x_0) + 4f(x_1) + f(x_2)\big)$	$\frac{1}{3}, \ \frac{4}{3}, \ \frac{1}{3}$
4	$(3h/8)\big(f(x_0) + 3f(x_1) + 3f(x_2) + f(x_3)\big)$	$\frac{3}{8}, \ \frac{9}{8}, \ \frac{9}{8}, \ \frac{3}{8}$
5	$(2h/45)\big(7f(x_0) + 32f(x_1) + 12f(x_2)$ $+ 32f(x_3) + 7f(x_4)\big)$	$\frac{14}{45}, \ \frac{64}{45}, \ \frac{24}{45}, \ \frac{64}{45}, \ \frac{14}{45}$

The elements of the linear array (A) are then:

A_0	A_1	A_2	A_3	A_4	A_5	A_6	A_7	A_8	A_9	A_{10}	A_{11}	A_{12}	A_{13}
$\frac{1}{2}$	$\frac{1}{2}$	$\frac{1}{3}$	$\frac{4}{3}$	$\frac{1}{3}$	$\frac{3}{8}$	$\frac{9}{8}$	$\frac{9}{8}$	$\frac{3}{8}$	$\frac{14}{45}$	$\frac{64}{45}$	$\frac{24}{45}$	$\frac{64}{45}$	$\frac{14}{45}$

2 points　　　3 points　　　　4 points　　　　　5 points

Note that if the first constant in an m-point formula is selected, the linear subscript, k, is $k = m(m - 1)/2 - 1$.

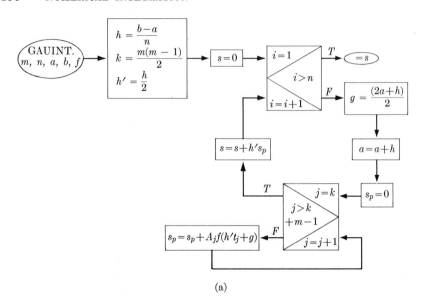

(a)

```
          EXTERNAL FUNCTION (M, N, A, B, F.)
          INTEGER M, N, I, J, K
          ENTRY TO GAUINT.
          H = (B − A)/N
          K = (M*(M − 1))/2
          HP = H/2
          S = 0
          THROUGH L1, FOR I = 1, 1, I .G. N
          G = (2.*A+H)12.0
          A = A + H
          SP = 0.
          THROUGH L2. FOR J = K, 1, J .E. K + M
     L2   SP = SP + ARRAY(J)*F.(HP*T(J) + G)
     L1   S = S + HP*SP
          FUNCTION RETURN S
          VECTOR VALUES ARRAY(1) = 1., 1., .55555556, .88888889,
          1 .55555556, .34785483, .65214516, .65214516, .34785483
          VECTOR VALUES T(1) = −.57735020, .57735020
          1 −.77459674, 0., .77459674, −.86113633, −.33998100, .33998100, .86113633
          END OF FUNCTION
```

(b)

Fig. 13–8.   (a) Flow chart.   (b) Program.

The program for this example is presented in Fig. 13–7(b). Note that to avoid confusion with the interval end point a (here A), the array designated before A is represented by ARRAY.

Example.   Write an external function, called GAUINT., which has dummy variables a, b, f, m, n as before. The numerical integration is to be accomplished by n applications of a Gaussian m-point formula $(2 \leq m \leq 4)$.

Since the Gaussian formulas do not involve ordinates at the end points of the intervals, the steps preventing the reevaluation of the function f at the same point are not relevant. There is in this case, however, the additional complication of having to transform each subinterval to the interval $(-1, 1)$. Also, in addition to the linear array (a) of weighting coefficients, a linear array (t) is required for the roots of the appropriate Legendre polynomials. The zeroth elements of these two arrays are not used so that the formula for the linear subscript for the first relevant item in the m-point formula is $k = m(m - 1)/2$.

Number of points	Ordinate weights	Legendre polynomial roots
2	1, 1	$-\dfrac{1}{\sqrt{3}}, \dfrac{1}{\sqrt{3}}$
3	$\frac{5}{9}, \frac{8}{9}, \frac{5}{9}$	$-\sqrt{\frac{3}{5}}, 0, \sqrt{\frac{3}{5}}$
4	$\dfrac{18 - \sqrt{30}}{36}, \dfrac{18 + \sqrt{30}}{36},$	$-(\frac{3}{7} + \frac{2}{7}\sqrt{\frac{6}{5}})^{1/2}, -(\frac{3}{7} - \frac{2}{7}\sqrt{\frac{6}{5}})^{1/2},$
	$\dfrac{18 + \sqrt{30}}{36}, \dfrac{18 - \sqrt{30}}{36},$	$(\frac{3}{7} - \frac{2}{7}\sqrt{\frac{6}{5}})^{1/2}, \quad (\frac{3}{7} + \frac{2}{7}\sqrt{\frac{6}{5}})^{1/2},$

The transformation to the t variables is

$$x = \frac{(b - a)}{2} t + \frac{(b + a)}{2} \quad \text{and} \quad dx = \frac{b - a}{2} dt$$

If $h = b - a$, $x = (h/2)t + \frac{1}{2}(2a + h)$. As a further simplification, let $h' = h/2$ and $g = (2a + h)/2$; then $x = h't + g$.

The flow chart and program are presented in Fig. 13–8.

NUMERICAL DIFFERENTIATION

The shortcomings of numerical differentiation were mentioned earlier, but they are verified by examination of the error terms after differentiation. Starting with the first-order forward-difference interpolating polynomial

$$f(x) = f(x_0) + (x - x_0)\frac{\Delta f(x_0)}{h} + (x - x_0)(x - x_1)\frac{f''(\zeta)}{2}$$

and differentiating with respect to x, one arrives at

$$f'(x) = \frac{\Delta f(x_0)}{h} + [(x - x_0) + (x - x_1)]\frac{f''(\zeta)}{2}$$

Evaluating the derivative at x_0, and remembering that $x_0 - x_1 = -h$, one obtains a familiar approximation for the first derivative:

$$f'(x_0) = \frac{\Delta f(x_0)}{h} - \frac{h}{2} f''(\zeta), \qquad f'(x_0) \approx \frac{\Delta f(x_0)}{h} = \frac{f(x_1) - f(x_0)}{h}$$

In the same way, a second-order approximation can be derived:

$$f(x) = f(x_0) + (x - x_0)\frac{\Delta f(x_0)}{h} + (x - x_0)(x - x_1)\frac{\Delta^2 f(x_0)}{2h^2}$$
$$+ (x - x_0)(x - x_1)(x - x_2)\frac{f'''(\zeta)}{3!}$$

$$f'(x) = \frac{\Delta f(x_0)}{h} + [(x - x_0) + (x - x_1)]\frac{\Delta^2 f(x_0)}{2h^2}$$
$$+ [(x - x_0)(x - x_1) + (x - x_0)(x - x_2)$$
$$+ (x - x_1)(x - x_2)]\frac{f'''(\zeta)}{6}$$

At $x = x_0$,

$$f'(x_0) = \frac{\Delta f(x_0)}{h} - \frac{\Delta^2 f(x_0)}{2h} + 2h^2\frac{f'''(\zeta)}{6}$$

By expanding the differences one obtains

$$f'(x_0) \approx \frac{2f(x_1) - 2f(x_0) - f(x_2) + 2f(x_1) - f(x_0)}{2h}$$
$$\approx \frac{-f(x_2) + 4f(x_1) - 3f(x_0)}{2h}$$

However, at $x = x_1$,

$$f'(x_1) = \frac{\Delta f(x_0)}{h} + \frac{\Delta^2 f(x_0)}{2h} - \frac{h^2 f'''(\zeta)}{6}$$

and

$$f'(x) \approx \frac{2f(x_1) - 2f(x_0) + f(x_2) - 2f(x_1) + f(x_0)}{2h} = \frac{f(x_2) - f(x_0)}{2h}$$

When the derivative was evaluated at the center point, a smaller error was made. The odd-point formulas are preferred due to the symmetry about a central point, which produces a corresponding reduction in the error term. The five-point expression, evaluated at the central point x_2, which could be obtained in the same manner as those above, is

$$f'(x_2) = \frac{f(x_0) + 8f(x_1) + 8f(x_3) + f(x_4)}{12h} + \frac{h^4}{30}f^{(5)}(\zeta)$$

Simultaneous
Linear
Equations

CHAPTER

FOURTEEN

The solution of simultaneous linear equations is probably the most frequently occurring problem in numerical computation. Most people who have had courses in algebra know a method of solving such systems of equations (at least in principle), but not all can give an unambiguous procedure for doing so. The description of such algorithms is the principle concern of this chapter.

A system of n equations can be represented as follows:

$$\sum_{j=1}^{n} a_{ij}x_j = b_i, \quad \text{for} \quad i = 1, 2, 3, \ldots, n$$

In the expanded form, the equations are written

$$a_{11}x_1 + a_{12}x_2 + a_{13}x_3 + \cdots + a_{1n}x_n = b_1$$
$$a_{21}x_1 + a_{22}x_2 + \cdots \qquad\qquad + a_{2n}x_n = b_2$$
$$\vdots$$
$$a_{n1}x_1 + a_{n2}x_2 + \cdots \qquad\qquad + a_{nn}x_n = b_n$$

The right-hand sides may be regarded as a linear array or vector. The coefficients when written as a two-dimensional array without the variable names are called the *matrix* of *coefficients*. When the right-hand sides are appended on the right, the combined array is called the *augmented matrix:*

$$
\begin{array}{cccccc}
a_{11} & a_{12} & a_{13} & \cdots & a_{1n} & b_1 \\
a_{21} & a_{22} & & \cdots & a_{2n} & b_2 \\
\vdots & & & & & \\
a_{n1} & a_{n2} & & \cdots & a_{nn} & b_n \\
\end{array}
$$

$$\underbrace{\qquad\qquad\qquad\qquad}_{\text{Matrix of coefficients}} \quad \underbrace{\qquad\qquad}_{\substack{\text{Vector of} \\ \text{right-hand sides}}}$$

In computing, it is often desirable to treat the augmented matrix as a single array having more columns than rows. The right-hand sides are designated as elements of the same matrix rather than by a separate name. With such notation, the n equations are

$$\sum_{j=1}^{n} a_{ij}x_j = a_{i,n+1}, \qquad i = 1, 2, 3, \ldots, n$$

and the augmented matrix is written

$$
\begin{array}{cccc}
a_{11} & a_{12} & \cdots & a_{1,n+1} \\
a_{21} & a_{22} & \cdots & a_{2,n+1} \\
\vdots & & & \\
a_{n1} & a_{n2} & \cdots & a_{n,n+1}
\end{array}
$$

It is possible to append more than one vector of right-hand sides, in which case the index of the right-hand column would be greater than $n + 1$.

Methods of solving simultaneous linear equations can be grouped under three headings: (1) by determinants, (2) by elimination, and (3) by iterative techniques. Actually, from a computational point of view, the first is not an effective method, and determinants will be discussed only to the extent required to show that they may be computed by the elimination methods.

ELIMINATION OR REDUCTION

In the context above the word "linear" is usually taken to mean that a variable appears to the first power in every term of the function. Thus

$$f(x_1, x_2) = a_1 x_1 + a_2 x_2 \qquad \text{and} \qquad g(x_1, x_2) = b_1 x_1 + b_2 x_2$$

are linear. Two properties of linear functions that are extensively used in the solution of simultaneous equations are:

$$f(x_1, x_2) + f(x_3, x_4) = f(x_1 + x_3, x_2 + x_4); \quad cf(x_1, x_2) = f(cx_1, cx_2)$$

In the latter, c is an arbitrary constant. The nonlinear function $h(x_1, x_2) = a_1 x_1^2 + a_2 x_1 x_2$ quite obviously does not have either of these properties. In the first property above, the same linear function is applied to two different x-vectors, first to x_1, x_2 and then to x_3, x_4. In simultaneous equations the opposite point of view is taken. There is only one solution vector, but there are several different linear functions (the left-hand parts of the equations which are applied). Since the linear functions are symmetric, that is, both the coefficients and the unknowns appear to the first power in every term, one may define another function, say g, which represents the x's operating on various coefficients:

$$g(a_{11}, a_{12}) = x_1 a_{11} + x_2 a_{12}$$
$$g(a_{21}, a_{22}) = x_1 a_{21} + x_2 a_{22}$$

The linear operations are:

$$g(a_{11} + a_{21}, a_{12} + a_{22}) = g(a_{11}, a_{12}) + g(a_{21}, a_{22})$$
$$g(ca_{11}, ca_{12}) = cg(a_{11}, a_{22})$$

In prose, the first equation states that if one adds the corresponding coefficients of two linear equations before multiplying each by a value of x, the result is the same as if the multiplication by the x's were carried out for each equation separately and then the resultant sums (the right-hand sides) were added. The second equation states that if the coefficients are multiplied by a constant c and then used as multipliers of x_1 and x_2, the results are the same as those obtained by multiplying by x_1, x_2 first and then multiplying the sum (the right-hand side) by the constant c. The repeated application of these two properties is the basis for the elimination methods of solving simultaneous linear equations. "Equations," multiplied by a constant, are added in such a way that a simpler set of equations is produced.

To illustrate an elimination (or reduction) procedure, we shall use the following steps to solve the set of equations given below.

$$2x_1 - 7x_2 + 4x_3 = 9$$
$$x_1 + 9x_2 - 6x_3 = 1$$
$$-3x_1 + 8x_2 + 5x_3 = 6$$

The ordinary (human) approach is to look for simple relations between coefficients. One could observe, for instance, that multiplying the second equation by 2 would yield $2x_1$ as the leading term, and therefore subtracting the first equation from the multiplied second equation would eliminate x_1 from the second equation:

$$2x_1 - 7x_2 + 4x_3 = 9$$
$$25x_2 - 16x_3 = -7$$
$$-3x_1 + 8x_2 + 5x_3 = 6$$

Only the coefficients and right-hand sides entered into this elimination step; the variable names did not. Hence only the augmented matrix need be written. The step could be written

$$
\begin{array}{rrrr}
2 & -7 & 4 & 9 \\
1 & 9 & -6 & 1 \\
-3 & 8 & 5 & 6
\end{array}
\quad\rightarrow\quad
\begin{array}{c}
2 \times \text{row } 2 \\
- \\
1 \times \text{row } 1 \\
= \\
\text{New row } 2
\end{array}
\quad\rightarrow\quad
\begin{array}{rrrr}
2 & -7 & 4 & 9 \\
0 & 25 & -16 & -7 \\
-3 & 8 & 5 & 6
\end{array}
$$

As a next step, multiplying the first row by 4 and adding the second would eliminate x_3 from the first equation, i.e., make the coefficient of x_3 zero:

$$
\begin{array}{rrrr}
2 & -7 & 4 & 9 \\
0 & 25 & -16 & -7 \\
-3 & 8 & 5 & 6
\end{array}
\quad\rightarrow\quad
\begin{array}{c}
4 \times \text{row } 1 \\
+ \\
1 \times \text{row } 2 \\
= \\
\text{New row } 1
\end{array}
\quad\rightarrow\quad
\begin{array}{rrrr}
8 & -3 & 0 & 29 \\
0 & 25 & -16 & -7 \\
-3 & 8 & 5 & 6
\end{array}
$$

Two more steps permit the solution for one of the variables, after which substitution in the other equations determines the remaining two.

$$
\begin{array}{rrrr}
8 & -3 & 0 & 29 \\
0 & 25 & -16 & -7 \\
-3 & 8 & 5 & 6
\end{array}
\quad\rightarrow\quad
\begin{array}{c}
8 \times \text{row } 3 \\
+ \\
3 \times \text{row } 1 \\
= \\
\text{New row } 3
\end{array}
\quad\rightarrow\quad
\begin{array}{rrrr}
8 & -3 & 0 & 29 \\
0 & 25 & -16 & -7 \\
0 & 55 & 40 & 135
\end{array}
$$

$$
\begin{array}{rrrr}
8 & -3 & 0 & 29 \\
0 & 25 & -16 & 7 \\
0 & 55 & 40 & 135
\end{array}
\quad\rightarrow\quad
\begin{array}{c}
2 \times \text{row } 3 \\
+ \\
5 \times \text{row } 2 \\
= \\
\text{New row } 3
\end{array}
\quad\rightarrow\quad
\begin{array}{rrrr}
8 & -3 & 0 & 29 \\
0 & 25 & -16 & -7 \\
0 & 235 & 0 & 235
\end{array}
$$

The result is:

$$
\begin{aligned}
235x_2 &= 235 && \therefore\ x_2 = 1 \\
8x_1 - 3x_2 &= 29 && \therefore\ x_1 = 4 \\
25x_2 - 16x_3 &= -7 && \therefore\ x_3 = 2
\end{aligned}
$$

The procedure is then to add and subtract the proper multiples of rows until the equations are reduced to a simpler form that is readily solved.

The simplest form is the system of independent equations,

$$a_{11}x_1 = b_1$$
$$a_{22}x_2 = b_2$$
$$a_{33}x_3 = b_3$$

However, a system in which one equation involves only one variable, another two variables, another three, etc., is also readily solved by systematic substitution (or *back solution* as this procedure is often called).

$$a_{11}x_1 = b_1$$
$$a_{21}x_1 + a_{22}x_2 = b_2$$
$$a_{31}x_1 + a_{32}x_2 + a_{33}x_3 = b_3$$

The matrices corresponding to these two readily solvable cases are *diagonal* and *triangular*, respectively. In a diagonal matrix all the coefficients are zero except those on the main diagonal; i.e., those whose row and column indices are equal.

$$\begin{matrix} a_{11} & 0 & 0 \\ 0 & a_{22} & 0 \\ 0 & 0 & a_{33} \end{matrix}$$

In the triangular form only the elements above (or below) the diagonal are zero.

$$\begin{matrix} a_{11} & 0 & 0 \\ a_{21} & a_{22} & 0 \\ a_{31} & a_{32} & a_{33} \end{matrix}$$

The matrix shown is said to be in lower triangular form.

Assuming for the moment that the elimination should proceed until the independent equations are obtained, one can describe the process of solving a system of equations as follows. Given an augmented matrix, add (or subtract) multiples of the other rows to (or from) a multiple of a particular row until the coefficient matrix has been reduced to diagonal form. What is now needed is a systematic description of the order in which the rows are modified. In the example, the order was determined by considerations of arithmetic simplicity. Elements were set to zero when the relations between the coefficients made such a step convenient. If a computer is to do the computation, such considerations are not important, but what is needed is a systematic sequence of steps to accomplish the diagonalization.

Assuming that $a_{11} \neq 0$, one may use multiples of the first row to set to zero the other elements in the first column. The row selected to simplify the other rows is called the *pivot row;* the element in the pivot row which is in the column to be set to zero is called the *pivot element.*

$$
\begin{array}{cccc}
a_{11} & a_{12} & a_{13} & a_{14} \\
a_{21} & a_{22} & a_{23} & a_{24} \\
a_{31} & a_{32} & a_{33} & a_{34}
\end{array}
\quad
\begin{array}{l}
a_{11} \text{ row } 2 \\
\overline{} \\
a_{21} \text{ row } 1 \\
= \\
\text{New row } 2
\end{array}
\rightarrow
\begin{array}{cccc}
a_{11} & a_{12} & a_{13} & a_{14} \\
0 & a'_{22} & a'_{23} & a'_{24} \\
a_{31} & a_{32} & a_{33} & a_{34}
\end{array}
\quad
\begin{array}{l}
a_{11} \text{ row } 3 \\
\overline{} \\
a_{31} \text{ row } 1 \\
= \\
\text{New row } 3
\end{array}
$$

$$
\rightarrow
\begin{array}{cccc}
a_{11} & a_{12} & a_{13} & a_{14} \\
0 & a'_{22} & a'_{23} & a'_{24} \\
0 & a'_{32} & a'_{33} & a'_{34}
\end{array}
$$

In this sequence of steps, *row 1 was a pivot row* (a_{11} the pivot element) and *rows 2 and 3 were reduced.* The same steps for the previously considered numerical example are:

$$
\begin{array}{rrrr}
2 & -7 & 4 & 9 \\
1 & 9 & -6 & 1 \\
-3 & 8 & 5 & 6
\end{array}
\rightarrow
\begin{array}{rrrr}
2 & -7 & 4 & 9 \\
0 & 25 & -16 & -7 \\
-3 & 8 & 5 & 6
\end{array}
\rightarrow
\begin{array}{rrrr}
2 & -7 & 4 & 9 \\
0 & 25 & -16 & -7 \\
0 & -5 & 22 & 39
\end{array}
$$

One can continue the process, using multiples of row 2 to alter the other rows so that the other elements in column 2 are set to zero. Note that row 3 could be used for the same purpose, but not row 1, since adding multiples of it to the other rows would destroy the zeros already created.

$$
\begin{array}{cccc}
a_{11} & a_{12} & a_{13} & a_{14} \\
0 & a'_{22} & a'_{23} & a'_{24} \\
0 & a'_{32} & a'_{33} & a'_{34}
\end{array}
\quad
\begin{array}{l}
a'_{22} \text{ row } 1 \\
\overline{} \\
a_{12} \text{ row } 2 \\
= \\
\text{New row } 1
\end{array}
\rightarrow
\begin{array}{cccc}
a'_{11} & 0 & a'_{13} & a'_{14} \\
0 & a'_{22} & a'_{23} & a'_{24} \\
0 & a'_{32} & a'_{33} & a'_{34}
\end{array}
\quad
\begin{array}{l}
a'_{22} \text{ row } 3 \\
\overline{} \\
a'_{32} \text{ row } 2 \\
= \\
\text{New row } 3
\end{array}
$$

$$
\rightarrow
\begin{array}{cccc}
a'_{11} & 0 & a'_{13} & a'_{14} \\
0 & a'_{22} & a'_{23} & a'_{24} \\
0 & 0 & a''_{33} & a''_{34}
\end{array}
$$

Row 2 was a pivot row, and *rows 1 and 3 were reduced.* Note that, except for the diagonal elements, the computation did not need to be carried out on the elements to the left of the pivot column (column 2), since the results are zero. In fact, the computations of elements *in* the pivot column can also be omitted since the method is designed to make these zero. The same steps for the example are:

$$
\begin{array}{rrrr}
2 & -7 & 4 & 9 \\
0 & 25 & -16 & -7 \\
0 & -5 & 22 & 39
\end{array}
\rightarrow
\begin{array}{rrrr}
50 & 0 & -12 & 176 \\
0 & 25 & -16 & -7 \\
0 & -5 & 22 & 39
\end{array}
\rightarrow
\begin{array}{rrrr}
50 & 0 & -12 & 176 \\
0 & 25 & -16 & -7 \\
0 & 0 & 470 & 940
\end{array}
$$

There is one independent equation at this point ($470x_3 = 940$), but one more cycle is required to obtain the diagonal matrix.

At this point, only row 3 may be used as a pivot since the use of any other would destroy existing zeros.

$$
\begin{array}{cccc}
a'_{11} & 0 & a'_{13} & a'_{14} \\
0 & a'_{22} & a'_{23} & a'_{24} \\
0 & 0 & a''_{33} & a''_{34}
\end{array}
\qquad
\begin{array}{l}
a''_{33} \text{ row 1} \\
\overline{} \\
a'_{13} \text{ row 3} \\
\overline{\overline{}} \\
\text{New row 1}
\end{array}
\rightarrow
\begin{array}{cccc}
a''_{11} & 0 & 0 & a''_{14} \\
0 & a'_{22} & a'_{23} & a'_{24} \\
0 & 0 & a''_{33} & a''_{34}
\end{array}
$$

$$
\begin{array}{l}
a''_{33} \text{ row 2} \\
\overline{} \\
\rightarrow a'_{23} \text{ row 3} \rightarrow \\
\overline{\overline{}} \\
\text{New row 2}
\end{array}
\qquad
\begin{array}{cccc}
a''_{11} & 0 & 0 & a''_{14} \\
0 & a''_{22} & 0 & a''_{24} \\
0 & 0 & a''_{33} & a''_{34}
\end{array}
$$

Row 3 was used as a pivot row to reduce rows 1 and 2. The matrix of coefficients is now in the desired form. The analogous steps bring the example to diagonal form also.

$$
\begin{array}{rrrr}
50 & 0 & -12 & 176 \\
0 & 25 & -16 & -7 \\
0 & 0 & 470 & 940
\end{array}
\rightarrow
\begin{array}{rrrr}
23500 & 0 & 0 & 94000 \\
0 & 25 & -16 & -7 \\
0 & 0 & 470 & 940
\end{array}
\rightarrow
\begin{array}{rrrr}
23500 & 0 & 0 & 94000 \\
0 & 11750 & 0 & 11750 \\
0 & 0 & 470 & 940
\end{array}
$$

From the above, one obtains

$$
\begin{array}{lll}
23500x_1 = 94000 & \therefore & x_1 = 4 \\
11750x_2 = 11750 & \therefore & x_2 = 1 \\
470x_3 = 940 & \therefore & x_3 = 2
\end{array}
$$

In this process three indices are employed. One index designates the pivot row (k), another the row being reduced (i), and the third determines the specific element being changed within the row being reduced (j). To develop a formula for the reduction, it may be helpful to write out a specific row reduction and then identify the elements with the subscripts i, j, k. With the first row used as a pivot ($k = 1$), the modification of the third row ($i = 3$) to set $a_{13} = 0$ is:

$$\text{New row 3} = (a_{11}\text{ row 3} - a_{31}\text{ row 1}) = \begin{cases} a'_{31} = a_{11}a_{31} - a_{31}a_{11} = 0 \\ a'_{32} = a_{11}a_{32} - a_{31}a_{12} \\ a'_{33} = a_{11}a_{33} - a_{31}a_{13} \\ a'_{34} = a_{11}a_{34} - a_{31}a_{14} \end{cases}$$

The formulas on the right can be replaced by

$$a'_{3j} = a_{11}a_{3j} - a_{31}a_{1j}$$

for

$$j = 1, 2, 3, 4$$

By observing that the pivot row (row 1) used in this specific case was also employed in the reduction of row 2, the formula can be generalized to include this reduction also:

$$a'_{ij} = a_{11}a_{ij} - a_{i1}a_{1j}$$

for

$$i = 2, j = 1,\ 2,\ 3,\ 4$$

and for

$$i = 3, j = 1,\ 2,\ 3,\ 4$$

Since every row was used once as a pivot row, the inclusion of the pivot index k permits the statement of the entire reduction by a single formula, with some accompanying statements to quantify the indices:

$$a'_{ij} = a_{kk}a_{ij} - a_{ik}a_{kj}$$

The ranges of i, j, k are

$$k = 1,\ 2,\ 3$$

and for each value of k, $i = 1, 2, 3$ (excluding $i = k$) and for each value of $i, j = 1, 2, 3, 4$. This method of reduction, which is called the Gauss-Jordan method, produces a diagonal matrix and can be extended to n equations by simply replacing the 3 by n. In such highly iterative procedures, it is useful to introduce a little more formalism in the description of the algorithms so that such statements as "... and for each value of ..." need not be included. In addition, the occasionally confusing mathematical practice of using the same index in a variety of independent expressions can be clarified by such notation. The convention to be used in algorithms of this repetitive type is that a quantifying statement (for example, $i = 1, 2, \ldots, n$) applies to all the statements below it that are indented to the right. In this form, the Gauss-Jordan algorithm is:

$$k = 1, 2, \ldots, n$$
$$i = 1, 2, \ldots, n; \quad i \neq k$$
$$j = 1, 2, \ldots, n + 1$$
$$a'_{ij} = a_{kk}a_{ij} - a_{ik}a_{kj}$$

The method described has some shortcomings, but the discussion of these will be postponed until this algorithm has been presented as a computer program. A fairly subtle problem is encountered in translating these steps into a computing procedure. As has been shown, the alteration of the ith row, using pivot row k, is written

$$a'_{ij} = a_{kk}a_{ij} - a_{ik}a_{kj}, \qquad j = 1, 2, 3, \ldots, n + 1$$

The prime is used to designate that a new array distinct from the original is produced, and in this mathematical statement questions about the dynamics of computation, such as, Does a'_{ij} replace a_{ij}?, simply do not arise. Since in the computer formulation only one array is involved, the formula, in effect, is

$$a_{ij} \leftarrow a_{kk}a_{ij} - a_{ik}a_{kj}, \qquad j = 1, 2, \ldots, n + 1$$

The reduction of row i causes all the elements in that row to be given new values, and, once given a new value, the old value is no longer available. The element a_{ij} is used just once and is immediately replaced by its new value. However, a_{ik} is used in the computation of every element in the row (i.e., it does not have a j-index), and at some point $(j = k)$ it will be given a new value. In the remaining computation in the row, the new value of a_{ik} will be used in the formula, and this was not intended! There are several ways of overcoming this difficulty. One solution is to postpone the computation of a_{ik} until the last step of a row; another is to save the value of a_{ik} before the row reduction commences. A better solution, because it reduces the amount of computation as well, is to compute only those elements which are used in the later stages of reduction. This selective computation is illustrated by the following partially reduced matrix with five rows:

		Pivot column		
		↓		
a_{11}	0	0	a_{14}	a_{15}
0	a_{22}	0	a_{24}	a_{25}
0	0	a_{33}	a_{34}	a_{35}
Pivot row → 0	0	0	a_{44}	a_{45}
0	0	0	a_{45}	a_{55}

Row 4 is the pivot row. To see the problem described above, consider the left-to-right reduction of row 2. The new elements are:

$$(a_{44} \cdot 0 - a_{24} \cdot 0) \quad (a_{44} \cdot a_{22} - a_{24} \cdot 0) \quad (a_{44} \cdot 0 - a_{24} \cdot 0)$$

$$a_{21} \leftarrow 0 \qquad\qquad a_{22} \leftarrow a_{44} \cdot a_{22} \qquad\qquad a_{23} \leftarrow 0$$

$$(a_{44} \cdot a_{24} - a_{24} \cdot a_{kk}) \quad (a_{44} \cdot a_{25} - 0 \cdot a_{45})$$

$$a_{24} \leftarrow 0 \qquad \text{The zero above should be the original } a_{24} \text{ element!}$$

Note that the correct values would be obtained by proceeding from right to left, since to the left of the pivot column the multiplier of a_{24} is zero anyway. However, with the exception of the diagonal element (a_{22} in row 2), every computation to the left of and including the pivot column results in a zero and need not be carried out. In other words, compute from left to right starting at column $k + 1$. To handle the diagonal elements to the left of the kth column (this refers only to those rows preceding the pivot row, that is, $i < k$) the additional step,

$$a_{ii} \leftarrow a_{kk} a_{ii} \qquad \text{for} \quad i < k$$

must be included. With these revisions, the process is:

$$k = 1, 2, \ldots, n$$
$$i = 1, 2, \ldots, n; \quad i \neq k$$
$$\text{whenever} \quad i < k, \quad a_{ii}' = a_{kk} a_{ii}$$
$$j = k + 1, \quad k + 2, \ldots, n + 1$$
$$a_{ij}' = a_{kk} a_{ij} - a_{ik} a_{kj}$$

This description is almost directly translatable into a program, but the flow chart is helpful in understanding the nested iterations.

Example. Write an external function which solves by the Gauss-Jordan method a system of n simultaneous linear equations. The solutions obtained are to replace the right-hand sides of the given augmented matrix, a. The calling sequence is SLEQ.(N, A), where A is the name of the augmented matrix and N the number of equations. Assume that the pivot elements are nonzero. The flow chart and program are given in Fig. 14–1. The last iteration divides the right-hand side by the diagonal element to produce the solutions and replaces the right side with these values. The conditional skipping of the scope of an iteration when $i = k$ illustrates the need for the CONTINUE statement. It is necessary to skip the scope of the iteration but not leave the iteration; i.e., the index i must be incremented from its present value and the computation continued.

This routine has two serious deficiencies: (1) Since the elements are computed by multiplication, the numbers increase in magnitude quite rapidly if the original elements are greater than unity. Correspondingly,

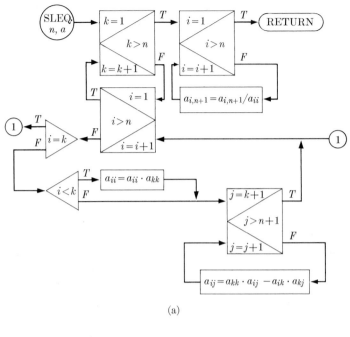

(a)

```
             EXTERNAL FUNCTION (N, A)
             INTEGER I, J, K, N
             ENTRY TO SLEQ.
             THROUGH ITER, FOR K = 1, 1, K .G. N
             THROUGH ITER, FOR I = 1, 1, I .G. N
             WHENEVER I .E. K, TRANSFER TO ITER
             WHENEVER I .L. K, A(I, I) = A(I, I)*A(K, K)
             THROUGH ST, FOR J = K+1, 1, J .G. N+1
ST           A(I, J) = A(K, K)*A(I, J) − A(I, K)*A(K, J)
ITER         CONTINUE
             THROUGH ST1, FOR I = 1, 1, I .G. N
ST1          A(I, N+1) = A(I, N+1)/A(I, I)
             FUNCTION RETURN
             END OF FUNCTION
```

(b)

Fig. 14–1. (a) Flow chart. (b) Program.

the computed elements diminish rapidly if the original elements are less than unity. The numerical example illustrates this growth. The numbers in the augmented matrix are all integers less than ten and yet, in spite of the fact that there are only three equations, the final diagonal elements are as large as 23,500. With such growth it is not uncommon for systems of as few as six equations to exceed the floating-point capacity of the machine in the reduction. What is needed is some normalizing step in the process to scale the elements to reasonable magnitudes.

(2) The assumption that the pivot element must be nonzero leads to the second deficiency. Certainly it is possible to have zero coefficients in

the given set of equations, and although the pivot elements after the first reduction are not the given coefficients, it is conceivable that some of these could be zero and yet have a solvable system of equations. The solution to this problem is fairly obvious, but its exact statement is fairly complex. The procedure is to rearrange the remaining rows and columns of a partially reduced matrix to guarantee that the pivot element will be nonzero. If such an arrangement is not possible, the system does not have a unique solution. Both shortcomings will be remedied in subsequent programs, but first it is appropriate to digress and consider several properties of determinants.

DETERMINANTS

The solution of simultaneous linear equations by determinants, or Cramer's rule, is a useful theoretical tool and practical procedure when the number of equations is small, say, four or less. But determinants do not provide an effective computing procedure when n is large because the number of arithmetic steps becomes excessively large. Using the number of multiplications as a measure of efficiency of the solution procedure, one finds that solving n equations by determinants requires approximately $2(n + 1)!$ multiplications, while the Gauss-Jordan method just described requires approximately n^3 multiplications. [Specifically, the method is accomplished with $n(n + 1)(n - 1) + n(n - 1)/2$ multiplications; the scaling modification alluded to would reduce this number to $n(n + 1) \times (n - 1)/2 + n(n - 1)$.] For $n = 10$, comparison shows that the order of magnitude is 70,000,000 multiplications for determinants versus 1000 for elimination. Nonetheless, it is important to be able to calculate the value of determinants. One of the most important reasons for being able to compute such values is that if the determinant of a system is zero (or in a computational problem, is very small) the equations are not independent. Perhaps before one examines some specific properties of determinants, a review of Cramer's rule is in order.

Given n simultaneous linear equations in n unknowns,

$$\sum_{j=1}^{n} a_{ij}x_j = b_i, \qquad i = 1, 2, \ldots, n$$

the determinant of the system is

$$\Delta = \begin{vmatrix} a_{11} & a_{12} & \cdots & a_{1n} \\ a_{21} & a_{22} & \cdots & a_{2n} \\ \vdots & & & \vdots \\ a_{n1} & a_{n2} & \cdots & a_{nn} \end{vmatrix}$$

If $\Delta \neq 0$, the solution is

$$x_1 = \frac{\begin{vmatrix} b_1 & a_{12} & \cdots & a_{1n} \\ b_2 & a_{22} & \cdots & a_{2n} \\ \vdots & & & \vdots \\ b_n & a_{n2} & \cdots & a_{nn} \end{vmatrix}}{\Delta}$$

$$x_2 = \frac{\begin{vmatrix} a_{11} & b_1 & \cdots & a_{1n} \\ a_{21} & b_2 & \cdots & a_{2n} \\ \vdots & & & \vdots \\ a_{n1} & b_n & \cdots & a_{nn} \end{vmatrix}}{\Delta}$$

$$\vdots \qquad x_n = \frac{\begin{vmatrix} a_{11} & a_{12} & \cdots & b_1 \\ a_{21} & a_{22} & \cdots & b_2 \\ \vdots & & & \vdots \\ a_{n1} & a_{n2} & \cdots & b_n \end{vmatrix}}{\Delta}$$

To evaluate such determinants by the methods of elimination, one must understand the evaluation of determinants by minors and determine the effect that the linear operations on the rows of the determinant have on the determinant's value.

Evaluation by minors. This technique is developed here by induction. The determinant of a single number is itself,

$$|a_{11}| = a_{11}$$

The rule for computing a second-order determinant can be found by solving the system

$$a_{11}x_1 + a_{12}x_2 = b_1$$
$$a_{21}x_1 + a_{22}x_2 = b_2$$

for x_1 by substitution and identifying the resultant denominator as the determinant:

$$x_1 = \frac{b_1 a_{22} - b_2 a_{12}}{a_{11} a_{22} - a_{12} a_{21}}$$

The denominator is the familiar "criss-cross" rule:

$$\begin{vmatrix} a_{11} & a_{12} \\ a_{21} & a_{22} \end{vmatrix} = a_{11}a_{22} - a_{12}a_{21} = a_{11}|a_{22}| - a_{12}|a_{21}|$$

In the rightmost form, the determinant is expanded by taking the element and multiplying it by the determinant that results when the row and column containing the first row element are deleted. The signs of the terms alternate.

The same method can be used to compute a third-order determinant:

$$\begin{vmatrix} a_{11} & a_{12} & a_{13} \\ a_{21} & a_{22} & a_{23} \\ a_{31} & a_{32} & a_{33} \end{vmatrix} = \begin{aligned} & a_{11}a_{22}a_{33} + a_{31}a_{12}a_{23} + a_{13}a_{21}a_{32} \\ & - a_{13}a_{22}a_{31} - a_{23}a_{32}a_{11} - a_{33}a_{21}a_{12} \end{aligned}$$

$$= a_{11} \begin{vmatrix} a_{22} & a_{23} \\ a_{32} & a_{33} \end{vmatrix} - a_{12} \begin{vmatrix} a_{21} & a_{23} \\ a_{31} & a_{33} \end{vmatrix} + a_{13} \begin{vmatrix} a_{21} & a_{22} \\ a_{31} & a_{33} \end{vmatrix}$$

The same description applies. The elements of a given row are multiplied by the determinants obtained by deleting the row and column which contain the element. This subdeterminant is called a *minor*, and when the sign is attached to the determinant, it is called a *cofactor*. Using the latter form one can write the third-order determinant:

$$\begin{vmatrix} a_{11} & a_{12} & a_{13} \\ a_{21} & a_{22} & a_{23} \\ a_{31} & a_{32} & a_{33} \end{vmatrix} = a_{11}\,\Delta_{11} + a_{12}\,\Delta_{12} + a_{13}\,\Delta_{13}$$

where

$$\Delta_{ij} = (-1)^{i+j} \times \begin{vmatrix} a_{11} \cdots a_{1,j-1}, & a_{1,j+1} & \cdots & a_{1n} \\ \vdots & & & \\ a_{i-1,1} & & & \\ a_{i+1,1} & & & \vdots \\ \vdots & & & \\ a_{n,1} & & \cdots & a_{nn} \end{vmatrix}$$

The ith row and the jth column are deleted from the determinant to form the cofactor of a_{ij}. If the quantity $i + j$ is even, the cofactor is positive; otherwise it is negative. In general, then,

$$\Delta = \sum_{j=1}^{n} a_{ij}\,\Delta_{ij}$$

But each determinant Δ_{ij} can, in turn, be expanded in terms of cofactors. This expansion process can continue recursively until the cofactors are single elements. To illustrate numerically, the now familiar third-order matrix is used.

$$\begin{vmatrix} 2 & -7 & 4 \\ 1 & 9 & -6 \\ -3 & 8 & 5 \end{vmatrix} = 2\begin{vmatrix} 9 & -6 \\ 8 & 5 \end{vmatrix} + 7\begin{vmatrix} 1 & -6 \\ -3 & 5 \end{vmatrix} + 4\begin{vmatrix} 1 & 9 \\ -3 & 8 \end{vmatrix}$$

$$= 2(93) + 7(-13) + 4(35) = 235$$

Consider now the determinants of two special cases, a diagonal matrix and a triangular matrix. For the diagonal matrix,

$$\begin{vmatrix} a_{11} & 0 & 0 \\ 0 & a_{22} & 0 \\ 0 & 0 & a_{33} \end{vmatrix} = a_{11}\begin{vmatrix} a_{22} & 0 \\ 0 & a_{33} \end{vmatrix} + 0\begin{vmatrix} 0 & 0 \\ 0 & a_{33} \end{vmatrix} + 0\begin{vmatrix} 0 & a_{22} \\ 0 & 0 \end{vmatrix}$$

$$= a_{11}a_{22}a_{33}$$

The determinant is simply the product of the diagonal elements.

In the triangular case,

$$\begin{vmatrix} a_{11} & 0 & 0 \\ a_{21} & a_{22} & 0 \\ a_{31} & a_{32} & a_{33} \end{vmatrix} = a_{11}\begin{vmatrix} a_{22} & 0 \\ a_{32} & a_{33} \end{vmatrix} + 0\begin{vmatrix} a_{21} & 0 \\ a_{31} & a_{33} \end{vmatrix} + 0\begin{vmatrix} a_{21} & a_{22} \\ a_{31} & a_{32} \end{vmatrix}$$

$$= a_{11}a_{22}a_{33}$$

In both cases, the determinant is the product of the diagonal elements. These matrix forms are the ones produced by the elimination methods, but in the process, rows were multiplied by constants and added together. The next step is to determine how these operations affect the value of a determinant.

Multiplication of a row by a constant. The effect of multiplication by a constant is relatively easy to determine once expansion by cofactors is understood. The procedure is simply to expand about the multiplied row and observe that the multiplier may be factored out of the determinant. In the third-order case,

$$\begin{vmatrix} a_{11} & a_{12} & a_{13} \\ ca_{21} & ca_{22} & ca_{23} \\ a_{31} & a_{32} & a_{33} \end{vmatrix} = ca_{21}\,\Delta_{21} + ca_{22}\,\Delta_{22} + ca_{23}\,\Delta_{23}$$

$$= c(a_{21}\,\Delta_{21} + a_{22}\,\Delta_{22} + a_{23}\,\Delta_{23}) = c\Delta$$

where Δ was the determinant before the multiplication by c. Thus one sees that multiplying a row by a constant modifies the determinant by the same factor. If more than one row multiplier is used, the original determinant is modified by the product of the multipliers.

Addition of rows. If a certain fact is known, it is readily seen that the addition of rows of a determinant does not affect the value of the determinant. This fact is that if the cofactors of a given row are multiplied by the elements of another row, the resultant sum of products is zero. One can easily demonstrate this result for the third-order determinant. By taking the cofactors of the first row and multiplying these by second-row elements one sees that the result is zero.

$$a_{21}\,\Delta_{11} + a_{22}\,\Delta_{12} + a_{23}\,\Delta_{13}$$

$$= a_{21}\begin{vmatrix} a_{22} & a_{23} \\ a_{32} & a_{33} \end{vmatrix} - a_{22}\begin{vmatrix} a_{21} & a_{23} \\ a_{31} & a_{33} \end{vmatrix} + a_{23}\begin{vmatrix} a_{21} & a_{22} \\ a_{31} & a_{32} \end{vmatrix}$$

$$= a_{21}a_{22}a_{33} - a_{21}a_{23}a_{32} - a_{22}a_{21}a_{33}$$

$$+ a_{22}a_{23}a_{31} + a_{23}a_{21}a_{32} - a_{23}a_{22}a_{31} = 0$$

This property is to be expected if the matrix elements are considered to be coefficients of linear equations because it is the result that would be obtained if one row of the matrix were duplicated, e.g.,

$$\begin{vmatrix} a_{21} & a_{22} & a_{23} \\ a_{21} & a_{22} & a_{23} \\ a_{31} & a_{32} & a_{33} \end{vmatrix}$$

But from the point of view of linear equations this duplication is equivalent to including the same equation twice in the system of equations. Obviously, in this case the equations are not independent (two are identical!) and the determinant of the system must therefore be zero. With this information, the lack of effect of adding multiples of rows can be seen by expanding the determinant about the augmented row.

$$\begin{vmatrix} a_{11} + ca_{21} & a_{12} + ca_{22} & a_{13} + ca_{23} \\ a_{21} & a_{22} & a_{23} \\ a_{31} & a_{32} & a_{33} \end{vmatrix}$$

$$= (a_{11} + ca_{21})\,\Delta_{11} + (a_{21} + ca_{22})\,\Delta_{12} + (a_{13} + ca_{23})\,\Delta_{13}$$

$$= (a_{11}\,\Delta_{11} + a_{12}\,\Delta_{12} + a_{13}\,\Delta_{13}) + c(a_{21}\,\Delta_{11} + a_{22}\,\Delta_{12} + a_{23}\,\Delta_{13})$$

$$= \Delta + 0$$

These observations demonstrate that the determinant of a matrix can be computed by an elimination procedure which reduces the given matrix to triangular or diagonal form, provided the product of the row multipliers used to produce these forms is recorded. This product is divided into the determinant of the triangular (or diagonal) form to obtain the true determinant.

To illustrate, the coefficients of the numerical example are presumed to be reduced to triangular form by the elimination process. The necessary multipliers for this reduction are recorded adjacent to the multiplied row.

$$\begin{vmatrix} 2 & -7 & 4 \\ 1 & 9 & -6 \\ -3 & 8 & 5 \end{vmatrix} \rightarrow \begin{vmatrix} 2 & -7 & 4 \\ 0 & 25 & -16 \\ 0 & -5 & 22 \end{vmatrix} \begin{matrix} \\ \times 2 \\ \times 2 \end{matrix} \rightarrow \begin{vmatrix} 2 & -7 & 4 \\ 0 & 25 & -16 \\ 0 & 0 & 470 \end{vmatrix} \begin{matrix} \\ \times 2 \\ \times 2 \times 25 \end{matrix}$$

$$\Delta = \frac{2 \cdot 25 \cdot 470}{2 \cdot 2 \cdot 25} = 235$$

It will be seen that the incorporation of the scaling into the elimination process, which was mentioned previously, will simplify the task of keeping track of the multiplicative constants.

SOME VARIATIONS OF THE ELIMINATION METHOD

The scaling difficulties of the Gauss-Jordan method can be alleviated by dividing the pivot row by its diagonal element (the pivot element) before using this row in the reduction of the other rows. Stated another way, the elements of the kth row are divided by a_{kk} to produce new elements a'_{kj}. The new diagonal, $a'_{kk} = 1$, is a result of this division. (It is still assumed that $a_{kk} \neq 0$.)   With the pivot element always unity, the reduction formula is

$$a'_{ij} = a_{ij} - a_{ik}a_{kj}$$

Note now that the reduced row (row i) is *not* multiplied by a constant, but a multiple of the pivot row is subtracted from it. From the results obtained in the discussion of determinants it follows that the value of the determinant is not changed by the reduction of the ith row. It is true, however, that the division of the pivot row by the diagonal element does affect the determinant value. This step is tantamount to multiplying by the constant $1/a_{kk}$. Therefore the value of the determinant is the determinant of the reduced matrix, Δ_r (a diagonal or triangular matrix), divided by the product of all the row multipliers:

$$\frac{1}{a_{11}} \cdot \frac{1}{a'_{22}} \cdot \frac{1}{a''_{33}} \cdots \frac{1}{a_{nn}^{(n-1)}}$$

The primes indicate that these diagonal elements are not the original matrix but are altered in the reduction process. More concisely,

$$\Delta = \frac{\Delta_r}{\prod_{i=1}^{n} [1/a_{ii}^{(i-1)}]} = \Delta_r \prod_{i=1}^{n} a_{ii}^{(i-1)}$$

But as a result of the division of the pivot rows all the diagonal elements
will be unity, and the product of these diagonal elements, Δ_r, is also unity.
Hence $\Delta = \prod_{i=1}^{n} a_{ii}^{(i-1)}$. In prose, once again, the determinant of the
system is simply the product of the pivot-row divisors used in reducing
the matrix of coefficients to diagonal or triangular form. If the primary
goal is the computation of the determinant, reduction to triangular form
is superior since it can be carried out in fewer operations than are required
to obtain the diagonal form. As observed earlier, the determinant is the
product of the diagonal elements.

By considering a matrix which is partially reduced to triangular form
one can determine the range of the indices.

$$
\begin{array}{cccc}
1 & a_{12} & a_{13} & a_{14} \\
0 & 1 & a_{23} & a_{24} \\
0 & 0 & a_{33} & a_{34} \\
0 & 0 & a_{43} & a_{44}
\end{array}
$$

The next step, at this point, is to select row 3 as a pivot row (row 4
could be used, but that is a complication which is postponed until later)
and divide the remaining elements in row 3 by a_{33}.

$$
\begin{array}{cccc}
1 & a_{12} & a_{13} & a_{14} \\
0 & 1 & a_{23} & a_{24} \\
0 & 0 & 1 & a'_{34} \\
0 & 0 & a_{43} & a_{44}
\end{array}
$$

Subtracting $a_{43} \cdot$ (row 3) from row 4 will make

$$a'_{43} = a_{43} - a_{43} \cdot 1 = 0$$

as desired. As observed earlier, this computation need not be carried out
since the result must be zero. Also, the zero elements to the left of a_{43}
will not be changed by the subtraction of row 3, and hence the computation
of new elements in a reduced row can start with the first element to the
right of the pivot column, i.e., the $(k + 1)$-column.

The description of a procedure for reducing a matrix to triangular form
with 1's on the diagonal can be described in terms of the pivot index, k,

the reduced row index, i, and the column index, j, as follows:

$$k = 1, 2, \ldots, n$$
$$j = k + 1, k + 2, \ldots, n + 1$$
$$a'_{kj} = \frac{a_{kj}}{a_{kk}}$$
$$i = k + 1, k + 2, \ldots, n$$
$$j = k + 1, k + 2, \ldots, n + 1$$
$$a'_{ij} = a_{ij} - a_{ik}a_{kj}$$

After these steps have been completed, the reduction of the triangular matrix to diagonal form must be carried out before the solution to the linear equations is obtained explicitly. The triangular form for three equations is:

$$x_1 + a_{12}x_2 + a_{13}x_3 = a_{14}$$
$$x_2 + a_{23}x_3 = a_{24}$$
$$x_3 = a_{34}$$

Putting this result in matrix form suggests a familiar approach to the diagonalization, namely, finishing the pivoting process. Use row 3 to put zeros in column 3 (rows 1 and 2); use row 2 to put a zero in column 2 (row 1). This procedure is merely the "triangularization" of the upper triangle, but this time there is no need for division since the diagonal elements are already unity.

$$
\begin{array}{cccc}
1 & a_{12} & a_{13} & a_{14} \\
0 & 1 & a_{23} & a_{24} \\
0 & 0 & 1 & a_{34}
\end{array}
$$

To reduce, use the triangularization algorithm without division.

$$k = 2, 3, \ldots, n$$
$$i = 1, 2, \ldots, k - 1$$
$$j = k + 1, k + 2, \ldots, n + 1$$
$$a'_{ij} = a_{ij} - a_{ik}a_{kj}$$

Although this approach to the back solution is familiar, it is a little more complicated than it needs to be. There are two alternative approaches: one is to substitute the known value x_3 into all the other equations and then x_2 into all the remaining equations, etc.; the other is to do the same thing but in a different order. That is, one substitutes x_3 in the preceding

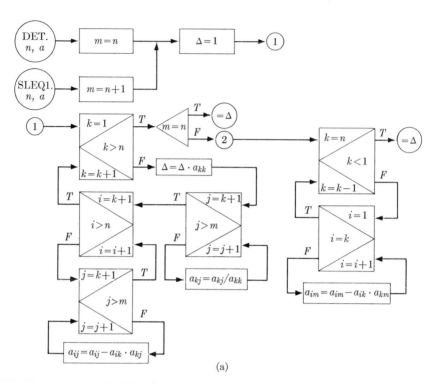

(a)

```
        EXTERNAL FUNCTION (N, A)
        INTEGER I, J, K, M, N
        ENTRY TO SLEQ1.
        M = N + 1
        TRANSFER TO E1
        ENTRY TO DET.
        M = N
E1      DELTA = 1.0
        THROUGH E2, FOR K = 1, 1, K .G. N
        DELTA = DELTA*A(K, K)
        THROUGH E3, FOR J = K + 1, 1, J .G. M
E3      A(K, J) = A(K, J)/A(K, K)
        THROUGH E2, FOR I = K + 1, 1, I .G. N
        THROUGH E2, FOR J = K + 1, 1, J .G. M
E2      A(I, J) = A(I, J) − A(I, K)*A(K, J)
        WHENEVER M .E. N, FUNCTION RETURN DELTA
        THROUGH E4, FOR K = N, −1, K .L. 1
        THROUGH E4, FOR I = 1, 1, I .E. K
E4      A(I, M) = A(I, M) − A(I, K)*A(K, M)
        FUNCTION RETURN DELTA
        END OF FUNCTION
```

(b)

Fig. 14–2. (a) Flow chart. (b) Program.

equation to obtain x_2, then substitutes x_2 and x_3 in the preceding equation, etc. The difference is simply whether the row index or the column index is the "inner" iteration. Using the first approach, one selects row n as a pivot, and only the pivot column and $(n + 1)$-column are altered. Since zeros are produced in the pivot column, there is no need to explicitly carry out the computation. When column $n - 1$ is used as a pivot, only the $(n + 1)$-column need be changed.

$$k = n, \ n - 1, \ldots, \ 1$$

$$i = n - 1, \ n - 2, \ldots, \ 1$$

$$a_{i,n+1} = a_{i,n+1} - a_{ik}a_{k,n+1}$$

When this process is completed, the roots will be in the positions originally occupied by the right-hand sides. The entire procedure is now complete enough to be programmed.

Example. Write an external function which, by an elimination method, computes the determinant of the matrix of coefficients of a given augmented matrix. The function should have two entries: DET. if only the value of the determinant is desired, and SLEQ1. if, in addition, the solution of the system is to replace the right-hand sides. The parameters should be n, the number of equations, and a, the name of the augmented matrix. The flow chart and the program are presented in Fig. 14–2.

The section from the entry points to ① computes the number of columns, m, involved in the reduction; $m = n$ if only the determinant is desired, otherwise $m = n + 1$ on the assumption that there is only one vector of right-hand sides in the augmented matrix. From ① to ② the triangular matrix with unit diagonal elements is computed. Every pivot-row divisor is multiplied by a partial product to form the determinant. At the conclusion of this section, if $m = n$, the process is completed, and the value of the determinant is the direct result. The last section, from ② to the end, carries out the back solution of the reduced matrix.

MATRIX NOTATION

The procedures that have been introduced for solving linear equations can be expressed more succinctly in terms of matrix notation. The purpose of this section is not to develop matrix algebra but to motivate a very useful linear algorithm which is a relatively simple extension of the preceding topics. This extension consists of finding the *inverse* of a matrix by reduction methods.

A set of n equations can be written as a matrix of coefficients, a vector of unknowns, and a vector of right-hand sides.

$$\begin{bmatrix} a_{11} & a_{12} & \cdots & a_{1n} \\ a_{21} & & & \\ \vdots & & & \\ a_{n1} & & \cdots & a_{nn} \end{bmatrix} \begin{bmatrix} x_1 \\ x_2 \\ \vdots \\ x_n \end{bmatrix} = \begin{bmatrix} b_1 \\ b_2 \\ \vdots \\ b_n \end{bmatrix}$$

Any one of the right-hand sides is simply expressed as $b_i = \sum_{k=1}^{n} a_{ik}x_k$. In matrix notation, the forms above are written

$$A\bar{x} = \bar{b}$$

where matrices are denoted by capital letters and the lower-case letters indicate vectors. The operation of matrix-vector multiplication, on the left above, is defined by the linear evaluation formula for each of the n elements of b. Matrix multiplication simply introduces another subscript into the formula. Thus

$$AB = C$$

written in array form becomes

$$\begin{bmatrix} a_{11} & a_{12} & \cdots & a_{1n} \\ a_{21} & & & \\ a_{31} & & & \vdots \\ \vdots & & & \\ a_{n1} & & \cdots & a_{nn} \end{bmatrix} \begin{bmatrix} b_{11} & b_{12} & \cdots & b_{1n} \\ b_{21} & & & \\ \vdots & & & \vdots \\ b_{n1} & & \cdots & b_{nn} \end{bmatrix} = \begin{bmatrix} c_{11} & c_{12} & \cdots & c_{1n} \\ c_{21} & & & \\ \vdots & & & \vdots \\ c_{n1} & & \cdots & c_{nn} \end{bmatrix}$$

If the columns of the B- and C-matrices are considered one at a time, the definition of the product elements remains unchanged. For instance, the first column of c is

$$c_{i1} = \sum_{k=1}^{n} a_{ik}b_{k1}, \qquad i = 1, 2, \ldots, n$$

For a general element, the additional column subscript j is included, and

$$c_{ij} = \sum_{k=1}^{n} a_{ik}b_{kj}$$

Although the matrices shown here are square (i.e., they have the same number of rows and columns), it is apparent that matrix multiplication is defined so long as the left factor has as many columns as the right factor has rows.

Let us return for the moment to the equation $A\bar{x} = \bar{b}$. If the range of these variables were real numbers instead of arrays, solving for $\bar{x}$ would be a simple task:

$$A\bar{x} = \bar{b}$$

$$\frac{1}{A} A\bar{x} = \frac{1}{A} \bar{b}$$

$$1 \cdot \bar{x} = A^{-1}\bar{b}$$

Thus $1 \cdot \bar{x} = \bar{x}$ would be obtained by multiplying the reciprocal (or inverse) of A and $\bar{b}$. In the domain of real numbers a unit element (1) and an inverse for any nonzero number x exist, and the latter is designated x^{-1}. The defining properties of these two entities are:

$$\left. \begin{array}{l} 1 \cdot x = x \\ x \cdot x^{-1} = 1 \end{array} \right\} \quad \text{for any real number } x$$

The question is whether analogous entities exist for arrays, and the answer is that in some cases they do. A square diagonal matrix with ones on the diagonal is called an identity matrix (I) and fulfills the first condition:

$$\begin{bmatrix} 1 & 0 & 0 \\ 0 & 1 & 0 \\ 0 & 0 & 1 \end{bmatrix} \begin{bmatrix} a_{11} & a_{12} & a_{13} & a_{14} \\ a_{21} & a_{22} & a_{23} & a_{24} \\ a_{31} & a_{32} & a_{33} & a_{34} \end{bmatrix} = \begin{bmatrix} a_{11} & a_{12} & a_{13} & a_{14} \\ a_{21} & a_{22} & a_{23} & a_{24} \\ a_{31} & a_{32} & a_{33} & a_{34} \end{bmatrix}$$

$$IA = A$$

Note that in this case, AI is not defined since the rows and columns do not match, and hence the matrix multiplication formula cannot be applied. The search for inverses is limited to square matrices and reduces to the question of whether there is a matrix B such that

$$AB = I$$

Writing out this matrix equation in array form illustrates that B, if it exists, can be found by solving a system of n equations with n different right-hand side vectors.

$$\begin{bmatrix} a_{11} & a_{12} & a_{13} \\ a_{21} & a_{22} & a_{23} \\ a_{31} & a_{32} & a_{33} \end{bmatrix} \begin{bmatrix} b_{11} & b_{12} & b_{13} \\ b_{21} & b_{22} & b_{23} \\ b_{31} & b_{32} & b_{33} \end{bmatrix} = \begin{bmatrix} 1 & 0 & 0 \\ 0 & 1 & 0 \\ 0 & 0 & 1 \end{bmatrix}$$

There are three different unknown vectors (the columns of B) and three corresponding right-hand-side vectors (the columns of I). To find $B = A^{-1}$, the combined system is solved. Assuming the system is solvable, one can obtain subsequent solutions $\bar{x}$ by matrix-vector multiplication, that is, $A^{-1}\bar{b} = \bar{x}$.

Before developing an algorithm for the purpose of including the production of an inverse with the diagonalization process, we wish to note in passing that the row transformations that have been basic in the preceding algorithms can be expressed in terms of matrices. Conceptually this approach has many advantages, but the algorithms are the same since the manipulation of single elements is ultimately required.

As an example of a matrix transformation, note that rows 2 and 3 of a four-row matrix would be interchanged if it were multiplied on the left by

$$
\begin{bmatrix}
1 & 0 & 0 & 0 \\
0 & 0 & 1 & 0 \\
0 & 1 & 0 & 0 \\
0 & 0 & 0 & 1
\end{bmatrix}
$$

The pivot operation

$$a'_{ij} = a_{ij} - a_{ik}a_{kj}$$

is carried out on an entire row by multiplying on the left by the matrix

$$
i\text{th row} \rightarrow
\begin{bmatrix}
1 & & & & & & \\
& 1 & & & & & \\
& & 1 & & & & \\
& & & 1 & & & \\
& & & & 1 & & \\
& & & & -a_{ik} & & 1 \\
& & & & \uparrow & &
\end{bmatrix}
$$

kth column

Matrix inversion. The augmented matrix for finding the inverse of a system of three equations is shown below. By carrying out one step of the reduction, one can see that the inverse can actually replace the original matrix and hence does not require the explicit inclusion of the identity matrix.

$$
\begin{array}{ccccccccccc}
a_{11} & a_{12} & a_{13} & 1 & 0 & 0 & & 1 & a'_{12} & a'_{13} & \dfrac{1}{a_{11}} = a'_{11} & 0 & 0 \\
a_{21} & a_{22} & a_{23} & 0 & 1 & 0 & \Rightarrow & 0 & a'_{22} & a'_{23} & a_{21}a'_{11} & 1 & 0 \\
a_{31} & a_{32} & a_{33} & 0 & 0 & 1 & & 0 & a'_{32} & a'_{33} & a_{31}a'_{11} & 0 & 1
\end{array}
$$

After the first step of "inversion in place," the matrix would be

$$a'_{11} = \frac{1}{a_{11}} \quad a'_{12} \quad a'_{13}$$

$$a_{21}a'_{11} \qquad a'_{22} \quad a'_{23}$$

$$a_{31}a'_{11} \qquad a'_{32} \quad a'_{33}$$

After row 2 is used as the next pivot row, column 2 becomes a column of the partial inverse, etc. In algorithm form this procedure is described by

$$k = 1, 2, \ldots, n$$

$$j = 1, 2, \ldots, n; \quad j \neq k$$

$$a'_{kj} = \frac{a_{kj}}{a_{kk}}$$

$$a'_{kk} = \frac{1}{a_{kk}}$$

$$i = 1, 2, \ldots, n; \quad i \neq k$$

$$i = 1, 2, \ldots, n; \quad j \neq k$$

$$a'_{ij} = a_{ij} - a_{ik}a_{kj}$$

$$a'_{ik} = a_{ik}a_{kk}$$

Example. Write an external function INV. (N, A) which replaces the $N \times N$ matrix A with its inverse. Since the algorithm is so similar to the Gauss-Jordan method, only the program is presented.

```
       EXTERNAL FUNCTION (N, A)
       INTEGER I, J, K, N
       ENTRY TO INV.
       THROUGH S1, FOR K = 1, 1, K.G.N
       THROUGH S2, FOR J = 1, 1, J.G.N
S2     WHENEVER J.NE.K, A(K, J) = A(K, J)/A(K, K)
       A(K, K) = 1.0/A(K, K)
       THROUGH S1, FOR I = 1, 1, I.G.N
       WHENEVER I.E.K, TRANSFER TO S1
       THROUGH S3, FOR J = 1, 1, J.G.N
S3     WHENEVER J.NE.K, A(I, J) = A(I, J) − A(I, K)*A(K, J)
       A(I, K) = A(I, K)*A(K, K)
S1     CONTINUE
       FUNCTION RETURN
       END OF FUNCTION
```

Maximum element selection. The restriction (which is still in effect) that the pivot elements must be nonzero at every point can be removed by adding a few statements to the program above which search for a nonzero pivot element before a new pivot row is selected. To understand the required program changes, however, some additional discussion is almost mandatory.

It was pointed out earlier that division is an approximate operation. The continuing digits of the quotient must usually be truncated. It seems reasonable to assume that the propagation error would be reduced if this error-introducing operation were postponed as long as possible. From this point of view the original Gauss-Jordan algorithm is attractive since there is no division until a diagonal matrix has been obtained. Once committed to the division, however, one can hold the propagated error to a minimum if the largest (in magnitude) possible divisor is always selected. The fact that the operation itself is approximate cannot be helped. The approximation-error number analysis of division illustrated that the largest divisor produced the smallest quotient error; this result can now be verified by a differential analysis of the division operation. If $f = y/x$, then

$$df = \frac{x(dy/dx) - y}{x^2}\, dx \qquad \text{or} \qquad df = \frac{x\, dy - y\, dx}{x^2}$$

and, as the previous approach showed, a divisor of large magnitude reduces the error.

Up to this point, the pivot elements have been selected systematically, i.e., the element in column 1 of row 1 was used first, the element in column 2 of row 2 was used next, etc. The result of these selections produced, in the division case, a diagonal matrix of unit elements. The first numerical illustration of this chapter showed that it is not necessary to use equation 1 to solve for x_1, equation 2 to solve for x_2, etc., as the preceding elimination algorithms have done. A different order of selection of pivot elements will lead to an independent set of equations as long as any row or column is not used in the pivoting process more than once. The final matrix will not be diagonal, but it will have only one unit element in any row or column. The algorithm for such a reduction is obviously more complicated. To illustrate the sequence of steps required, the inverse of a simple system is determined below. For clarity, the inverse is obtained as augmented columns, but in practice it would probably be developed, as in the inversion example above, in the "zero" positions of the reduced matrix. One of the "bookkeeping" tasks in such an algorithm is to designate the rows and columns that are used as pivots. Once a row or column has been selected, it cannot again be used as a pivot. The scheme for keeping track of these pivot inclusions is to carry along two additional linear arrays which give the order of inclusion of the rows and columns. The number of the first pivot row will be in element 1 of the row array, and similarly, the number of the first column used as a pivot will be in element 1 of the column array. The numbers of the second pivot row and column will be in the second elements, etc. The elements of these two arrays are initially set to the integers in their natural order, i.e., 1, 2, 3, 4, ... In the following example, the row and column arrays are shown at the left and above the matrix of coefficients, respectively. The system of equations is:

$$x_1 + 2x_2 + 8x_3 = -3$$
$$2x_1 - 4x_2 - 6x_3 = 0$$
$$-2x_1 + 4x_2 + 2x_3 = 4$$

for which the solution is:

$$x_1 = 1, \qquad x_2 = 2, \qquad x_3 = -1$$

The augmented matrix, including an identity matrix, is given below. The row and column arrays have their initial values. The largest (in magnitude) element of the possible pivot elements is circled.

i \ j	1	2	3	4			
1	1	2	⑧	−3	1	0	0
2	2	−4	−6	0	0	1	0
3	−2	4	2	4	0	0	1

The largest element is in the (1, 3)-position. Accordingly, the number in the first position (1) of the column array is interchanged with the number in the third position (3); there is no change in the row array. Subtracting multiples of row 1 to set column 3 to zero produces the following result:

i \ j	3	2	1	4			
1	$\frac{1}{8}$	$\frac{1}{4}$	1	$-\frac{3}{8}$	$\frac{1}{8}$	0	0
2	$\frac{11}{4}$	$-\frac{5}{2}$	0	$-\frac{9}{4}$	$\frac{3}{4}$	1	0
3	$-\frac{9}{4}$	⑦⁄₂	0	$\frac{19}{4}$	$-\frac{1}{4}$	0	1

Remaining numbers
that can be
pivot elements

Of the remaining elements, the one in position $(3, 2)$ has the largest magnitude. Since 2 is already in the second position in the column vector, there is no change there, but 3 is the second pivot row, so the 3 and 2 are interchanged. Note that for each successive pivot selection only the *remaining* numbers (elements 2 and 3 after the first selection) of the row and column vectors are examined.

i \ j	3	2	1	4			
1	$\frac{2}{7}$	0	1	$-\frac{5}{7}$	$\frac{1}{7}$	0	$-\frac{1}{14}$
3	$\left(\frac{8}{7}\right)$	0	0	$\frac{8}{7}$	$-\frac{8}{14}$	1	$\frac{5}{7}$
2	$-\frac{9}{14}$	1	0	$\frac{19}{14}$	$-\frac{1}{14}$	0	$\frac{2}{7}$

The only remaining element is in the $(2, 1)$-position. Since this is the last pivot element, no interchanges are called for.

i \ j	3	2	1	4			
1	0	0	1	-1	0	$-\frac{1}{4}$	$-\frac{1}{4}$
3	1	0	0	1	$\frac{1}{2}$	$\frac{7}{8}$	$\frac{5}{8}$
2	0	1	0	2	$\frac{1}{4}$	$\frac{9}{16}$	$\frac{11}{16}$
					③	①	②

If the inversion had been done in place, the ones and zeros now in the matrix of coefficients would not appear, but would have been immediately replaced by the properly altered column of the developing inverse. After the first step, the first column of the "potential" inverse would appear in column 3 of the matrix of coefficients. After the second, column 3 of the inverse would be in column 2 of the matrix. And the final step would put column 2 of the inverse in column 1 of the matrix.

i \ j	3	2	1	4
1	$-\frac{1}{4}$	$-\frac{1}{4}$	0	-1
3	$\frac{7}{8}$	$\frac{5}{8}$	$\frac{1}{2}$	1
2	$\frac{9}{16}$	$\frac{11}{16}$	$\frac{1}{4}$	2

The information required to rearrange the rows and columns so that the inverse is the inverse of the original matrix of coefficients and the solutions are correctly identified is contained in the auxiliary linear arrays. The rearrangement can be regarded as a two-step process: (1) the rows of the entire matrix are rearranged, and then (2) the columns of the matrix of coefficients are reordered. The solution vector, column 4, is helpful in considering the first step. Row 1 and column 3 were the first pivot choices. Stated differently, equation 1 was used to solve for x_3. Therefore, row 1 should be interchanged with row 3 so that the solution, x_3, is in the third row.

i \ j	3	2	1	4
3	$\frac{9}{16}$	$\frac{11}{16}$	$\frac{1}{4}$	2
1	$\frac{7}{8}$	$\frac{5}{8}$	$\frac{1}{2}$	1
2	$-\frac{1}{4}$	$-\frac{1}{4}$	0	-1

To record this move, the 3 and 1 in the auxiliary vector are also interchanged. Looking at the next elements of the auxiliary arrays, one sees that element 2 in row 1 was used as a pivot (i.e., x_2 was solved for in equation 1). Row 1 must be interchanged with the second row.

i \ j	3	2	1	4
3	$\frac{7}{8}$	$\frac{5}{8}$	$\frac{1}{2}$	1
2	$\frac{9}{16}$	$\frac{11}{16}$	$\frac{1}{4}$	2
1	$-\frac{1}{4}$	$-\frac{1}{4}$	0	-1

The row interchanges are complete. The solutions are in the desired order.

$$x_1 = 1, \qquad x_2 = 2, \qquad x_3 = -1$$

Stated simply, enough row interchanges were made to put the auxiliary vectors in correspondence by altering only the row labels. A similar procedure puts the columns in correct order, but this time the row array remains fixed and the column headings are altered. It is necessary to start from the original row and column arrays.

i \ j	3	2	1	4
1				
3				
2				

In row 1 the pivot element is in column 3. To correspond to the identity matrix it should be in column 1; hence interchange columns 1 and 3.

i \ j	1	2	3	4
1	$\frac{1}{2}$	$\frac{5}{8}$	$\frac{7}{8}$	1
3	$\frac{1}{4}$	$\frac{11}{16}$	$\frac{9}{16}$	2
2	0	$-\frac{1}{4}$	$-\frac{1}{4}$	-1

In row 3 the pivot column is 2. To put this pivot column in column 3, interchange columns 2 and 3.

i \ j	1	3	2	4
1	$\frac{1}{2}$	$\frac{7}{8}$	$\frac{5}{8}$	1
3	$\frac{1}{4}$	$\frac{9}{16}$	$\frac{11}{16}$	2
2	0	$-\frac{1}{4}$	$-\frac{1}{4}$	-1

The reordering is now complete. In the algorithm to be given, the row interchanges precede the column interchanges. To eliminate the need for an additional array, the permutations required to put the rows in 3 2 1 order are preserved in the i-array. The permutations are then performed in reverse order on the columns, with the result that the columns appear in 1 3 2 order. As a check,

$$
A A^{-1} = \begin{bmatrix} 1 & 2 & 8 \\ 2 & -4 & 6 \\ -2 & 4 & 2 \end{bmatrix} \begin{bmatrix} \frac{1}{2} & \frac{7}{8} & \frac{5}{8} \\ \frac{1}{4} & \frac{9}{16} & \frac{11}{16} \\ 0 & -\frac{1}{4} & -\frac{1}{4} \end{bmatrix} = \begin{bmatrix} 1 & 0 & 0 \\ 0 & 1 & 0 \\ 0 & 0 & 1 \end{bmatrix} = I
$$

One can also obtain the solution to the original set of equations:

$$
A^{-1}b = \begin{bmatrix} \frac{1}{2} & \frac{7}{8} & \frac{5}{8} \\ \frac{1}{4} & \frac{9}{16} & \frac{11}{16} \\ 0 & -\frac{1}{4} & -\frac{1}{4} \end{bmatrix} \begin{bmatrix} -3 \\ 0 \\ 4 \end{bmatrix} = \begin{bmatrix} 1 \\ 2 \\ -1 \end{bmatrix} = \bar{x}
$$

The following example illustrates the statement of this algorithm as a program. In procedures as complicated as this it is advantageous to closely relate the flow chart to the program statements. Accordingly, some of the capitalized multi-character variable names are used in the flow chart. This machine-imposed notation is stylistically objectionable, perhaps, but in context the use is clear. Where it is possible without confusion, lower-case letters are used for index and subscript variables.

Example.   Write an external function, MAXINV.(A, NI, NJ) which finds the inverse of the matrix of coefficients of the augmented matrix A. The augmented matrix has NI rows and NJ columns, where NJ $\geq$ NI. When NJ $>$ NI, solutions are to be found for the additional NJ-NI columns of right-hand sides. The inverse is to replace the matrix of coefficients; the magnitude of the determinant is to be directly returned, and the elements with greatest magnitude are to be used as pivot elements.

Flow chart. This procedure is complex enough so that it is useful to break the flow chart up into sections and intersperse some descriptive comments.

(1) The first step is to set the elements of the two auxiliary linear arrays I and J to the values 1, 2, 3, . . . , NJ. The partial product, Δ, which is to become the magnitude of the determinant, is set to one and the iteration which counts the number of pivot cycles is entered. When this iteration is terminated ($k >$ NI), a transfer is made to S7 where the rearrangement of the rows and columns of the reduced matrix starts (Fig. 14–3).

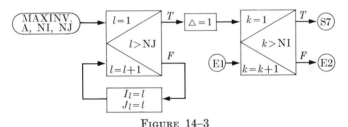

FIGURE 14–3

(2) With the pivot index (a value of k) selected, all the rows and columns designated in the k, $k + 1$, . . . , NI elements of the I- and J-arrays are searched for the maximal element. Once found, it becomes the next pivot element and its row and column are preserved as the integer variables KI and KJ. These values are interchanged with the kth position of the auxiliary arrays. However, this interchange should not take place when only one row and column remain, i.e., when $k =$ NI. At several points in this program, a substitution is made simply for the sake of computing efficiency. Such a case appears in the flow chart (Fig. 14–4) as IL $= I_l$. A single integer variable IL is created so that the subscripted variable I_l need not be subsequently referred to. The pivot element is stored as AKK and then set to one, thus yielding the unit element which the inverse required.

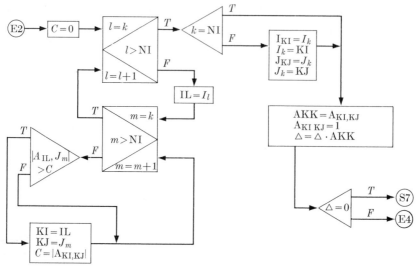

FIGURE 14–4

(3) Having determined the pivot element and made the proper interchanges in the auxiliary arrays, one next divides all the elements in the
pivot row (row KI) by the pivot element. Note that the pivot element
itself becomes $1/A_{KI,KJ}$. Then, in accordance with the Gauss-Jordan
procedure, all the "non-pivot" elements are reduced. Before a row is
reduced, the element in the pivot column (column KJ) is saved as AIK,
and then the original matrix element is set to zero. Again, this is the
proper value for obtaining the inverse in place. These steps are illustrated in Fig. 14–5.

(4) The previous flow chart returns to the incrementation of k (E1),
and the cycle repeats until $k > NI$, at which time the rearrangement
(S7) commences. The row interchanges are determined by examining
initially the first elements of the auxiliary arrays and, after the interchanges, the second elements, then the third, etc. The position under
examination is given by an index k, and when $k > NI$, the rearrangement
of rows is complete. As the interchanges are made, the subscript of the
element in the i-array that is interchanged with i_k is recorded in i_k after
the interchange. For example, in the first step rows 1 and 3 are interchanged.

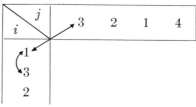

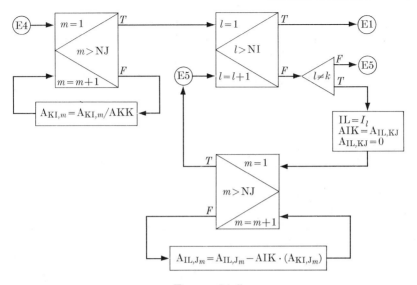

FIGURE 14–5

To record this move $i_1 = 1$ is interchanged with $i_2 = 3$. The final arrangement will be 3 2 1, and so i_1 is given the value 2, the subscript of the position where it was placed.

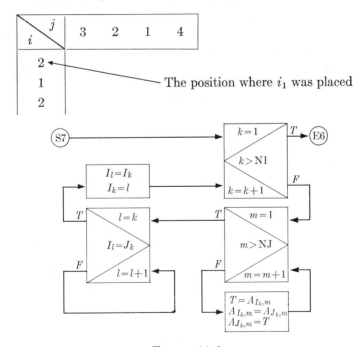

FIGURE 14–6

The next step would be to interchange row 1 with row 2; therefore $i_2 \rightarrow i_3$. The auxiliary arrays obtained by carrying through all the row interchanges are shown in Fig. 14–6.

i $\diagdown$ j	3	2	1	4
2				
3				
3				

(5) The last step is to interchange the columns according to the interchanges which have been recorded in the i-array. The i-array is considered to start with the last element. For the example, the entire process can be illustrated schematically as shown in Fig. 14–7(a). The program is presented in Fig. 14–7(b). By counting the row and column interchanges as the final reordering is being done, one could also determine the sign of the determinant, but this complication is not included here.

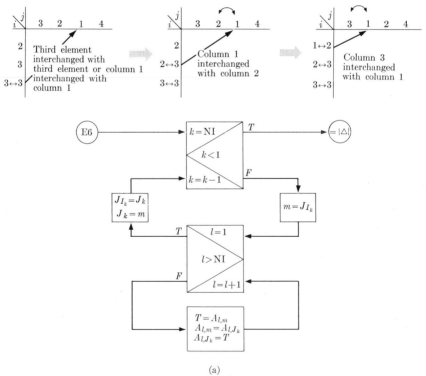

(a)

FIG. 14–7. (a) Flow chart.

```
          EXTERNAL FUNCTION (A, NI, NJ)
          INTEGER I, J, K, L, M, KI, KJ, NI, NJ, IL
          DIMENSION I(50), J(50).
          ENTRY TO MAXINV.
          THROUGH S2, FOR L=1, 1, L.G.NJ
          I(L) = L
S2        J(L) = L
          DET = 1.0
          THROUGH S5, FOR K=1, 1, K.G.NI
          C = 0.
          THROUGH S3, FOR L=K, 1, L.G.NI
          IL = I(L)
          THROUGH S3, FOR M=K, 1, M.G.NI
          WHENEVER .ABS.A(IL, J(M)).G.C
              KI = IL
              KJ = J(M)
              C = .ABS.A(KI, KJ)
S3        END OF CONDITIONAL
          WHENEVER K.E.NI, TRANSFER TO S1
          I(KI) = I(K)
          I(K) = KI
          J(KJ) = J(K)
          J(K) = KJ
S1        AKK = A(KI, KJ)
          A(KI, KJ) = 1.0
          DET = DET*AKK
          WHENEVER DET.E. 0, TRANSFER TO S7
          THROUGH S4, FOR M=1, 1, M .G. NJ
S4        A(KI, M) = A(KI, M)/AKK
          THROUGH S5, FOR L=1, 1, L .G. NI
          WHENEVER L .NE. K
              IL = I(L)
              AIK = A(IL, KJ)
              A(IL, KJ) = 0
              THROUGH S6, FOR M=1, 1, M .G. NJ
S6        A(IL, J(M)) = A(IL, J(M)) − AIK*A(KI, J(M))
S5        END OF CONDITIONAL
S7        THROUGH S8, FOR K=1, 1, K .G. NI
          THROUGH S9, FOR M=1, 1, M .G. NJ
          T = A(I(K), M)
          A(I(K), M) = A(J(K), M)
S9        A(J(K), M) = T
S10       THROUGH S10, FOR L=K, 1, I(L) .E. J(K)
          I(L) = I(K)
S8        I(K) = L
          THROUGH S12, FOR K=NI, −1, K .L. 1
          M = J(I(K))
          THROUGH S11, FOR L=1, 1, L .G. NI
          T = A(L, M)
          A(L, M) = A(L, J(K))
S11       A(L, J(K)) = T
          J(I(K)) = J(K)
S12       J(K) = M
          FUNCTION RETURN .ABS. DET
          END OF FUNCTION
```

(b)

FIG. 14–7. (b) Program.

ITERATIVE METHODS

Iterative methods similar to those illustrated for equations involving one unknown can be used when the functions involve many variables. The problems of convergence of the iteration are often compounded by the additional variables, but such methods do have a virtue that the elimination methods do not possess. Error is not propagated. Since the general procedure is one of taking an approximate solution to a set of equations and then improving it, computational errors which are introduced during the improvement simply mean that the next approximate solution is not quite so good as it might be. If the process is assumed to converge, the error could conceivably result in an additional iterative cycle, but no loss in accuracy of the final solution would occur. When the number of equations is very large, the propagated error in elimination methods becomes a serious problem, and iterative methods are useful to obtain the solution or improve the solution after an approximate solution has been determined by elimination.

Given n simultaneous equations,

$$f_1(x_1, x_2, \ldots, x_n) = 0$$
$$f_2(x_1, x_2, \ldots, x_n) = 0$$
$$\vdots$$
$$f_n(x_1, x_2, \ldots, x_n) = 0$$

which are not necessarily linear, one scheme for the improvement of an initial approximate solution $x_1^{(0)}$, $x_2^{(0)}$, $x_3^{(0)}$, $\ldots$, $x_n^{(0)}$ would be to apply Newton's method to each equation individually. To make this application, assume that the first equation can be considered to be a function of x_1 only, the second of x_2 only, etc. The equations and their root improvement formulas are indicated below.

$$f_1(x_1, \ldots, x_n) \approx \bar{f}_1(x_1), \qquad x_1^{(k+1)} = x_1^{(k)} - \frac{\bar{f}_1(x_1^{(k)})}{\bar{f}'_1(x_1^{(k)})}$$

$$f_2(x_1, \ldots, x_n) \approx \bar{f}_2(x_2), \qquad x_2^{(k+1)} = x_2^{(k)} - \frac{\bar{f}_2(x_2^{(k)})}{\bar{f}'_2(x_2^{(k)})}$$

$$\vdots \qquad\qquad\qquad\qquad \vdots$$

$$f_n(x_1, \ldots, x_n) \approx \bar{f}_n(x_n), \qquad x_n^{(k+1)} = x_n^{(k)} - \frac{\bar{f}_n(x_n^{(k)})}{\bar{f}'_n(x_n^{(k)})}$$

The improvement formulas are the iterative formulas of Newton's method. The index of the approximation is indicated by a superscript since the subscript identifies a particular unknown. The procedure would be to use equation 1 to improve x_1, then equation 2 to improve x_2, etc., and to repeat this improvement until all the equations are simultaneously satisfied. Again, as a practical matter, the values of the functions will probably not be zero, but the sum of the absolute values of the differences from zero (the residuals) should be acceptably small.

In the particular case of interest, i.e. for linear equations, the root improvement formula is of a simple form. For the ith equation,

$$f_i(x_1, \ldots, x_n) = a_{i1}x_1 + a_{i2}x_2 + \cdots + a_{ii}x_i + \cdots$$
$$+ a_{in}x_n - a_{i,n+1} = 0$$

the improvement formula is

$$x_i^{(k+1)} = x_i^{(k)} - \frac{\sum_{j=1}^{n} a_{ij}x_j - a_{i,n+1}}{a_{ii}} = x_i^{(k)} - \frac{r_i^{(k)}}{a_{ii}}$$

The numerator of the rightmost term will be zero if the equation is satisfied and is called the residual, $r_i^{(k)}$. When Newton's iteration formula is applied to a straight line, the improved approximation is the root, but, of course, the function actually depends on n variables and hence the repeated trials are necessary.

Reverting to substitution forms and neglecting the superscripts, one proceeds by computing

$$\sum_{j=1}^{n} a_{ij}x_j - a_{i,n+1} = r_i$$
$$x_i \leftarrow x_i - \frac{r_i}{a_{ii}}$$

for $i = 1, 2, \ldots, n$. At the same time, $\sum_{i=1}^{n} |r_i|$ is computed, and when this sum is sufficiently close to zero the solution is complete. Otherwise, the improvement cycle is repeated until there is convergence, or until some maximum number of iterations have been completed. This method is called the Gauss-Seidel method of solving linear equations.

Example. Write a program which attempts to solve a system of linear equations by the Gauss-Seidel method. If the solution is not obtained in 100 trials, the program is terminated with the printed comment "NO SOLUTION FOUND." The necessary input information is the number of equations, n, the name of the augmented matrix, a, the criterion for convergence, ϵ, and the initial approximation to the solution vector $x_1, x_2, \ldots, x_n$. If the method is successful, the solution is printed. The flow chart and the program for this example are given in Fig. 14–8. The Gauss-Seidel method is a *single-step* method in that the solution is

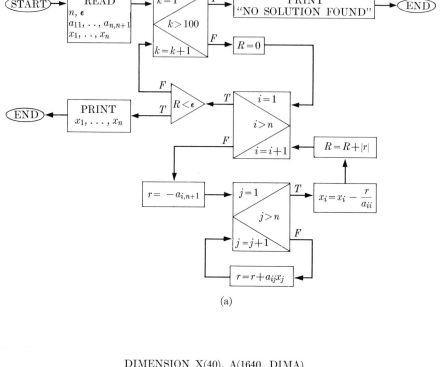

(a)

```
           DIMENSION  X(40), A(1640, DIMA)
           INTEGER  I, J, K, N
           VECTOR VALUES  DIMA = 2, 1, 0
START      READ DATA
           DIMA(2) = N+1
           READ DATA
           THROUGH L1, FOR  K = 1, 1, K .G. 100
           CAPR = 0.
           THROUGH L2, FOR  I = 1, 1, I .G. N
           R = −A(I, N+1)
           THROUGH L3, FOR  J = 1, 1, J .G. N
L3         R = R+A(I, J)*X(J)
           X(I) = X(I) − R/A(I, I)
L2         CAPR = CAPR+.ABS. R
L1         WHENEVER CAPR .L. EPS, TRANSFER TO L4
           PRINT COMMENT$ NO SOLUTION FOUND$
           TRANSFER TO END
L4         PRINT RESULTS  X(1) . . . X(N)
END        END OF PROGRAM

Data
N = 3,  EPS = 1E−4 *
A(1, 1) = 2, −7, 4, 9,    A(2, 1) = 1, 9, −6, 1,
A(3, 1) = −3, 8, 5, 6     X(1) = 1, 1, 1 *
```

(b)

FIG. 14–8. (a) Flow chart. (b) Program.

improved after the evaluation of each equation. Other *total-step* methods compute an improved approximation only after all equations have been evaluated. Among the latter is the method of *steepest descent*, which is similar to Newton's method, but the assumption that each equation may be treated as a function of a single variable is not made. If one pictures the approximation as being a point on a surface, the path of steepest descent from the point is projected (analogous to the tangent in Newton's method) to determine the next approximation.

Approximation

In the preceding chapters the criterion used in approximating a function by a polynomial was that the polynomial agree exactly with the function at a prescribed number of points. As mentioned before, when this criterion is used, the problem is one of *interpolation*, and the polynomial is called an interpolating polynomial. When other criteria are used to find polynomials (or other forms) to represent functions, the problem is one of *approximation*. A fairly obvious need for other criteria arises when the given points are empirical, such as observations from an experiment. In such cases it does not seem reasonable to ask that the approximating function pass through the given points since these values are known to contain some measurement error. A numerical process analogous to the draftsman's technique of drawing a smooth curve through the "center" of a collection of plotted points is needed. Ideally, this process should take into account the reliability of the observations, if such information can be quantified, so that the more reliable points will have a greater effect or *weight* in the production of an approximating function. In fact, this idea of weighting has applications beyond the considerations of reliability; for instance, it may be used to give greater emphasis to points within a particular interval. However, in the initial introduction to least-square approximations it is assumed that the given values are of equal importance.

LEAST-SQUARES POLYNOMIAL APPROXIMATION

The draftsman's procedure of visually fitting a curve to a set of points may be described as follows. (1) By observation of the plotted points, a curve (i.e., a function) is selected, and (2) the curve is then drawn so that there are about as many points above the line as below; however, in this division, the distance of the points from the line is taken into account. In Fig. 15–1, these distances, or deviations, are labeled d_0, $d_1, \ldots, d_N$.

These deviations are the differences between the selected function, $p(x)$, evaluated at a certain abscissa, and the given ordinate corresponding to

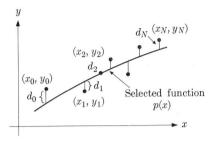

FIGURE 15–1

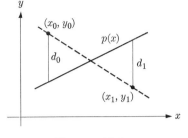

FIGURE 15–2

the same abscissa:

$$d_0 = p(x_0) - y_0$$
$$d_1 = p(x_1) - y_1$$
$$\vdots$$
$$d_k = p(x_k) - y_k$$
$$\vdots$$
$$d_N = p(x_N) - y_N$$

For the points above $p(x)$ the deviations are negative, and for those below $p(x)$ they are positive. It is tempting to say that the curve is "centered" if the negative deviations are equal to the positive deviations or, more simply, if

$$\sum_{k=0}^{N} d_k = \sum_{k=0}^{N} (p(x_k) - y_k) = 0$$

but a simple two-point case (Fig. 15–2) illustrates that this condition can be satisfied without yielding the desired curve. Here $d_0 = -d_1$ so that $\sum_{k=0}^{1} d_k = 0$, but the straight line $p(x)$ is obviously not as good an approximation as the dashed line shown. The alternative criterion that $\sum_{k=0}^{1} |d_k|$ be as small as possible would have given the better result. In general, of course, $\sum_{k=0}^{N} |d_k|$ will not be zero as it was in this example, but the requirement that it be a minimum avoids the difficulties encountered when the sum of deviations is set to zero. However, the absolute values give rise to a problem. Differentiation is useful in the search for minimum values, but the absolute value function is not differentiable at its minimum. Another function which is dependent only on the magnitude of a number is the square, $f(x) = x^2$, and it is differentiable. Moreover, the square of a variable (or even the sum of the squares of several variables) does not have a maximum—only a minimum. In other words, the square increases without bound as the magnitude of the argument increases. These, then, are

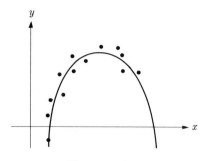

FIGURE 15–3

reasons for using the least-squares criterion to determine an approximating function $p(x)$; i.e.,

$$\sum_{k=0}^{N} d_k^2 = \sum_{k=0}^{N} \left(p(x_k) - y_k\right)^2 = \text{minimum}$$

For the purposes at hand, the postulated function $p(x)$ will be limited to polynomials. All that needs to be determined then by looking at the given points is an estimate of the degree, n, of the polynomial. The method to be developed is just as applicable when $p(x)$ is a linear combination of functions other than polynomials.

In summary, if the given points are

$$
\begin{array}{cc}
x_0 & y_0 \\
x_1 & y_1 \\
\vdots & \vdots \\
x_N & y_N
\end{array}
$$

and a plot of these points looks like the graph in Fig. 15–3, it would seem reasonable that the inserted curve could be represented by the parabola (i.e., the second-degree polynomial) $p(x) = a_0 + a_1 x + a_2 x^2$. The problem is to find the best values for a_0, a_1, a_2 and the least-squares criterion for "best" is to be used:

$$F = \sum_{k=0}^{N} d_k^2 = \sum_{k=0}^{N} \left(p(x_k) - y_k\right)^2$$

$$= \sum_{k=0}^{N} \left(a_0 + a_1 x_k + a_2 x_k^2 - y_k\right)^2 = \text{minimum}$$

It is necessary to find the values of a_0, a_1, a_2 for which $F(a_0, a_1, a_2)$ is minimum. If F were a function of only one variable instead of three, the procedure would be the familiar one of finding the value of the variable for which the derivative is equal to zero. With three variables it is necessary to find the values for which the three partial derivatives are simultaneously zero:

$$\frac{\partial F}{\partial a_0} = 0$$

$$\frac{\partial F}{\partial a_1} = 0$$

$$\frac{\partial F}{\partial a_2} = 0$$

Since F is a sum of terms, the derivative of F will be the sum of the derivatives of the terms.

$$\frac{\partial F}{\partial a_0} = \sum_{k=0}^{N} 2(a_0 + a_1 x_k + a_2 x_k^2 - y_k) = 0$$

$$\frac{\partial F}{\partial a_1} = \sum_{k=0}^{N} 2x_k(a_0 + a_1 x_k + a_2 x_k^2 - y_k) = 0$$

$$\frac{\partial F}{\partial a_2} = \sum_{k=0}^{N} 2x_k^2(a_0 + a_1 x_k + a_2 x_k^2 - y_k) = 0$$

This is a set of simultaneous linear equations in the unknowns a_0, a_1, a_2. Since one may multiply a linear equation by a constant without affecting the equality, all the equations above may be multiplied by $\frac{1}{2}$, with the result that the 2 will be eliminated. If the summation operator is applied to each term within the parentheses separately and the term involving y_i moved to the right-hand side, the equations are in a more conventional form.

$$\left(\sum_{k=0}^{N} 1\right) a_0 + \left(\sum_{k=0}^{N} x_k\right) a_1 + \left(\sum_{k=0}^{N} x_k^2\right) a_2 = \sum_{k=0}^{N} y_k$$

$$\left(\sum x_k\right) a_0 + \left(\sum x_k^2\right) a_1 + \left(\sum x_k^3\right) a_2 = \sum x_k y_k$$

$$\left(\sum x_k^2\right) a_0 + \left(\sum x_k^3\right) a_1 + \left(\sum x_k^4\right) a_2 = \sum x_k^2 y_k$$

The first term in the first equation may look strange. When the expression being summed does not depend on the index of summation as in $\sum_{k=0}^{N} a_0$, it may be written $a_0 \sum_{k=0}^{N} 1$, which is simply $a_0(N + 1)$.

Thus the coefficients of the second-degree polynomial are obtained by simply computing the coefficients of the linear equations above (called *normal equations*) and solving the system to determine a_0, a_1, a_2. Since the solution of a linear system has already been discussed, only the algorithm for computing the elements of the augmented matrix need be developed.

The first equation can be written

$$\sum_{j=0}^{2} \left(\sum_{k=0}^{N} x^j \right) a_j = \sum_{k=0}^{N} y_k$$

the second

$$\sum_{j=0}^{2} \left(\sum_{k=0}^{N} x^{j+1} \right) a_j = \sum_{k=0}^{N} x_k y_k$$

and the third

$$\sum_{j=0}^{2} \left(\sum_{k=0}^{N} x^{j+2} \right) a_j = \sum_{k=0}^{N} x_k^2 y_k$$

The exponents increased by one for each equation as did the exponent of x_k on the right-hand side. Expressing these changes in terms of i, an equation index (row index), one can write the entire system as

$$\sum_{j=0}^{n} \left(\sum_{k=0}^{N} x_k^{i+j} \right) a_j = \sum_{k=0}^{N} x_k^i y_k; \qquad i = 0, 1, 2, \ldots, n$$

The degree of the polynomial, n, would be two for the example considered, but the formula above is general. The usual case is $n < N$, but when $n = N$ one obtains the coefficients of an interpolating polynomial, since a polynomial of degree n can pass through $n + 1$ points with $\sum_{k=0}^{N} d_k^2 = 0$. For $n > N$, an independent set of equations will not be obtained.

The parenthesized sums in the last form of the system are the coefficients. A minor complication is introduced by the fact that matrix-element subscripts conventionally start with 1; that is, the upper left-hand element in a matrix, b, is $b_{1,1}$, not $b_{0,0}$. This discrepancy in the notation can be adjusted by writing

$$\sum_{j=1}^{n+1} \left(\sum_{k=0}^{N} x_k^{i+j-2} \right) a_{j-1} = \sum_{k=0}^{N} x_k^{i-1} y_k, \qquad i = 1, 2, \ldots, n, n+1$$

Now the computation of the augmented matrix can be described by the following steps:

(1) Compute

$$b_{ij} = \sum_{k=0}^{N} x_k^{i+j-2} = \sum_{k=0}^{N} x_k^{i-1} x_k^{j-1}$$

for

$$i = 1, 2, \ldots, n+1$$

and for each i,

$$j = 1, 2, \ldots, n+1$$

(2) Compute the right-hand sides:

$$b_{i,n+2} = \sum_{k=0}^{N} x_k^{i-1} y_k, \quad \text{for} \quad i = 1, 2, \ldots, n+1$$

Strictly speaking, for this algorithm to be valid for any x_k one must assume that the result of computing 0^0 is unity. If it is further observed that the coefficient matrix is symmetric, that is, $a_{ij} = a_{ji}$, then some saving in computation time can be effected.

Before proceeding to a programming example, let us illustrate this method by a simple numerical problem.

Approximate the points,

x	y
0	1.00
1	3.85
2	6.50
3	9.35
4	12.05

by a first-degree polynomial $(n = 1)$. Since five points are given, $N = 4$. The augmented matrix to be computed is:

$$\begin{bmatrix} \sum_{k=0}^{4} 1 & \sum_{k=0}^{4} x_k & \sum_{k=0}^{4} y_k \\[2mm] \sum_{k=1}^{4} x_k & \sum_{k=0}^{4} x_k^2 & \sum_{k=0}^{1} x_k y_k \end{bmatrix} = \begin{bmatrix} 5 & 10 & 32.75 \\[2mm] 10 & 50 & 93.10 \end{bmatrix}$$

Using the Gauss-Jordan method, one obtains the augmented matrix in diagonal form:

$$\begin{bmatrix} 250 & 0 & 257.2 \\ 0 & 50 & 138.0 \end{bmatrix}$$

from which

$$a_0 = \frac{257.2}{250} = 1.03$$

and

$$a_1 = \frac{138}{50} = 2.76$$

The straight-line approximation is

$$y = 1.03 + 2.76x$$

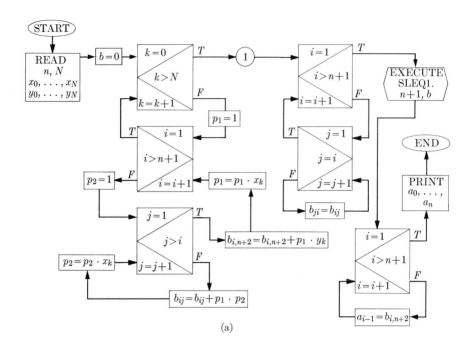

(a)

```
            DIMENSION X(100), Y(100), B(110, BD), A(10)
            VECTOR VALUES BD = 2, 1, 10
            INTEGER I, J, K, N, CAPN
            READ DATA
            EXECUTE ZERO. (B(0) ... B(110))
            THROUGH S1, FOR K = 0, 1, K .G. CAPN
            P1 = 1.0
            THROUGH S1, FOR I = 1, 1, I .G. N + 1
            P2 = 1.0
            THROUGH S2, FOR J = 1, 1, J .G. I
            B(I, J) = B(I, J) + P1*P2
S2          P2 = P2*X(K)
            B(I, N + 2) = B(I, N + 2) + P1*Y(K)
S1          P2 = P2*X(K)
            THROUGH S3, FOR I = 1, 1, I .G. N + 1
            THROUGH S3, FOR J = 1, 1, J .E. I
S3          B(J, I) = B(I, J)
            EXECUTE SLEQ1.(N + 1, B)
            THROUGH S4, FOR I = 1, 1, I .G. N + 1
S4          A(I - 1) = B(I, N + 2)
            PRINT RESULTS A(0) ... A(N)
            END OF PROGRAM
Data
CAPN = 6, N = 4, X(0) = -.45, -.15, .15, .45, .75, .90, 1.35,
Y(0) = 1.0, .86602540, .5, 0., -.5, -.70710678, -1.0*
```

(b)

FIG. 15–4. (a) Flow chart. (b) Program.

Example. Write a program which applies the least-squares criterion to determine the coefficients of an nth-degree polynomial which approximates the given points (x_0, y_0), (x_1, y_1), $\ldots$, (x_N, y_N), where $n \leq N$. Assume that the linear equations can be solved by use of the external function SLEQ1. described earlier.

The principal task is to compute the coefficients of the augmented matrix from the given points. After this has been accomplished, the linear equations must be solved, and finally the solutions, which are the desired coefficients, must be printed. There is a variety of computational sequences which would accomplish this calculation. The one selected is not the shortest in expression, but it is more efficient in terms of computing time than algorithms which can be described in fewer statements. The flow chart and the program for this example are given in Fig. 15–4. Since all the elements of the matrix b are sums, before the process of accumulation, these elements must be initially set to zero. The somewhat cryptic block containing $b = 0$ indicates this step of setting the matrix to zero. The step could, of course, be written as an iteration, but it is convenient, even in the statements, to write the common operation of setting array elements to zero more succinctly. The use of a zero function in an EXECUTE statement accomplishes this initialization; e.g.,

$$\text{EXECUTE ZERO.}(B(0) \ldots B(110))$$

The variables p_1 and p_2 are used to develop partial products; p_1 has the value x_k^{i-1} and p_2 the value x_k^{j-1}. Thus the box in the innermost repetition might be written

$$b_{ij} = b_{ij} + x_k^{i-1}x_k^{j-1}$$

and if b_{ij} is initially zero, the repetition of this computation for $k = 0, 1,$ $\ldots$, N produces the proper value for the (i, j)-element. The box immediately above the one just described computes the values of the right-hand sides, and the indicated computation is carried out once for each row for each value of k. Only the elements of the lower triangle, including the main diagonal, are computed, since the column index is $j = 1, 2, \ldots, i$. Therefore the section starting with ① transfers the lower triangle elements to the upper triangle. This step is permissible since the matrix is symmetric about the main diagonal. The final step after the normal equations are solved is to transfer the augmented column, which now represents the desired solutions, to the linear array $a_0, \ldots, a_n$ and print these results. The fourth-degree polynomial obtained from the data shown in the program is

$$p(x) = 0.70532586 - 1.253901x - 1.01683828x^2 + 0.71508116x^3 + 0.02453243x^4$$

The approximation or curve-fitting procedure described above is the basis for the statistical technique called *regression analysis*, although the use of this name generally implies, in addition, the evaluation of certain quantities which are measures of how well the postulated function represents the given points.

NEAR-SINGULAR SETS OF EQUATIONS

Now that the least-squares method of producing polynomials seems to be settled, it is necessary to point out that it frequently gives rise to a certain problem. As the number of normal equations increases, the determinant of the matrix of coefficients often becomes very small. Such a system of equations is said to be *near-singular* which, in other terms, means that one or more of the linear equations can *almost* be expressed as a linear combination of the other equations, For two equations, this situation is represented geometrically by straight lines which are almost, but not quite, parallel. The reason that this state of affairs tends to occur can be seen by examining a general coefficient from the normal equations:

$$b_{ij} = \sum_{k=0}^{N} x^{i+j-2}$$

Assuming that x_0, x_1, x_2, ..., x_N tend to be evenly distributed in some interval, say (0, 1), one can represent the sum above by the shaded area in the bar graph of Fig. 15-5; that is, the sum is composed of rectangles with base 1 and altitude x_k^{i+j-2}. The exponent $(i + j - 2) \geq 0$ is a constant, and $0 \leq x_k \leq 1$. Still subject to the assumption that the x_k's are evenly

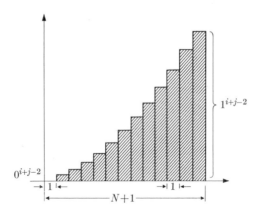

FIGURE 15-5

distributed in (0, 1), this sum can be closely approximated by an integral,

$$b_{ij} = \sum_{k=0}^{N} x_k^{i+j-2} \approx (N + 1) \int_0^1 x^{i+j-2} \, dx$$

which is simply the area under the continuous curve x^{i+j-2}, and the $(N + 1)$-factor is necessary since the "base" of the integration is length 1 rather than $N + 1$. The integral is readily evaluated:

$$\int_0^1 x^{i+j-2} \, dx = \left[\frac{x^{i+j-1}}{i + j - 1} \right]_0^1 = \frac{1}{i + j - 1}$$

and

$$b_{ij} \approx \frac{N + 1}{i + j - 1}$$

The determinant of the system of normal equations is approximated by

$$\Delta = \begin{vmatrix} \dfrac{N + 1}{1} & \dfrac{N + 1}{2} & \cdots & \dfrac{N + 1}{n + 1} \\ \dfrac{N + 1}{2} & & & \\ \vdots & & & \\ \dfrac{N + 1}{n + 1} & & \cdots & \dfrac{N + 1}{2n + 1} \end{vmatrix}$$

$$= (N + 1)^{n+1} \begin{vmatrix} 1 & \dfrac{1}{2} & \dfrac{1}{3} & \dfrac{1}{4} & \cdots & \dfrac{1}{n + 1} \\ \dfrac{1}{2} & \dfrac{1}{3} & \dfrac{1}{4} & & & \\ \dfrac{1}{3} & \dfrac{1}{4} & \dfrac{1}{5} & & & \\ \dfrac{1}{n + 1} & & & & \cdots & \dfrac{1}{2n + 1} \end{vmatrix}$$

The matrix whose determinant is the factor on the right is a well-known one, called the *Hilbert matrix*. The determinant of this matrix of order n can be indicated by Δ_n^H. Using this notation, one has

$$\Delta = (N + 1)^{n+1} \Delta_{n+1}^H$$

The Hilbert matrix is so well known because the system of equations which it represents rapidly becomes near-singular as the number of equations increases. This can be seen by evaluating the determinant for various numbers of equations:

$$\Delta_1^H = 1$$
$$\Delta_2^H = 1 \cdot \tfrac{1}{3} - \tfrac{1}{2} \cdot \tfrac{1}{2} = \tfrac{1}{12} = 8.3 \times 10^{-2}$$
$$\Delta_3^H = 1(\tfrac{1}{3} \cdot \tfrac{1}{5} - \tfrac{1}{4} \cdot \tfrac{1}{4}) - \tfrac{1}{2}(\tfrac{1}{2} \cdot \tfrac{1}{5} - \tfrac{1}{3} \cdot \tfrac{1}{4}) + \tfrac{1}{3}(\tfrac{1}{2} \cdot \tfrac{1}{4} - \tfrac{1}{3} \cdot \tfrac{1}{3})$$
$$\quad = 4.6 \times 10^{-4}$$
$$\Delta_4^H = 1.7 \times 10^{-7}$$
$$\Delta_5^H = 3.7 \times 10^{-12}$$
$$\Delta_6^H = 5.4 \times 10^{-18}$$
$$\vdots$$
$$\Delta_9^H = 9.7 \times 10^{-43}$$

Suppose, for example, that $N + 1 = 20$ and $n + 1 = 9$; then

$$\Delta = (20)^9 \, \Delta_9^H = 5.12 \times 10^{11} \times 0.97 \times 10^{-42} = 5 \times 10^{-31}$$

A determinant of such a small magnitude would not permit solution by the elimination methods that have been described.

This difficulty can be resolved by producing a system of equations which are independent, such as a system represented by a diagonal coefficient matrix. To achieve this result it is necessary to express the desired polynomial in terms of coordinate functions other than $1, x, x^2, \ldots, x^n$; that is, the desired function is

$$p(x) = a_0 P_0(x) + a_1 P_1(x) + a_2 P_2(x) + \cdots$$

where $P_0(x)$, $P_1(x)$, $P_2(x)$ are the first three members of a family of orthogonal polynomials.

CHEBYSHEV ECONOMIZATION

The usefulness of coordinate functions other than the familiar set $1, x, x^2, x^3, \ldots$ was illustrated earlier in the discussion of numerical integration. It turns out that the use of other criteria for the determination of approximating functions leads quite naturally to the use of other coordinate functions. There is a general approach to this subject which is indicated in a later section. At this point, a specific problem is considered which leads to the employment of Chebyshev polynomials as coordinate functions.

It would seem desirable to approximate a function uniformly well over a particular interval of interest, say (a, b); that is, the error in approxi-

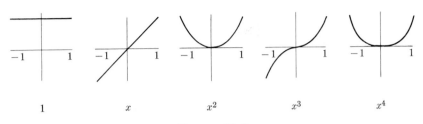

$$1 \qquad x \qquad x^2 \qquad x^3 \qquad x^4$$

FIGURE 15–6

mating the function $f(x)$ should ideally be about the same anywhere in (a, b) and not large at some points and very small at others. After all, since the approximation is to be evaluated at points anywhere in (a, b) (otherwise this would not be the interval of interest), it will be the maximum error in the interval that will limit the usefulness of the approximation. As before, it simplifies matters if the interval considered is $(-1, 1)$, but this is not an essential restriction since, if the original z was in the range $a \leq z \leq b$, then a new variable,

$$x = \frac{2z - b - a}{b - a}$$

is in the range $-1 \leq x \leq 1$.

To illustrate that the coordinate functions 1, x, x^2, x^3, ... do not have this uniform error property, suppose that

$$p(x) = a_0 + a_1 x + a_2 x^2 + a_3 x^3 + a_4 x^4$$

is a good approximation to $f(x)$ for $-1 \leq x \leq 1$. The graphs of the five coordinate functions involved are shown in Fig. 15–6. The approximation $p(x)$ may be regarded as a weighted sum of these functions. Note that in this interval the maximum magnitudes of these functions occur at -1 and 1. Given that $p(x)$ is a good approximation, dropping the term $a_4 x^4$ will apparently cause considerable error near the end points but almost no additional error near $x = 0$, where x^4 has small values. It is apparent that the error will always be concentrated at the end points when these functions are used to produce approximations.

The criterion can be altered at this point to remove the emphasis from the uniform distribution of error and simply state that the maximum error in the interval is to be minimized. It is obvious, though, that this smallest error will not be achieved if the error is concentrated and not spread through the interval.

The question now arises, what sort of coordinate functions would be useful to minimize the maximum error? In view of the preceding discussion,

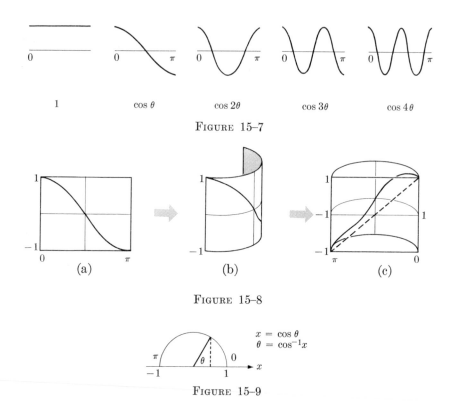

FIGURE 15–7

FIGURE 15–8

FIGURE 15–9

two useful properties would be: (1) The maxima and minima should not always occur at the same points in the interval, and (2) the magnitudes of the extreme values of a given function should be equal—otherwise the sums of such functions might lead to concentration of the error.

The trigonometric functions, sine and cosine, have these properties in the interval $(0, \pi)$. In particular, the set 1, $\cos \theta$, $\cos 2\theta$, $\cos 3\theta$, $\cos 4\theta$, $\ldots$ exhibits these properties, as shown in Fig. 15–7. These functions could be used as coordinate functions, but as transcendental functions their computation requires approximation, and it is more convenient to transform $\cos n\theta$ to polynomials in x. This transformation can be viewed as a projection of these curves from a cylinder to the xy-plane, which contains the cylindrical axis. The projection of $\cos \theta$ in this manner is indicated in Fig. 15–8. The dashed line is the projection on the plane. A look at the top of diagram (c) clearly shows the transformations between x and θ (Fig. 15–9). As a result, $y = \cos \theta$ is transformed in the xy-plane to $y = \cos (\cos^{-1} x) = x$. This is the first Chebyshev polynomial; it is usually written

$$T_1(x) = x$$

TABLE 15-1

$T_0 = 1$	$1 = T_0$
$T_1 = x$	$x = T_1$
$T_2 = 2x^2 - 1$	$x^2 = (\frac{1}{2})(T_0 + T_2)$
$T_3 = 4x^3 - 3x$	$x^3 = (\frac{1}{4})(3T_1 + T_3)$
$T_4 = 8x^4 - 8x^2 + 1$	$x^4 = (\frac{1}{8})(3T_0 + 4T_2 + T_4)$
$T_5 = 16x^5 - 20x^3 + 5x$	$x^5 = (\frac{1}{16})(10T_1 + 5T_3 + T_5)$

The second Chebyshev polynomial is obtained by transforming $y = \cos 2\theta = 2 \cos^2 \theta - 1$, so that

$$T_2(x) = 2 \cos^2 (\cos^{-1} x) - 1 = 2x^2 - 1$$

Similarly,

$$\cos 3\theta = 4 \cos^3 \theta - 3 \cos \theta$$
$$T_3(x) = 4x^3 - 3x$$

These trigonometric identities become more complicated, and it is useful to devise a recursion formula, i.e., a formula which expresses the polynomial desired in terms of the lower-order polynomials. If the formulas for the sum and difference of two angles are used for $\cos (n\theta + \theta)$ and $\cos (n\theta - \theta)$, the results are

$$\cos (n\theta + \theta) = \cos ((n + 1)\theta) = \cos (n\theta) \cos (\theta) - \sin (n\theta) \sin (\theta)$$
$$\cos (n\theta - \theta) = \cos ((n - 1)\theta) = \cos (n\theta) \cos (\theta) + \sin (n\theta) \sin (\theta)$$

Adding these two expressions gives

$$\cos (n + 1)\theta = 2 \cos n\theta \cos \theta - \cos (n - 1) \theta$$

which, in terms of the T's, is

$$T_{n+1}(x) = 2T_n(x) \cdot x - T_{n-1}(x)$$

Now $T_4(x)$ can be determined from the polynomials already known:

$$T_4(x) = 2T_3(x) \cdot x - T_2(x)$$
$$= 2(4x^3 - 3x)x - (2x^2 - 1)$$
$$= 8x^4 - 8x^2 + 1$$

The Chebyshev polynomials produced thus far, with one more added, are listed in Table 15-1. Because the relations will be used shortly, 1, x, x^2, x^3, x^4, x^5 are also expressed in terms of the Chebyshev polynomials. These relations were obtained by the straightforward algebraic manipulation of the left-hand column.

The graph of these Chebyshev polynomials would be very similar to the cosine curves with maximum and minimum values of ± 1. The curves would be somewhat compressed at the ends of the interval $(-1, 1)$. If these polynomials are divided by the high-order coefficient, which is 2^{n-1} for T_n, the greatest magnitude assumed by the resulting polynomial with high-order coefficient unity is $1/2^{n-1}$.

It still is not obvious that a function which is a combination of Chebyshev polynomials will have the smallest maximum error in $(-1, 1)$. Indeed, such a statement cannot be made because any function in 1, x, x^2, ... can be written as a combination of 1, T_1, T_2, T_3, ... by merely using the right-hand column of Table 15–1. Such an algebraic change would not alter the error properties of the function. However, it is possible to show rather simply that there is no polynomial with leading coefficient unity which will have a smaller maximum magnitude in $(-1, 1)$ than a Chebyshev polynomial of the same order (also with leading coefficient unity). This property is shown by contradiction. Assume that there is such an nth-degree polynomial $P_n(x)$ which has a smaller maximum magnitude. The contradiction arises when the difference $D = P_n(x) - T_n(x)/2^{n-1}$ is formed. The polynomial $T_n(x)/2^{n-1}$ takes its maximum magnitude $n + 1$ times in $(-1, 1)$. (Remember its $\cos n\theta$ origin.) If $P_n(x)$ is between the maxima and minima of $T_n(x)/2^{n-1}$, as it must be if it has a smaller maximum magnitude, then the difference D must change signs n times; that is, D must be negative at the maxima of $T_n(x)/2^{n-1}$ and positive at the minima. But both $T_n(x)/2^{n-1}$ and $P_n(x)$ have high-order terms of x^n, and hence the difference will be a polynomial of degree $n - 1$. However, $(n - 1)$-degree polynomials cannot have n zeros (or roots) as this one must have. Therefore there cannot be such a polynomial as $P_n(x)$. The logic of this proof may emerge more clearly if a graph representing a specific case is drawn. If $T_4/8 = x^4 - x^2 + \frac{1}{8}$ and the postulated

$$P_4(x) = x^4 + a_3 x^3 + a_2 x^2 + a_1 x + a_0$$

with extreme values of smaller magnitude are plotted on the same graph, the difference, $D = P_4 - T_4/8$ (represented by a dashed line), can be drawn as shown in Fig. 15–10. The difference has four roots in the interval, but this is a contradiction since a third-degree polynomial,

$$D = P_4 - \frac{T_4}{8} = a_3 x^3 + (a_2 + 1)x^2 + a_1 x + (a_0 - \tfrac{1}{8})$$

can have only three roots.

This property of smallest extreme values is used in the economization procedure and is best introduced by an example. Suppose that it is desired

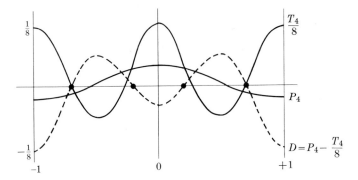

FIGURE 15–10

to approximate e^x in $(-1, 1)$ with a maximum error of 0.01. An examination of Taylor's series shows that terms through the fifth degree are necessary:

$$e^x \approx 1 + x + \frac{x^2}{2} + \frac{x^3}{6} + \frac{x^4}{24} + \frac{x^5}{120}$$

$$|R_6(x)| = \left|\frac{e^\varsigma x^6}{720}\right| \le \frac{e}{720} = 0.0038$$

Dropping the fifty-degree term would permit an error of $e/120 \approx 0.0226$, and hence this term must be included. But an economization of terms can be accomplished if the polynomial is written in terms of Chebyshev polynomials and then one or more high-order Chebyshev terms are dropped. The writing in this form is accomplished by substituting for x, x^2, x^3, x^4, x^5 the equivalent in terms of T_1, T_2, T_3, T_4, T_5 and then collecting terms:

$$e^x \approx \tfrac{81}{64}T_0 + \tfrac{217}{192}T_1 + \tfrac{13}{48}T_2 + \tfrac{17}{384}T_3 + \tfrac{1}{192}T_4 + \tfrac{1}{1920}T_5$$

Since the magnitude of $T_n(x)$ does not exceed unity, dropping the rightmost two terms introduces at most the additional error of $\tfrac{1}{192} + \tfrac{1}{1920} = \tfrac{11}{1920} \approx 0.0057$. Making these deletions, one obtains

$$e^x \approx \tfrac{81}{64}T_0 + \tfrac{217}{192}T_1 + \tfrac{13}{48}T_2 + \tfrac{17}{384}T_3$$

and the total error is at most $0.0038 + 0.0057 = 0.0095$. This result can be converted to x's again by using the left-hand column in Table 15–1:

$$e^x \approx \tfrac{1}{384}(382 + 383x + 208x^2 + 68x^3)$$

which produces the desired result without the original fourth- and fifth-degree terms.

This technique of Chebyshev economization has been the basis for obtaining many useful approximations. Another example (from Hastings) is

$$\sin \frac{\pi}{2} x = 1.5706268x - 0.6432292x^3 + 0.0727102x^5$$

where $-1 \le x \le 1$ and the maximum error = 0.0001.

A computer program designed to carry out this economization procedure is an interesting algorithm. The obvious procedure is to incorporate the two transformation columns of Table 15–1 in the program and then to accumulate the Chebyshev coefficients by transforming each of the polynomial coefficients by means of the table. After economization, the reverse transformation back to polynomial coefficients is done by using the table of Chebyshev polynomials. To illustrate this approach with a sample, consider the polynomial

$$p(x) = 1 + 2x + 3x^2 + 4x^3$$

In tabular form the transformation is:

	$\times T_0$	$\times T_1$	$\times T_2$	$\times T_3$
$1 \cdot 1 =$	1			
$2 \cdot x =$		2		
$3 \cdot x^2 =$	$\frac{3}{2}$		$\frac{3}{2}$	
$4 \cdot x^3 =$		3		1
Total	$\frac{5}{2}$	5	$\frac{3}{2}$	1

Thus $p(x) = \frac{5}{2}T_0 + 5T_1 + \frac{3}{2}T_2 + T_3$, and the change back to polynomial form would be a similar tabular process. Actually, tables need not be used since the transformation can be carried out by means of the recursion relations. In a slightly rewritten form, these are

$$xT_n = \tfrac{1}{2}T_{n+1} + \tfrac{1}{2}T_{n-1} \quad \text{for} \quad n \ge 1 \quad \text{and} \quad xT_0 = T_1$$

If the polynomial is considered in nested form,

$$p(x) = 1 + x(2 + x(3 + x \cdot 4))$$

these formulas are applied starting with the inner parentheses:

$$x4 = 4T_1$$
$$x(3T_0 + 4T_1) = 3T_1 + \tfrac{4}{2}T_2 + \tfrac{4}{2}T_0$$
$$x(2T_0 + 2T_0 + 3T_1 + 2T_2) = 4T_1 + \tfrac{3}{2}T_2 + \tfrac{3}{2}T_0 + T_3 + T_1$$
$$(T_0 + \tfrac{3}{2}T_0 + 5T_1 + \tfrac{3}{2}T_2 + T_3) = \tfrac{5}{2}T_0 + 5T_1 + \tfrac{3}{2}T_2 + T_3$$

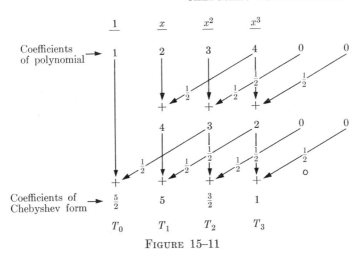

FIGURE 15–11

The diagram of this process (Fig. 15–11) may help to clarify the program implementation of this step. A new element in a row is obtained by adding one-half of the element displaced two columns to the right to one-half of the element directly above. The two leftmost elements are exceptions in that the element directly above is simply added (i.e., multiplied by one and then added). One can carry out this transformation, using only one array if the original values of the two coefficients to the right of the one being produced are saved. In the program that follows (Fig. 15–13b), these two are saved as variables designated R1 and R2. After this conversion has been completed, some high-order terms may be truncated to effect the Chebyshev economization, and then the process is reversed to obtain the adjusted polynomial form. A similar diagram can be used to illustrate the reversal of this process (Fig. 15–12).

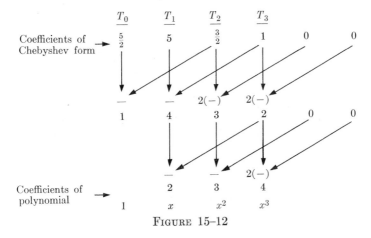

FIGURE 15–12

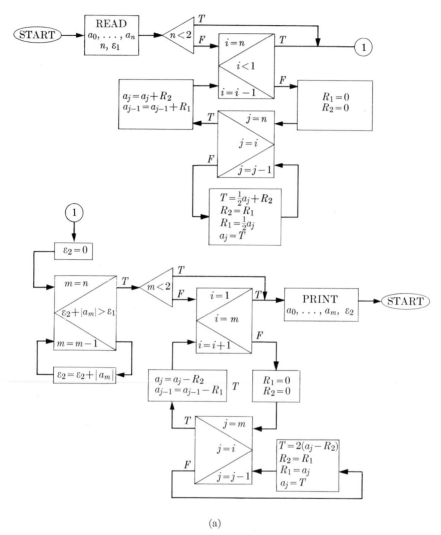

(a)

FIG. 15–13. (a) Flow chart.

Example. Write a program which reads $n + 1$ coefficients $a_0, a_1, a_2, \ldots,$ a_n and a value ε_1 which is the maximum additional error that is allowed. The printed output should be the economized coefficients $a_0, a_1, \ldots, a_m$, where $m \leq n$ and $\varepsilon_2 \leq \varepsilon_1$. The value of ε_2 is the amount of additional error introduced by the Chebyshev economization. The flow chart and the program are presented in Fig. 15–13.

The section from START to ① converts the given polynomial coefficients to Chebyshev coefficients. The section from ① to ② deter-

```
              DIMENSION A(20)
              INTEGER I, J, M, N
START         READ DATA
              WHENEVER N .L. 2, TRANSFER TO S1
              THROUGH S2, FOR I = N − 1, −1, I .L. 1
              R1 = 0.
              R2 = 0.
              THROUGH S3, FOR J = N, −1, J .E. I
              T = .5*A(J) + R2
              R2 = R1
              R1 = .5*A(J)
S3            A(J) = T
              A(J) = A(J) + R2
S2            A(J − 1) = A(J − 1) + R1
S1            ESP2 = C.
              THROUGH S4, FOR M = N, −1, EPS2 + .ABS. A(M)   ⅁. EPS1
S4            EPS2 = EPS2 + .ABS. A(M)
              WHENEVER M .L. 2, TRANSFER TO S5
              THROUGH S6, FOR I = 1, 1, I .E. M
              R1 = 0.
              R2 = 0.
              THROUGH S7, FOR J = M, −1, J .E. I
              T = 2*(A(J) − R2)
              R2 = R1
              R1 = A(J)
S7            A(J) = T
              A(J) = A(J) − R2
S6            A(J − 1) = A(J − 1) − R1
S5            PRINT RESULTS A(0) . . . A(M), EPS2
              TRANSFER TO START
              END OF PROGRAM
```

Data

A(0) = 1, 1, .5, .16666667, .04166667, .0083333, N = 5, EPS1 = .0062*

(b)

FIG. 15–13. (b) Program.

mines how many high-order terms can be dropped before the additional error exceeds ε_1. From ② to (START) , the array elements $a_0, a_1, \ldots,$ a_m are reconverted to coefficients of 1, x, $x^2, \ldots, x^m$.

A UNIFYING APPROACH

The two approximation techniques just described seem radically different, and yet they can be understood as special cases of general procedures. The criterion for selecting an approximating function $p(x)$ was that the sum of the squared deviations be a minimum:

$$\sum_{k=0}^{N} d_k^2 = \sum_{k=0}^{N} (p(x_k) - y_k)^2 = \text{minimum}$$

Although the technique was not applied in the earlier discussion, it was mentioned that it might be useful to weight some of the points (x_k, y_k), i.e., attach a multiplier, w_k, which will increase or decrease the contribution of a specific point in the process of obtaining the minimum. With this addition,

$$\sum_{k=0}^{N} w_k[p(x_k) - y_k]^2 = \text{minimum}$$

where it is assumed that w_k is always nonnegative. If, in addition, the y-function is a known function rather than a set of points, the summation above can be replaced by integration. Again, the interval is transformed to $(-1, 1)$ for convenience:

$$\int_{-1}^{1} w(x)[p(x) - y(x)]^2 \, dx = \text{minimum}$$

With these changes, the augmented matrix (i.e., the coefficients and right-hand sides of the normal equations) would be:

$$\int_{-1}^{1} w(x)x^0x^0 \, dx \quad \int_{-1}^{1} w(x)x^0x^1 \, dx \quad \int_{-1}^{1} w(x)x^0x^2 \, dx \quad \int_{-1}^{1} w(x)x^0y(x) \, dx$$

$$\int_{-1}^{1} w(x)x^1x^0 \, dx \quad \int_{-1}^{1} w(x)x^1x^1 \, dx \quad \int_{-1}^{1} w(x)x^1x^2 \, dx \quad \int_{-1}^{1} w(x)x^1y(x) \, dx$$

$$\int_{-1}^{1} w(x)x^2x^0 \, dx \quad \int_{-1}^{1} w(x)x^2x^1 \, dx \quad \int_{-1}^{1} w(x)x^2x^2 \, dx \quad \int_{-1}^{1} w(x)x^2y(x) \, dx$$

This form comes from the partial differentiation process, with $p(x)$ assumed to be the polynomial

$$p(x) = a_0 + a_1x + a_2x^2$$

The next step is to reduce the coefficient matrix to diagonal form so that the linear equations represented by the matrix are independent and directly solvable. This matrix reduction would not be necessary if the off-diagonal coefficients,

$$\int_{-1}^{1} w(x)x^ix^j \, dx, \qquad i \neq j$$

were zero at the outset. If two functions $p(x)$ and $q(x)$ have this property,

$$\int_{-1}^{1} w(x)p(x)q(x) \, dx = 0$$

then they are said to be *orthogonal*. As observed, this property would certainly simplify the task of finding the coefficients of the least-squares polynomial. The functions 1, x, x^2, x^3, ... are coordinate functions which could be named as follows:

$$P_0 = 1$$
$$P_1 = x$$
$$P_2 = x^2$$
$$P_3 = x^3$$

With this notation, an off-diagonal element is

$$\int_{-1}^{1} w(x) P_i P_j \, dx, \qquad i \neq j$$

It has been verified that these functions are not orthogonal, but the expression does raise the possibility that one could use another set which is orthogonal.

In the development of Chebyshev polynomials, emphasis was placed on the error introduced at the end points of $(-1, 1)$ when P_0, P_1, P_2, ... were used. This error can be reduced by giving it relatively more weight than the error elsewhere. In other words, one selects a weighting function which has its largest values near ± 1. The function

$$w(x) = \frac{1}{\sqrt{1 - x^2}}$$

has such a property. Hopefully, then, coordinate functions which are polynomials can be found which permit this weighting function and are also orthogonal. With this weighting function, the coefficients are of the form

$$\int_{-1}^{1} \frac{p_r(x) q_{r-1}(x)}{\sqrt{1 - x^2}} \, dx$$

where $p_r(x)$ and $q_{r-1}(x)$ are polynomials of degree r and $r - 1$ or less, respectively. The form of $w(x)$ suggests that the problem will be simplified if the trigonometric substitution $x = \cos \theta$ is made:

$$-\int_{\pi}^{0} \frac{p_r (\cos \theta) q_{r-1} (\cos \theta) \sin \theta \, d\theta}{\sqrt{1 - \cos^2 \theta}} = \int_{0}^{\pi} p_r (\cos \theta) q_{r-1} (\cos \theta) \, d\theta$$

If the rth-degree polynomial is orthogonal to *any* polynomial of lesser degree, q_{r-1}, then p_r, p_{r-1}, ..., p_0 is a family of orthogonal polynomials.

The first step in determining the form of p_r is to rewrite

$$q_{r-1}(\cos\theta) = a_0 + a_1 \cos\theta + a_2 \cos^2\theta + \cdots + a_{r-1}\cos^{r-1}\theta$$

as

$$q_{r-1}(\cos\theta) = b_0 + b_1 \cos\theta + b_2 \cos 2\theta + \cdots + b_{r-1}\cos(r-1)\theta$$

The second column of Table 15–1, which shows $1, x, x^2, x^3, \ldots$ expressed in terms of Chebyshev polynomials, becomes the following set of trigonometric identities when $\cos\theta$ is written for x:

$$\cos^0\theta = 1$$
$$\cos^1\theta = \cos$$
$$\cos^2\theta = \tfrac{1}{2}(1 + \cos 2\theta)$$
$$\cos^3\theta = \tfrac{1}{4}(3\cos\theta + \cos 3\theta)$$
$$\vdots$$

Replacing the powers of $\cos\theta$ in the first form by these identities and collecting terms give the second form. Using the second form, one finds that $p_r(\cos\theta)$ is a member of an orthogonal family if

$$\int_0^\pi p_r(\cos\theta)[b_0 + b_1\cos\theta + b_2\cos 2\theta + \cdots + b_{r-1}\cos(r-1)\theta]\,d\theta = 0$$

However, for this to be true, each term must be zero or

$$\int_0^\pi p_r(\cos\theta)b_k\cos k\theta\,dt = 0, \qquad k = 0, 1, \ldots, r-1$$

By consulting a table of definite integrals one finds

$$\int_0^\pi \cos r\theta\,\cos k\theta = 0, \qquad k \neq r$$

so that $p_r(\cos\theta) = C_r\cos r\theta$. The constant C_r is chosen to be unity for the ordinary Chebyshev polynomial. Resubstituting $\cos\theta = x$, one obtains

$$p_r(x) = T_r(x) = \cos(r\cos^{-1}x)$$

This was the result obtained in the section on economization, but the procedure here has been more general. The selection of other weighting functions gives rise to other families of orthogonal polynomials which are, however, not so readily obtained as those due to Chebyshev.

If the Chebyshev polynomials are used as coordinate functions in which the postulated least-squares polynomial is expressed (for example, $p(x) = a_0T_0 + a_1T_1 + a_2T_2$), then the orthogonality condition guarantees that the off-diagonal coefficients of the normal equations are zero:

$$\int_{-1}^{1} \frac{T_i T_j}{\sqrt{1 - x^2}}\, dx = 0 \qquad \text{when} \quad i \neq j$$

The resulting system of independent equations requires no elimination procedure:

$$\left[\int_{-1}^{1} \frac{T_0 T_0}{\sqrt{1 - x^2}}\, dx \right] a_0 \qquad\qquad\qquad = \int_{-1}^{1} \frac{T_0 y(x)}{\sqrt{1 - x^2}}\, dx$$

$$\left[\int_{-1}^{1} \frac{T_1 T_1}{\sqrt{1 - x^2}}\, dx \right] a_1 \qquad\qquad = \int_{-1}^{1} \frac{T_1 y(x)}{\sqrt{1 - x^2}}\, dx$$

$$\left[\int_{-1}^{1} \frac{T_2 T_2}{\sqrt{1 - x^2}}\, dx \right] a_2 = \int_{-1}^{1} \frac{T_2 y(x)}{\sqrt{1 - x^2}}\, dx$$

Since

$$\int_{-1}^{1} \frac{T_0^2}{\sqrt{1 - x^2}}\, dx = \int_{0}^{\pi} (\cos^0 \theta)^2\, dt = \pi$$

$$\int_{-1}^{1} \frac{T_r^2}{\sqrt{1 - x^2}}\, dx = \int_{0}^{\pi} (\cos r\theta)^2\, dt = \frac{\pi}{2}, \qquad r = 1, 2, 3, \ldots$$

the desired coefficients are simply

$$a_0 = \frac{1}{\pi} \int_{-1}^{1} \frac{y(x)}{\sqrt{1 - x^2}}\, dx$$

$$a_1 = \frac{2}{\pi} \int_{-1}^{1} \frac{x y(x)}{\sqrt{1 - x^2}}\, dx$$

$$a_2 = \frac{2}{\pi} \int_{-1}^{1} \frac{(2x^2 - 1) y(x)}{\sqrt{1 - x^2}}\, dx$$

The integrals have complicated matters slightly; only sums were involved in the normal equations as they were first derived. The integrations can be carried out numerically, of course, and there is a computational advantage to the orthogonal expansion in addition to the elimination of the "near-singular" problem. The advantage is that since the equations are independent, one can compute additional terms in the postulated function without having to recompute those already obtained.

The burden of numerical integration can be removed if the selected coordinate functions are orthogonal under summation; that is,

$$\sum_{k=0}^{N} p_r(x_k)p_s(x_k) = 0 \qquad \text{for} \quad r \neq s.$$

The best-known functions of this type are not polynomials but the familiar trigonometric functions, the sine and cosine. If the families, 1, $\cos \theta$, $\cos 2\theta$, $\cos 3\theta$, $\ldots$, $\cos N\theta$ and $\sin \theta$, $\sin 2\theta$, $\sin 3\theta$, $\ldots$, $\sin (9N - 1)\theta$, are evaluated only at the values

$$\theta_0 = 0$$

$$\theta_1 = \frac{\pi}{N}$$

$$\theta_2 = \frac{\pi}{N}$$

$$\theta_3 = \frac{\pi}{N}$$

$$\vdots$$

$$\theta_{2N-1} = \frac{(2N - 1)\pi}{N}$$

then

$$\sum_{k=0}^{2N-1} \sin r\theta_k \sin s\theta_k = \begin{cases} 0 & r \neq s \\ N & r = s \neq 0 \end{cases}$$

$$\sum_{k=0}^{2N-1} \sin r\theta_k \cos s\theta_k = 0$$

$$\sum_{k=0}^{2N-1} \cos r\theta_k \cos s\theta_k = \begin{cases} 0 & r \neq s \\ N & r = s \neq 0 \\ 2N & r = s = 0 \end{cases}$$

The arguments are equally spaced in increments of π/N, and if values of the function to be approximated can be obtained at θ_0, θ_1, θ_2, $\ldots$, θ_{2N-1}, then the coefficients of these coordinate functions can be obtained by summation. This is the basis of discrete Fourier analysis.

Since $T_r = \cos r (\cos^{-1} x)$, the Chebyshev polynomials can also be orthogonal under summation if

$$x_0 = \cos \theta_0$$

$$x_1 = \cos \theta_1$$

$$x_2 = \cos \theta_2$$

$$\vdots$$

$$x_{2N-1} = \cos \theta_{2N-1}$$

FIGURE 15–14

But in this case the x's are not equally spaced, and it is not often convenient to determine values of an empirical function corresponding to these abscissas.   It would be useful to have a family which does not require integration, consists of polynomials, and yet has equally spaced abscissas. The Gram (or Gram-Schmidt) polynomials constitute such an orthogonal family and, although they are not developed here, the first three members are given so that their general form may be seen.   The total interval is of length $2Mh$, where h is the size of the equal intervals (Fig. 15–14).

$$p_0(t, 2M) = 1$$

$$p_1(t, 2M) = \frac{t}{M}$$

$$p_2(t, 2M) = \frac{3t^2 - M(M + 1)}{M(2M - 1)}$$

$$\vdots$$

$$p_M(t, 2M) = \ldots$$

The summation index is t and the orthogonality relation is

$$\sum_{t=-M}^{M} p_r(t, 2M)p_s(t, 2M) = 0, \qquad \text{where} \quad r \neq s$$

The Numerical Solution of Ordinary Differential Equations

The *analytic* solution of ordinary differential equations is an extensive topic, and no attempt is made to cover it here. However, many of the numerical procedures described in the preceding chapters can be applied to the *numerical* solution of such equations, and hence this introduction is included. Thus, in the best mathematical tradition, one can attack this frequently occurring problem with tools already discussed.

For the reader who has not been exposed to differential equations, the problem can briefly be described as follows: Given a relation involving a derivative, find the functions for which the relation is true. A very simple example is

$$\frac{dy}{dx} = 2x$$

This is a *first-order* equation because only the first derivative is involved, and it is *ordinary* because only a total derivative (i.e., no partial derivatives) is present. In this case, the analytic solution, which is an expression or formula, is easily obtained by simple integration.

$$dy = 2x\,dx, \qquad \int_{y_0}^{y} dy = \int_{x_0}^{x} 2x\,dx, \qquad y = y_0 + x^2 - x_0^2$$

The terms $(y_0 - x_0^2)$ on the right are an unspecified constant; this means that many functions differing only by a constant are solutions. If some additional information is given, such as, for example, at a specific abscissa x_0, the function has a specific value y_0, this constant is determined and a single function results.

On the other hand, the numerical solution of this problem is simply a tabulation of the values of the desired function x^2 at specific values.

$$\begin{aligned} x_0, & \quad y_0 = x_0^2 \\ x_1, & \quad y_1 = x_1^2 \\ x_2, & \quad y_2 = x_2^2 \\ & \;\;\vdots \end{aligned}$$

264

With this approach a formula for the function is not explicitly obtained, but it can be plotted from the tabulated values or, perhaps, represented by a polynomial or some other function which approximates the table of values. The important point is that the analytic form is preferable if it can be obtained. Even if only specific values of the solution function are sought, evaluating the analytic form is, in general, simpler than solving the differential equation and produces more accurate results. Unfortunately, many, if not most, of the differential equations arising in practice cannot be so readily integrated. However, equations of the type

$$\frac{dy}{dx} = f(x), \qquad y = y_0 \quad \text{at} \quad x = x_0$$

(and this includes the example) can be integrated numerically by methods already described. Given x_0 and y_0, the problem is to compute

$$y_1 = y_0 + \int_{x_0}^{x_1} f(x)\,dx$$

$$y_2 = y_1 + \int_{x_1}^{x_2} f(x)\,dx$$

$$y_3 = y_2 + \int_{x_2}^{x_3} f(x)\,dx$$

$$\vdots$$

$$y_n = y_{n-1} + \int_{x_{n-1}}^{x_n} f(x)\,dx$$

Since any value of the derivative which is a function of x alone can be readily computed, the interpolating polynomials which are integrated over the single interval could be composed from many values of $f(x)$. In the general form of the first-order equation, the derivative is a function of y as well as of x:

$$y' = \frac{dy}{dx} = f(x, y), \qquad y = y_0 \quad \text{at} \quad x = x_0$$

and the derivative can be evaluated only where the values of y are known. In this instance, the interpolating polynomial to be used in the integration can be formed only from "past history," and another set of integration formulas is needed to deal with this case. With the assumption that the abscissas are equally spaced at intervals of width h, one step in the integration is

$$y_{n+1} = y_n + \int_{x_n}^{x_n+h} f(x, y)\,dx$$

When the derivative does not depend on y, adjacent points may be used

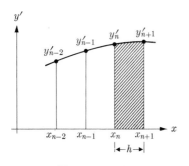

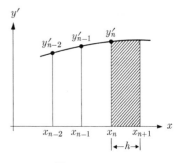

FIGURE 16–1   FIGURE 16–2

to form the polynomial (Fig. 16–1). Such integration formulas which include the end points of the integration interval are called *closed* formulas. In the more general case, the right end point cannot be used since the value of y is unknown there (Fig. 16–2). When the right end point is not used, the integration formulas are said to be *open*.

OPEN INTEGRATION FORMULAS

The process of deriving open integration formulas is the same one that produced the closed forms. One determines the indefinite integral of an equal-interval interpolating polynomial and then obtains different formulas by varying the number of terms retained in the integrated polynomial, as well as the number of intervals included in the integration. The backward-difference notation (∇) is useful since all known information precedes the point under consideration. After the transformation is made, $x = x_n + hs$, a single step is

$$y_{n+1} = y_n + h\int_0^1 f(x_n + hs, y)\,ds = y_n + h\int_0^1 y'_{n+s}\,ds$$

When an integration over $p + 1$ intervals is considered (rather than over just one interval as shown), one step becomes

$$y_{n+1} = y_{n-p} + h\int_{-p}^1 y'_{n+s}\,ds$$

Representing the integrand with the backward-difference polynomial written with respect to the last known point y'_n gives

$$y_{n+1} = y_{n-p} + h\int_{-p}^1 \left[y'_n + s\nabla y'_n + s(s+1)\frac{\nabla^2 y'_n}{2!} + s(s+1)(s+2)\frac{\nabla^3 y'_n}{3!} \right.$$
$$\left. + s(s+1)(s+2)(s+3)\frac{\nabla^4 y'_n}{4!} + \cdots \right] ds$$

When the indefinite integral, a function of p, is evaluated for $p = 0$, the result is

$$y_{n+1} = y_n + h(y_n' + \tfrac{1}{2}\nabla y_n' + \tfrac{5}{12}\nabla^2 y_n' + \tfrac{3}{8}\nabla^3 y_n' + \tfrac{251}{720}\nabla^4 y_n' + \cdots)$$

For $p = 1$,

$$y_{n+1} = y_{n-1} + h(2y_n' + 0\nabla y_n') + \frac{h^3}{3} y_n'''(\varsigma)$$

and for $p = 3$,

$$y_{n+1} = y_{n-3} + h(4y_n' - 4\nabla y_n' + \tfrac{8}{3}\nabla^2 y_n' + 0\nabla^3 y_n') + \tfrac{14}{45}h^5 y^{(5)}(\varsigma)$$

Again the zero coefficients permit a jump in the order of the error term when an even number of intervals is used (that is, p is odd), and this fact accounts for the widespread use of these forms. Open formulas can be rewritten in terms of the ordinates and the last, which is analogous to Simpson's rule in the closed form, becomes

$$y_{n+1} = y_{n-3} + \tfrac{4}{3}h(2y_n' - y_{n-1}' + 2y_{n-2}') + \tfrac{14}{45}h^5 y^{(5)}(\varsigma)$$

Assuming for the moment that a way has been provided to obtain the necessary preliminary values, one sees that the numerical solution by open formulas is a process of computing y_{n+1} from the preceding known values of the function and its derivatives. The computation may be based either upon the derivative values directly or upon backward differences which are formed from the derivative values. The latter approach has an advantage in that the first neglected difference can be used to produce an error estimate. As an illustration of one step of such a process, consider the differential equation

$$\frac{dy}{dx} = \frac{\pi}{180} \cos\left(\frac{\pi}{180} x\right), \qquad y = 0 \quad \text{at} \quad x = 0$$

The solution is, of course, $y = \sin[(\pi/180)x]$, and for $h = 5$, the initial difference table (obtained before using the method) is:

x	y	y'	$\nabla y'$	$\nabla^2 y'$	$\nabla^3 y'$
0	0.00000	0.0174533			
5	6.08716	0.0173868	0.0000665		
10	6.17365	0.0171882	0.0001986	−0.0001321	
15	0.25882	0.0168587	0.0003295	−0.0001309	+0.0000012

Using the single-interval formula ($p = 0$) with the first three differences retained, we have

$$y_{n+1} = y_n + h(y'_n + \tfrac{1}{2}\nabla y'_n + \tfrac{5}{12}\nabla^2 y'_n + \tfrac{3}{8}\nabla^3 y'_n)$$

$$y(20) = 0.25882 + 5(0.0168587 + \tfrac{1}{2}(0.0003295) + \tfrac{5}{12}(-0.0001309)$$
$$+ \tfrac{3}{8}(0.0000012)) = 0.34366$$

At this point the next derivative value, $y'(20)$, is computed. If the derivative were a function of y as well as of x, which is not the case here, it could not be computed earlier since it would depend on $y(20)$:

$$y'(20) = 0.0174533 \cos \left(\tfrac{20}{180}\pi\right) = 0.0164007$$

The next line of the difference table can now be formed.

	0.0164007	−0.0004580	−0.0007875	−0.0006566
	—	—	—	—
	0.0168587	0.0003295	−0.0001309	0.0000012
	‖	‖	‖	‖
20 0.34366	0.0164007	−0.0004580	−0.0007875	−0.0006566 −0.0006578

The rightmost difference is not used, but evaluating the neglected term, $\tfrac{251}{720}h\nabla^4 y'$, is useful to estimate the error:

$$\tfrac{251}{720}(5)(-0.0006578) = -0.00117$$

The actual error is $\sin 20° - 0.34366 = 0.34202 - 0.34366 = -0.00164$. The value of $h = 5$ seems to be too large to give a very accurate solution.

Before extending this numerical procedure to include both open and closed integration formulas, let us note that the simplest open form, neglecting all differences, is

$$y_{n+1} = y_n + hy'_n$$

The application of this formula is called Euler's method; it is rarely used in this crude form.

PREDICTOR-CORRECTOR METHODS

In this group of methods an open formula is used to *predict* a value of y_{n+1}, and then a closed formula is used, where the resultant y_{n+1} permits the computation of a *corrected* y_{n+1}. In fact, the closed formula may be repeatedly employed until two successive applications produce the same value. More often, however, the interval, h, is small enough so that after the prediction only one correction cycle is carried out for each point. A frequently used pair of open and closed formulas (Milne's method) is:

Predicted: $\quad y_{n+1} = y_{n-3} + \dfrac{4h}{3}\,(2y_n' - y_{n-1}' + 2y_{n-2}') + \dfrac{14}{45}\,h^5 y^{(5)}(\zeta_1)$

Corrected: $\quad y_{n+1} = y_{n-1} + \dfrac{h}{3}\,(y_{n+1}' + 4y_n' + y_{n-1}') - \dfrac{h^5}{90}\,y^{(5)}(\zeta_2)$

The second of these is Simpson's rule. When the error terms are dropped, the predicted value and the corrected value differ by

$$(\text{Predicted } y_{n+1} - \text{ corrected } y_{n+1}) = -\left(\frac{14}{45}h^5 y^{(5)}(\zeta_1) + \frac{h^5}{90}\,y^{(5)}(\zeta_2)\right)$$

If the fifth derivative $y^{(5)}$ is assumed to be constant in the interval, then

$$(\text{Predicted } y_{n+1} - \text{ corrected } y_{n+1}) = -\tfrac{29}{90}h^5 y^{(5)}(\zeta_2)$$

With this assumption, the following additional correction should produce an exact value for y_{n+1}.

$$y_{n+1} = \text{corrected } y_{n+1} + \tfrac{1}{29}\,(\text{predicted } y_{n+1} - \text{ corrected } y_{n+1})$$

Of course, the assumption is not generally valid, but if h is correctly chosen, the fifth derivative should be slowly varying. If the correction is actually used, it should be small relative to the value of y_{n+1}. As is the case with high-order differences, this difference is a measure of the error of y_{n+1}. If it encroaches on the number of accurate figures that are desired in the solution, a smaller interval should be chosen. The type of error measured by such differences is that due to truncation in the computation of a single step. Since the terminus of one integration is the initial point of another, error produced in one step is propagated to the next. The analysis of propagation of error is a complicated task and will not be pursued here.

The use of the minimal predictor-corrector pair is called the modified Euler method and is useful in starting a solution, since a history of previous values is not needed for these simple formulas:

$$y_{n+1} = y_n + hy_n' + h^3 y'''(\zeta_1)$$

The process of starting a solution from x_0, y_0 with this pair would be to compute

$$y_1^{(0)} = y_0 + hf(x_0, y_0), \qquad y' = f(x, y)$$

$$y_1^{(1)} = y_0 + \frac{h}{2}\,(f(x_0, y_0) + f(x_0 + h, y_1^{(0)}))$$

$$y_1^{(2)} = y_0 + \frac{h}{2}\,(f(x_0, y_0) + f(x_0 + h, y_1^{(1)}))$$

$$\vdots$$

The superscript indicates successive corrected values. When there is no change in two successive corrected values, the process is repeated again starting now with (x_1, y_1).

Milne's method, as well as a very useful method of starting a solution, is illustrated in detail by a program at the end of this chapter.

TAYLOR'S SERIES

Another method of starting the solution, or of solving it completely, is to write the object function as a Taylor series and simply evaluate the series at the desired points. The initial series expansion is made at the given point (x_0, y_0), and it is necessary to evaluate the derivatives at this point. The first derivative is given in a first-order equation, but the higher-order derivatives must be obtained by differentiation. The situation is complicated by the fact that the function, $y' = f(x, y)$, depends, in general, on both x and y. Hence one must differentiate with respect to two variables, using the chain rule:

$$\frac{df}{dx} = \frac{\partial f}{\partial x} + \frac{\partial f}{\partial y}\frac{dy}{dx}$$

In many practical instances, the differentiation quickly becomes very complicated, but for a simple example, such as the one below, it is straightforward. Given

$$y' = xy + 1 \qquad \text{and at} \qquad x = 0, \quad y = 1$$

then at $x = 0$, $y' = 1$. The successive derivatives and their values at $x = 0$ can be determined.

$$\frac{dy'}{dx} = \frac{\partial y'}{\partial x} + \frac{\partial y'}{\partial y}\frac{dy}{dx}$$

$$y'' = y + xy' \qquad\qquad \text{at} \quad x = 0, \quad y'' = 1$$

$$\frac{dy''}{dx} = \frac{\partial y''}{\partial x} + \frac{\partial y''}{\partial y}\frac{dy}{dx} + \frac{\partial y''}{\partial y'}\frac{dy'}{dx}$$

$$y''' = y' + y' + xy'' \qquad \text{at} \quad x = 0, \quad y''' = 2$$

$$\vdots$$

Combining these function and derivative values to produce a Taylor series of the form

$$f(x_0 + h) = f(x_0) + hf'(x_0) + \frac{h^2}{2!}f''(x_0) + \frac{h^3}{3!}f'''(x_0) + \cdots$$

results in

$$y(h) = 1 + h + \frac{h^2}{2} + \frac{h^3}{3} + \cdots$$

After tabulating the function for several points, one may find it desirable to expand about another point, say x_k, before continuing.

RUNGE-KUTTA METHODS

The difficulty with Taylor's series as a solution-starting procedure is that the series is specific to the problem, and differentiation in more realistic cases may be extremely difficult. It would be very useful to be able to obtain values of the solution function with an accuracy equivalent to a specified number of terms in the Taylor series representation, and yet compute these values by using a weighted-sum-of-ordinates formula similar to those employed in numerical integration. The popular Runge-Kutta methods fulfill these requirements and also have the added advantage that the interval of integration, h, may be readily changed. Unlike the techniques which are based on the integration of equal-interval interpolating formulas, the Runge-Kutta procedures are *single step*; they do not require any "past history" of values. When a past history is required, changing the value of h is complicated, and separate solution-starting procedures are required.

The derivation of the integration formulas is a little more complicated than it was for simple integration. Again this is due to the fact that the derivative is a function of both x and y.

$$y' = f(x, y)$$

It is worthwhile to go through the derivation of a Runge-Kutta formula, if for no other reason than that at first glance, it seems difficult to make a sum of derivative evaluations correspond to terms of the Taylor series which contain higher-order derivatives.

THIRD-ORDER RUNGE-KUTTA DERIVATION

The problem is: Given $y' = f(x, y)$ at $x = x_n$, $y = y_n$ produce a sum-of-ordinates integrating formula of the form

$$y_{n+1} \approx y_n + h(af_0 + bf_1 + cf_2)$$

where

$f_0 = f(x_n, y_n)$
$f_1 = f(x_n + mh, y_n + mhf_0)$
$f_2 = f(x_n + ph, y_n + phf_1) = hf(x_n + ph, y_n + qhf_1 + (p - q)hf_0)$

such that the result is identical with the first four terms of the Taylor series,

$$y_{n+1} \approx y_n + hy_n' + \frac{h^2}{2} y_n'' + \frac{h^3}{3!} y_n'''$$

(The second form on the right, introducing another parameter, q, simplifies the subsequent derivation.) One produces this equivalence by expanding f_0, f_1, f_2 and, from the immediately preceding formula, y_n', y_n'', y_n''', in terms of the two variables x and y and then equating the two expressions for y_{n+1}. The expansion of the last three is done by chain-rule differentiation as in the specific case of the previous section. The f's are expanded by using the two-variable Taylor series.

Taylor's series for two variables is most easily remembered from its operational form:

$$f(x+h, y+k) = (e^{h(\partial/\partial x)+k(\partial/\partial y)})f(x,y)$$

$$= \left(1 + h\frac{\partial}{\partial x} + k\frac{\partial}{\partial y} + \frac{1}{2}\left(h^2\frac{\partial^2}{\partial x^2} + 2hk\frac{\partial^2}{\partial x\,\partial y} + k^2\frac{\partial^2}{\partial y^2}\right) + \cdots\right)f(x,y)$$

$$= f + hf_x + kf_y + \frac{h^2}{2}\left(f_{xx} + hkf_{xy} + \frac{k^2}{2}f_{yy}\right) + \cdots$$

Here the subscripted f's indicate partial derivatives of $f(x,y)$. Expanding f_0, f_1, f_2 in this manner yields

$$f_0 = f$$

$$f_1 = f + mhf_x + mhf \cdot f_y + \frac{m^2h^2}{2}f_{xx} + m^2h^2f \cdot f_{xy} + \frac{m^2h^2f^2}{2}f_{yy} + \cdots$$

$$= f + mh(f_x + f \cdot f_y) + \frac{m^2h^2}{2}(f_{xx} + 2f_{xy}\cdot f + f_{yy}\cdot f^2) + \cdots$$

$$f_2 = f + phf_x$$

$$+ (qhf_1 - (p-q)hf)f_y + \frac{p^2h^2}{2}f_{xx} + ph(qhf_1 - (p-q)hf)f_{xy}$$

$$+ (qhf_1 - (p-q)hf)^2f_{yy} + \cdots$$

Substituting for f_1 permits, after a considerable manipulative effort, simplification to

$$f_2 = f + ph(f_x + f_y f) + \frac{p^2h^2}{2}(f_{xx} + 2f_{xy} + f_{yy}f^2)$$

$$+ mqh^2(f_x + f_y f)f_y + \cdots$$

The higher derivatives can be expressed in terms of partial derivatives by chain-rule differentiation:

$$y' = f = f(x, y)$$

$$y'' = f_x + f_y y' = f_x + f_y f$$

$$y''' = f_{xx} + f_{xy} f + f_y f_x + (f_{xy} + f_{yy} f + f_y^2) f$$

$$= f_{xx} + 2 f_{xy} f + f_{yy} f^2 + f_y (f_x + f_y f)$$

When the derivative expressions are replaced by single symbols,

$$f_x + f_y f = A$$

$$f_{xx} + 2 f_{xy} f + f_{yy} f^2 = B$$

the two formulas that must correspond are: Taylor's series,

$$y_{n+1} \approx y_n + hf + \frac{h^2}{2} A + \frac{h^3}{6} B + \frac{h^3}{6} A f_y,$$

and the integration formula,

$$y_{n+1} \approx y_n + ahf$$

$$+ bh \left(f + mhA + \frac{m^2 h^2}{2} B \right)$$

$$+ ch \left(f + phA + \frac{p^2 h^2}{2} B + mqh^2 A f_y \right)$$

For this to be true, the coefficients of hf must correspond, that is,

$$a + b + c = 1$$

Similarly the coefficients of $h^2 A$, $h^3 B$, and $h^3 A f_y$ must correspond.

$$bm + cp = \tfrac{1}{2}$$

$$bm^2 + cp^2 = \tfrac{1}{3}$$

$$cmq = \tfrac{1}{6}$$

Since there are six variables in these four equations, the values of two variables may be selected arbitrarily. It is convenient to select $m = \tfrac{1}{2}$ and $p = 1$, since the evaluations of $f(x, y)$ will then be at x_n, $x_n + h/2$, and $x_n + h$. By using these values one can determine the remaining ones from the equations and write the integrating formula. For

$$\begin{Bmatrix} m = \tfrac{1}{2} \\ p = 1 \end{Bmatrix}$$

$a = \tfrac{1}{6}$ and $y_{n+1} \approx y_n + \dfrac{h}{6}\,(f_0 + 4f_1 + f_2)$

$b = \tfrac{2}{3}$

$c = \tfrac{1}{6}$

$q = 2$

where

$$f_0 = f(x_n, y_n)$$

$$f_1 = f\left(x_n + \frac{h}{2}, y_n + \frac{hf_0}{2}\right)$$

$$f_2 = f(x_n + h, y_n + hf_1 - hf_0)$$

TWO FOURTH-ORDER FORMULAS

With correspondingly greater algebraic effort one can obtain fourth-order formulas. Again there is some free choice of parameters, and the simplest choice (Runge) is:

$$y_{n+1} \approx y_n + \frac{h}{6}\,(f_0 + 2f_1 + 2f_2 + f_3)$$

$$f_0 = f(x_n, y_n)$$

$$f_1 = f\left(x_n + \frac{h}{2}, y_n + \frac{hf_0}{2}\right)$$

$$f_2 = f\left(x_n + \frac{h}{2}, y_n + \frac{hf_1}{2}\right)$$

$$f_3 = f(x_n + h, y_n + hf_2)$$

Many other variants of these fourth-order formulas have been produced. One of them, the Gill version, was designed to save storage in digital computers using this algorithm. If m equations are being solved simultaneously, the method above requires the use of four linear arrays of length m, one array for y_n, one for the intermediate y-values, one for the values of the derivative f, and one in which the partial sums of the integrating formula are stored. The Gill version reduces this storage requirement to three arrays by eliminating the necessity for retaining y_n through the four evaluations. The formulas are reproduced here, although much of the

motivation for their use has disappeared as high-speed storage in machines
has increased.

$$\begin{cases} f_1 = f(x_n, y_n) \\ y_{n+1}^{(1)} = y_n + \dfrac{hf_1}{2} \\ q_1 = f_1 \end{cases}$$

$$\begin{cases} f_2 = f\left(x_n + \dfrac{h}{2}, y_{n+1}^{(1)} \right) \\ y_{n+1}^{(2)} = y_{n+1}^{(1)} + h\left(1 - \dfrac{1}{\sqrt{2}} \right)(f_2 - q_1) \\ q_2 = (2 - \sqrt{2})f_2 + \left(-2 + \dfrac{3}{\sqrt{2}} \right) q_1 \end{cases}$$

$$\begin{cases} f_3 = f\left(x_n + \dfrac{h}{2}, y_{n+1}^{(2)} \right) \\ y_{n+1}^{(3)} = y_{n+1}^{(2)} + h\left(1 + \dfrac{1}{\sqrt{2}} \right)(f_3 - q_2) \\ q_3 = (2 + \sqrt{2})f_3 + \left(2 + \dfrac{3}{\sqrt{2}} \right) q_2 \end{cases}$$

$$\begin{cases} f_4 = f(x_n + h, y_{n+1}^{(3)}) \\ y_{n+1} = y_{n+1}^{(4)} = y_{n+1}^{(3)} + h\left(\dfrac{f_4}{6} - \dfrac{q_3}{3} \right) \end{cases}$$

The three arrays required are for y, f, and the "bridging q's." The latter is
the temporary storage arranged so that the y_n-values need not be preserved.

Note that the original third-order formulation, as well as the fourth-
order one, reduces to Simpson's rule when the derivative is a function of
x alone. In such a case, f_1 and f_2 are equal, and, since the interval is
effectively $h/2$, Simpson's rule is obtained.

SIMULTANEOUS ORDINARY DIFFERENTIAL EQUATIONS

A higher-order differential equation, or a system of equations including
some high-order members, may be reduced to a set of first-order equations
by making a simple change of variable. An nth-order equation,

$$y^{(n)} = f(x, y, y', y'', \ldots, y^{(n-1)})$$

may be transformed by letting

$$y = y_0$$
$$y' = y_1$$
$$y'' = y_1' = y_2$$
$$y''' = y_1'' = y_2' = y_3$$
$$\vdots$$
$$y^{(n)} = \cdots = y_{n-1}' = f(x, y_0, y_1, y_2, \ldots, y_{n-1})$$

Such simultaneous systems can be handled by all the methods described. The computation proceeds in parallel; one makes one step for each equation before advancing to the next increment. When the derivative functions are evaluated, the current values of the array of the functional values (the y's) are used. In the fourth-order Runge-Kutta case, the increment might be described more accurately as a one-fourth step taken in parallel since on every intermediate step (there are four) all the equations are evaluated.

To illustrate the fourth-order Runge-Kutta procedure (Runge version), consider the two simultaneous equations:

$$\dot{y}_1 = y_2 + t \qquad\qquad \text{at} \quad t = 0, \quad y_1 = 0$$
$$\ddot{y}_2 = -y_2\dot{y}_2 - y_1 t^2 \qquad\qquad\qquad y_2 = 1$$
$$\qquad\qquad\qquad\qquad\qquad\qquad\qquad \dot{y}_2 = 1$$

The dot notation indicates differentiation with respect to t. For a second-order differential equation, the initial value of both the function and its first derivative are required.

Making the substitution $\dot{y}_2 = y_3$ results in a system of three first-order equations. The derivatives are also labeled f to conform with the earlier notation:

$$f_1 = \dot{y}_1 = y_2 + t \qquad\qquad \text{at} \quad t = 0, \quad y_1 = 0$$
$$f_2 = \dot{y}_2 = y_3 \qquad\qquad\qquad\qquad\qquad y_2 = 1$$
$$f_3 = \dot{y}_3 = -y_2 y_3 - y_1 t^2 \qquad\qquad\qquad y_3 = 1$$

Selecting $h = 0.2$, one evaluates the first of the Runge formulas. The parenthesized superscript indicates which Runge formula applies, while the subscript is the equation number. Initially, at $t = 0$,

$$\left.\begin{aligned} y_1(0) &= 0 \\ y_2(0) &= 1 \\ y_3(0) &= 1 \end{aligned}\right\} \quad \text{from which} \quad \left\{\begin{aligned} f_1^{(1)} &= 1 + 0 = 1 \\ f_2^{(1)} &= 1 \\ f_3^{(1)} &= -1 \times 1 = -1 \end{aligned}\right.$$

A trial value of y, indicated by the bar, is obtained and the second evaluation of the derivative functions is made by means of these trial values. With $t = 0.2/2 = 0.1$,

$$\bar{y}_1 = 0 + \left(\frac{0.2}{2}\right) \times 1 = 0.1, \qquad f_1^{(2)} = 1.1 + 0.1 = 1.2$$

$$\bar{y}_2 = 1 + \left(\frac{0.2}{2}\right) \times 1 = 1.1, \qquad f_2^{(2)} = 0.9$$

$$\bar{y}_3 = 1 + \left(\frac{0.2}{2}\right) \times (-1) = 0.9, \qquad f_3^{(3)} = -1.1 \times 0.9 - 0.1 \times 0.01$$
$$= -0.991$$

Continuing with $t = 0.1$, we have

$$\bar{y}_1 = 0 + \left(\frac{0.2}{2}\right) \times 1.2 = 1.2, \qquad f_1^{(3)} = 1.09 + 0.1 = 1.19$$

$$\bar{y}_2 = 1 + \left(\frac{0.2}{2}\right) \times 0.9 = 1.09, \qquad f_2^{(3)} = 0.9009$$

$$\bar{y}_3 = 1 + \left(\frac{0.2}{2}\right) \times (-0.991) \qquad f_3^{(3)} = -1.09 \times 0.9009 - 1.2 \times 0.01$$
$$= 0.9009, \qquad\qquad = -0.983181$$

The last evaluation is based on $t = 0.2$:

$$\bar{y}_1 = 0 + \left(\frac{0.2}{2}\right) \times 1.19 = 0.238, \qquad f_1^{(4)} = 1.18018 + 0.2 = 1.38018$$

$$\bar{y}_2 = 1 + \left(\frac{0.2}{2}\right) \times 0.9009, \qquad f_2^{(4)} = 0.8033638$$
$$= 1.18018$$

$$\bar{y}_3 = 1 + \left(\frac{0.2}{2}\right) \times (-0.983181) \qquad f_3^{(4)} = -1.18018 \times 0.8033638$$
$$= 0.8033638, \qquad\qquad\qquad -0.238 \times 0.04$$
$$= -0.9576339$$

Substituting these results in the integration formula yields

$$y_1(0.2) = 0 + \frac{0.2}{6}(1 + 2(1.2) + 2(1.19) + 1.38018) = 1.009339$$

$$y_2(0.2) = 1 + \frac{0.2}{6}(1 + 2(0.9) + 2(0.9009) + 0.8033638) = 1.793745$$

$$y_3(0.2) = 1 + \frac{0.2}{6}(-1 + 2(-0.991) + 2(-0.983181) + (-0.9576339))$$
$$= 0.143352$$

This completes one step of the integration; the process is then repeated for the desired number of intervals.

EXAMPLE PROGRAMS

To illustrate these solution procedures, we present external functions which integrate a system of differential equations by the Milne and Runge-Kutta methods.

Example 1. Write an external function which integrates one step of a system of m first-order equations by the Milne method. The function should have two entries, PRED., which produces a predicted value of y_{n+1} for each equation, and CORR., which then computes the corrected value of y_{n+1}. The necessary parameters are m, two arrays, y and f, the current value of the independent variable, x, and the interval size, h. The two linear arrays should initially contain all the preceding values required by the method; these will be stored according to the following scheme. (The superscripts here indicate the equation number.)

$$y_1 \text{ to } y_m \quad \text{contain} \quad y_n^{(1)} \text{ to } y_n^{(m)}$$

$$y_{m+1} \text{ to } y_{2m} \quad \text{contain} \quad y_{n-1}^{(1)} \text{ to } y_{n-1}^{(m)}$$

$$y_{2m+1} \text{ to } y_{3m} \quad \text{contain} \quad y_{n-2}^{(1)} \text{ to } y_{n-2}^{(m)}$$

$$y_{3m+1} \text{ to } y_{4m} \quad \text{contain} \quad y_{n-3}^{(1)} \text{ to } y_{n-3}^{(m)}$$

$$f_1 \text{ to } f_m \quad \text{contain} \quad f_n^{(1)} \text{ to } f_n^{(m)}$$

$$f_{m+1} \text{ to } f_{2m} \quad \text{contain} \quad f_{n-1}^{(1)} \text{ to } f_{n-1}^{(m)}$$

$$f_{2m+1} \text{ to } f_{3m} \quad \text{contain} \quad f_{n-2}^{(1)} \text{ to } f_{n-2}^{(m)}$$

For uniformity, the calling program should reserve $4m$ locations for both the y- and f-arrays. In summary, references to the function would be of the form

$$\text{PRED.}(M, Y, F, X, H)$$

and

$$\text{CORR.}(M, Y, F, X, H)$$

The function should, in addition, increment the value of the independent variable x and return, as a direct result, the value of y_{n+1} for the last equation computed. This return will simplify the calling statements when a single first-order equation is being solved.

The flow chart and the program are presented in Fig. 16–3. The variable y_T is a temporary location used to retain a value which is to be replaced. In the program calling this routine, the statements computing the deriva-

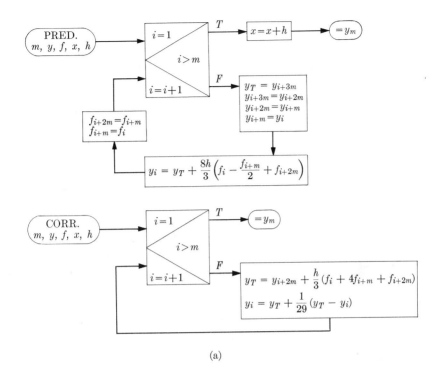

(a)

```
        EXTERNAL FUNCTION (M, Y, F, X, H)
        INTEGER I, K, M
        ENTRY TO PRED.
        THROUGH S1, FOR I = 1, 1, I .G. M
        YT = Y(I + 3*M)
        Y(I + 3*M) = Y(I + 2*M)
        Y(I + 2*M) = Y(I + M)
        Y(I + M) = Y(I)
        Y(I) = YT + 8.0*H*(F(I) − .5*F(I + M) + F(I + 2*M))/3.0
        F(I + 2*M) = F(I + M)
S1      F(I + M) = F(I)
        X = X + H
        FUNCTION RETURN Y(M)
        ENTRY TO CORR.
        THROUGH S2, FOR I = 1, 1, I .G. M
        YT = Y(I + 2*M) + H*(F(I) + 4.0*F(I + M) + F(I + 2*M))/3.0
S2      Y(I) = YT + (YT − Y(I)))/29.0
        FUNCTION RETURN Y(M)
        END OF FUNCTION
```

(b)

FIG. 16–3. (a) Flow chart. (b) Program.

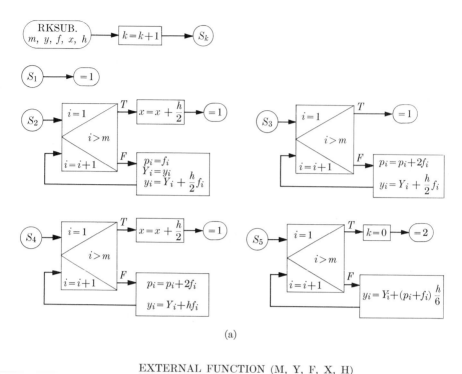

(a)

```
                    EXTERNAL FUNCTION (M, Y, F, X, H)
                    DIMENSION CAPY(40), P(40)
                    INTEGER I, M, K
                    VECTOR VALUES K = 0
                    ENTRY TO RKSUB.
                    K = K + 1
                    TRANSFER TO S(K)
        S(2)        THROUGH ST1, FOR I = 1, 1, I.G.M
                    P(I) = F(I)
                    CAPY(I) = Y(I)
        ST1         Y(I) = CAPY(I) + .5*H*F(I)
        ST2         X = X + .5*H
        S(1)        FUNCTION RETURN 1
        S(3)        THROUGH ST3, FOR I = 1, 1, I.G.M
                    P(I) = P(I) + 2.0*F(I)
        ST3         Y(I) = CAPY(I) + .5*H*F(I)
                    FUNCTION RETURN 1
        S(4)        THROUGH ST4, FOR I = 1, 1, I.G.M
                    P(I) = P(I) + 2.0*F(I)
        ST4         Y(I) = CAPY(I) + H*F(I)
                    TRANSFER TO ST2
        S(5)        THROUGH ST5, FOR I = 1, 1, I.G.M
        ST5         Y(I) = CAPY(I) + (P(I) + F(I))))*H/6.0
                    K = 0
                    FUNCTION RETURN 2
                    END OF FUNCTION
```

(b)

FIG. 16–4. (a) Flow chart. (b) Program.

tive functions, the f's, appear between the entry to PRED. and the entry to CORR. If only a single equation is involved, say $y' = xy + 1$, the direct results may be used in expressions, i.e.,

$$F(1) = X*PRED.(M, Y, F, X, H) + 1.$$

$$INT = CORR.(M, Y, F, X, H)$$

Example 2. Write an external function, to be called RKSUB., which has the same parameters as the preceding Milne routine, namely, m, y, f, x, and h, but uses the Runge formulas to integrate the differential equations. For m first-order simultaneous equations, the following parameters are required: two arrays, y and f, for the current values of the functions and the derivatives, respectively, the current values of the independent variable x, and the interval size h. Here, however, the arrays need contain only the m current values since the Runge-Kutta procedure is a single-step method and does not depend on the preceding values other than the last.

The flow chart and the program are presented in Fig. 16–4. Note that two working arrays are needed by the external function: Y to store the original values of y_n, and P to store the partial sums as terms are added in the process of producing y_{n+1}. When the integration is incomplete and additional evaluations of the derivative functions are required, the integer 1 is directly returned; when the integration is complete, the integer 2 is returned. These integer results may be used as statement label subscripts in the calling program to perform the necessary switching. The two working arrays were arbitrarily dimensioned to 40, permitting a maximum of 40 equations. The integer variable K, which is used to switch to the proper subsection of the program, is guaranteed to be initially zero by the vector-initializing statement, even though K is not a vector element. The last substitution statement returns K to zero after an integration step has been completed.

The use of these two functions is illustrated by the following example.

Example 3. Write a main program which numerically solves the three simultaneous equations

$$f_1 = \dot{y}_1 = y_2 + t$$
$$f_2 = \dot{y}_2 = y_3$$
$$f_3 = \dot{y}_3 = -y_2 y_3 - y_1 t^2$$

where at $t = 0$,

$$y_1 = 0, \qquad y_2 = 1, \qquad y_3 = 1$$

Read the values of the interval size and the limits of the integration. Use

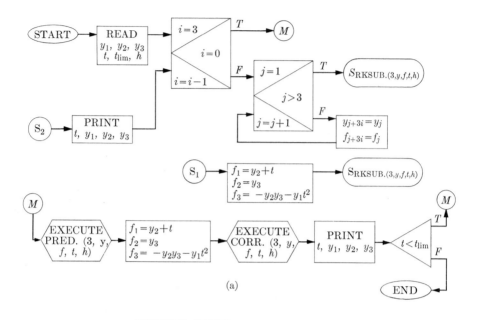

(a)

```
            INTEGER RKSUB., I, J
            DIMENSION Y(12), F(12)
            READ DATA
            THROUGH S(2), FOR I = 3, −1, I.E.O
            THROUGH ST2, FOR J = 1, 1, J.G.3
            Y(J + I∗3) = Y(J)
ST2         F(J + I∗3) = F(J)
ST1         TRANSFER TO S(RKSUB.(3, Y, F, T, H))
S(1)        F(1) = Y(2) + T
            F(2) = Y(3)
            F(3) = −Y(2)∗Y(3) − Y(1)∗T∗T
            TRANSFER TO ST1
S(2)        PRINT RESULTS T, Y(1) . . . Y(3)
ST3         EXECUTE PRED.(3, Y, F, T, H)
            F(1) = Y(2) + T
            F(2) = Y(3)
            F(3) = −Y(2)∗Y(3) − Y(1)∗T∗T
            EXECUTE CORR.(3, Y, F, T, H)
            PRINT RESULTS T, Y(1) . . . Y(3)
            WHENEVER T.L.TLIM, TRANSFER TO ST3
            END OF PROGRAM

$DATA
    T = 0, TLIM = 2.0, H = .2, Y(1) = 0, 1, 1∗
```

(b)

Fig. 16–5. (a) Flow chart. (b) Program.

the Runge-Kutta function to start the solution and, once enough values have been computed, continue the solution with the Milne function.

The first values of the functions, which are read as data, as well as the results of the first three applications of the Runge-Kutta method, must be transferred to the appropriate places in the y-array. Similarly, the derivative values must be stored for three points also. After this solution-starting phase, the remaining values are computed by the Milne procedure until the independent variable t reaches its final value. The flow chart and the program are presented in Fig. 16–5. Since RKSUB. produces integer results, this name must be placed in the integer declaration. The derivative evaluations could be written as an internal function or, with a little more switching of statement labels, the same set of statements could be used for both procedures.

This program could be solved by means of the Runge-Kutta procedure alone, but the Milne process has several advantages. Only one derivative evaluation for each integration step is required, and it is possible to monitor (by computing the difference between predicted and corrected values) the error introduced at each step. As mentioned before, the Runge-Kutta procedure is self-starting, and the interval size may be changed from step to step.

This has been a brief introduction to two of the most widely employed methods of solving ordinary differential equations when initial values are given. The questions of propagated error and stability of such procedures are left to the realm of numerical analysis. Perhaps the most important single problem for which digital computers are currently being used is the numerical solution of partial differential equations. The approach is similar in that integration is accomplished by forming sums of the derivatives evaluated at specific points, but the fact that there are two or more independent variables greatly complicates the matter.

Nonnumerical Problems

The methods and programs which have been discussed thus far are appropriate for solving the types of problems that arise in science and engineering, where useful results can be expressed in numbers. However, the use of digital computers for nonnumerical problems is increasing. Indeed, the majority of presently installed digital computers are used for administrative purposes where the job of ordering, merging, and summarizing data is the primary task. The term "nonnumerical" may seem paradoxical when all the symbols stored and manipulated by the computer can be interpreted as numbers. The important distinction in the processes mentioned, which is the definition of "nonnumerical," is that no attempt is made to represent real numbers or infinite processes. The elimination of the vexing problems of truncation and round-off errors is a welcome simplification in such algorithms, but on the other hand, unlike numerical procedures, such algorithms may become arbitrarily complex because they are not limited by the generation and propagation of error. Problems in symbol manipulation, such as formal differentiation, formal integration, language translation, and chess playing, are illustrative of problems which are extremely complex. To emphasize again the difference between the two types of algorithms, observe that no matter how many times the letters in a word to be translated are examined during a translation, the letters do not, by propagated or generated error, become other letters.

The programming language which has been introduced is useful for describing searching and sorting algorithms, and some illustrations of these nonnumerical procedures are included here. The idea of order is basic to these procedures and requires some explanation. Suppose that there is a set of elements $a_1, a_2, a_3, \ldots, a_n$ and, given any two of them, there is a way of determining that one precedes the other. It also seems reasonable that if it can be said that one precedes the other, then the two elements cannot be the same. A last feature of this rule for precedence is that if a_1 precedes a_2 and a_2 precedes, say a_3, then a_1 must precede a_3. These statements give, in an informal way, the requirements that one must meet to be able to arrange a set of elements in linear order. Very often, the symbol

$<$ is used for the word *precede*, and then the rules are:

> If a_i and a_j are distinct, $a_i < a_j$ or $a_j < a_i$.
>
> If $a_i < a_j$, then a_i and a_j are distinct.
>
> If $a_i < a_j$ and $a_j < a_k$, then $a_i < a_k$.

There is such a rule for the integers; i.e., "precedes" is determined by the relative position of the two integers under consideration in the sequential, ascending set of integers. As an example, $7 < 10$ because 7 comes before 10 in the string 1, 2, 3, 4, 5, 6, 7, 8, 9, 10. Similarly the alphabetic characters can be ordered $C < F$ because the governing sequence is A, B, C, D, E, F, G, ... In the case of the integers, it is a familiar step to ascertain that $7 < 10$ by forming the difference $7 - 10 = -3$ and observing that the result is negative. This step is possible because the operation of subtraction is also defined for the integers; but in the alphabetic example, $C - F$ is meaningless. In the flow charts and programs that follow, the relations $<$, $\leq$, $>$, $\geq$ will be used in connection with ordering processes, and, as the reader probably knows, the truth or falsity of a relation, say $a_i < a_j$, is determined by subtraction and testing for a negative result. The important point is that if some nonnumerical elements, such as the alphabetic characters, are to be ordered, they must first be put in correspondence with an ascending sequence of numbers for which subtraction is, of course, possible. The letters and special characters and a space or blank are represented in BCD form in the 709/7090 computer by the following octal integers (Table 17–1).

TABLE 17–1

A	$(21)_8$	J	41	S	62	+	20	0	00
B	22	K	42	T	63	—	40	1	01
C	23	L	43	U	64	*	54	2	02
D	24	M	44	V	65	/	61	3	03
E	25	N	45	W	66	(	74	4	04
F	26	O	46	X	67	)	34	5	05
G	27	P	47	Y	70	=	13	6	06
H	30	Q	50	Z	71	.	33	7	07
I	31	R	51		60	,	73	8	10
						$	53	9	11

Other ascending (but not necessarily contiguous) numbers could be used to represent these characters, but when the numbers do not correspond to the desired precedence, subtraction cannot be used. In these instances, the position of the characters in the original order-defining sequence must be found. Such a case arises in the decomposition of algebraic expressions to a sequence of binary operations. When the expression $(a + b * c)$ is encountered, conventional usage requires that the multiplication operation be carried out before the addition. In other words, $*$ *precedes* $+$. But in this case, $* \sim 54$ and $+ \sim 20$, so that subtraction cannot be used to determine order, and reference to the defining sequence, $*$, $+$, must be made.

In many nonnumerical problems, it is important to distinguish between a number and its character representation. For instance, the integer 29 as a binary number is $(11101)_2 = (35)_8$, but the two adjacent characters 29 are represented, as shown in Table 17–1, as

$$(0211)_8 = (000010001001)_2.$$

In the programming language, 29 as an integer is simply written 29, but when it is to be represented as the two characters, it is written \$29\$. The dollar signs fulfill the role of quotation marks in this context. When, as in this example, there are fewer than six characters (i.e., 36 bits) enclosed between the dollar signs, the given characters are justified to the left of the word and the remaining character positions on the right are entered as blanks, e.g., $(60)_8$.

SEARCHING

The simplest case of a searching algorithm is scanning of an unordered linear array $a_1, a_2, \ldots, a_n$ for a particular argument x. The obvious attack is to simply compare every element in turn with x until an equal element is found or all the elements have been examined. The flow chart for this simple search and the corresponding statements are presented in Fig. 17–1. With this procedure, if the arguments (the x-values) were uniformly distributed, it would take, on the average, $n/2$ trials to find the matching element. Note, however, that if no match is found, all n elements must be examined. If the elements are ordered, i.e., $a_1 \leq a_2 \leq a_3 \leq \cdots \leq a_n$, then a missing element can be determined without searching the entire

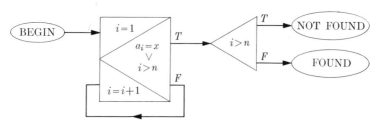

BEGIN   THROUGH BEGIN, FOR I = 1, 1, A(I) .E.X .OR. I.G.N
         WHENEVER I.G.N, TRANSFER TO NF

FIGURE 17–1

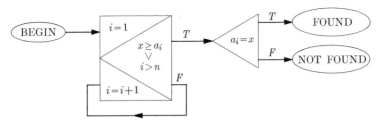

BEGIN   THROUGH BEGIN, FOR I = 1, 1, X .GE.A(I) .OR. I .G. N
WHENEVER A(I) .E.X, TRANSFER TO FOUND

FIGURE 17–2

array. The flow chart and statements are only slightly altered (Fig. 17–2).
Now the average number of elements searched is always $n/2$, regardless
of whether or not the search was successful.

The average number of comparisons in a search can be greatly reduced
from $n/2$ by using a method which is closely related to the half-interval
method of solving equations. If the array is in ascending order and the
argument x is subtracted from the elements, the resultant array,

$$(a_1 - x) \le (a_2 - x) \le (a_3 - x) \le \cdots \le (a_n - x)$$

will have negative elements up to the matching element, which would now
be zero, and positive elements beyond this point. This separation into
positive and negative elements is the procedure in the half-interval root-
finding method; however, in the present case, there is only a discrete number of points. Nonetheless, the procedure is very similar. In the *binary
search*, as it is called, an index $i = k$ is selected, and if $x < a_i$, the next
element compared is $a_{(i-k/2)}$. If $x > a_i$, the next element compared is
$a_{(i+k/2)}$ and, of course, if $x = a_k$, the search is ended. If the equal element
is not found, $k/4$ is then added or subtracted to the current value of the
subscript i to find the next element for comparison. The following example
illustrates the process.

Given:

2	5	9	11	12	14	18	29	31	64	68	72	75	83	96
a_1	a_2	a_3	a_4	a_5	a_6	a_7	a_8	a_9	a_{10}	a_{11}	a_{12}	a_{13}	a_{14}	a_{15}

Suppose that the argument $x = 14$, and the first element compared is a_8;
that is, $k = 8$. Then for $i = k$,

$$(14 - a_i) = (14 - 29)$$

is negative, and i is replaced by

$$i - \frac{k}{2} = 4$$

As the next step,

$$(14 - a_i) = (14 - 11)$$

is positive, and i is replaced by

$$i + \frac{k}{4} = 6$$

And finally,

$$(14 - a_i) = (14 - 14) = 0$$

With this scheme, every element could be found in three comparisons or less, i.e. in considerably fewer comparisons than $n/2 \approx 8$. The essence of this method is that a value k (the original subscript) is halved on each trial and, depending upon the sign of the difference $(x - a_i)$, this reduced value is either added or subtracted to the current value of the subscript i. In the example, k was initially an integral power of 2, that is, $i = k = 2^3$, so that the repeated division by 2 never produced a remainder. If the initial value of k were not so chosen, but was, for instance, selected as the integer closest to the mid-point, say the integral part of $n/2$, then a remainder would be produced at some point in the division, and the remainder would be dropped. Under these circumstances, the method could still be made to work, but it could possibly require several terminal cycles when the increment of the index was 1. For example, if the argument is $x = 2$, and $k = 10$, then, successively dividing k by 2 and truncating where a remainder occurs, gives the sequence of quotients 10, 5, 2, 1, 0. When these values are subtracted from the initial $k = 10$, the final value of the subscript i is $i = 10 - 5 - 2 - 1 = 2$, not the desired value of $i = 1$. An alternative adjustment, i.e., rounding the integer quotient before truncation, leads to the sequence of quotients 10, 5, 3, 2, 1, 0 which would "overshoot" the matching a_1, since $i = 10 - 5 - 3 - 2 = 0$, and a_0 is not included in the array to be searched. This deficiency could also be corrected, but the usual way of starting a binary search is to select as an initial value of k the largest integral power of 2 which is less than or equal to n, the number of elements in the array. There is a simple procedure of finding such a number, and it is illustrated here: A number, initially unity, is added to itself (i.e., doubled) until the sum is greater than n. If p doublings are required, the resultant number is $k = 2^p > n$. The stated goal was the largest power of 2 less than n, but this can be accomplished readily by choosing the first subscript to be $k/2$. The diagram and statement form are given in Fig. 17–3.

While the doubling process is fresh in mind, it is worthwhile to consider the reverse situation, a halving process. An integral power of 2 is reduced by half its value on every cycle until a value of unity results. This is actually what happens to the initial subscript value k in the binary search.

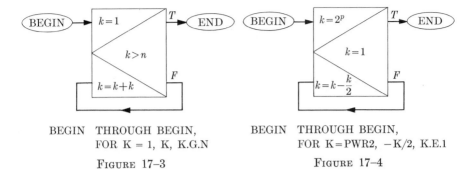

BEGIN   THROUGH BEGIN,
    FOR K = 1, K, K.G.N

FIGURE 17–3

BEGIN   THROUGH BEGIN,
    FOR K = PWR2, −K/2, K.E.1

FIGURE 17–4

In each iteration, one half of the current value of k is subtracted from k. The flow chart and corresponding statement are given in Fig. 17–4. As written, the value of k will never go to zero since only the integral part of an integer quotient is retained. When k has the value 1, the subtraction of the integer quotient $[\frac{1}{2}] = 0$ does not change the value of k from 1. When it is important for the iteration variable to become zero, the increment can be written as $k/2 − k$ instead of $k/2$. In some of the following algorithms this change is made in the statements. Note that this reduction requires p iterations. This implies that a binary search (which reduces such a power of 2) will require at most p iterations. Since $2^{p-1} \leq n < 2^p$, the number of iterations can be related to n, the number of elements in the searched array. Remembering that if $r = 2^q$, then $q = \log_2 r$, one can express the relation between n and p by $p − 1 \leq \log_2 n < p$. Due to this relation, the binary search is said to be proportional to $\log n$. The difference between $\log_2 n$ and $n/2$ becomes very impressive as n becomes large.

These flow chart and program segments can now be combined to describe the binary-search algorithm with but one slight additional complication. Since the initial value of k is an integral power of two, it is generally not equal to $n/2$; thus, if the sought-for value has a subscript greater than k, it is possible to compute a subscript for an element not in the array. That is, a trial value of i may be greater than n. To illustrate, consider the steps in the binary search for the array below, for which $n = 10$ and the argument is $x = 31$.

$$2 \quad 5 \quad 9 \quad 11 \quad 12 \quad 14 \quad 18 \quad 29 \quad 31 \quad 64$$
$$a_1 \quad a_2 \quad a_3 \quad a_4 \quad a_5 \quad a_6 \quad a_7 \quad a_8 \quad a_9 \quad a_{10}$$

Initially, $i = k = 2^3 = 8$. Since $x − a_8 = 31 − 29$ is positive, it follows that $i = 8 + k/2 = 12$. But a_{12} is not in the array, and so no comparison can be made. The solution to this difficulty is straightforward. Every subscript i is checked to see whether it is greater than the array of

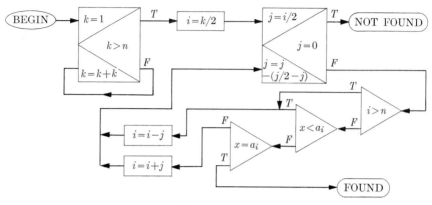

FIGURE 17–5

size n; if it is greater, the next fractional value of k is subtracted from the subscript without regard for the comparison. With this addition, one obtains the flow chart shown in Fig. 17–5.

In review, the first iteration finds that k which is an integral power of 2 and is greater than n. The next substitution sets the initial subscript to $k/2$, which is, of course, less than or equal to n. The following iteration decreases the increment j from its initial value $k/4$ by halving until the increment becomes zero. (Note that in this instance, the increment in statement form will have to be $j/2 - j$ if the zero value is to be attained.) The scope of the iteration determines whether the subscript increment is to be added to or subtracted from the current value of the subscript i. If many binary searches were to be made on the same array, the determination of k would only need to be done once. The statements for this look-up procedure are:

```
BEGIN      THROUGH BEGIN, FOR K = 1, K, K .G. N
               I = K/2
           THROUGH SEARCH, FOR J = I/2, J/2 — J, J .E. 0
           WHENEVER I .G. N
               I = I — J
           OR WHENEVER X .L. A(I)
               I = I — J
           OR WHENEVER X .E. A(I)
               TRANSFER TO FOUND
           OTHERWISE
               I = I + J
SEARCH     END OF CONDITIONAL
```

The importance of ordered arrays, or tables, in the search for specific entries hardly needs emphasis. Let us just imagine an unordered telephone directory. In this context, it is interesting to observe that a human being searching a large directory will often carry out a process similar to the binary search, leafing through decreasing numbers of pages until the number is found. The next programming topic to be considered is the important one of ordering an unordered array.

SORTING

The simplest sort procedure is very straightforward; it consists of repeated applications of the elementary search procedure, i.e., one is looking for the largest element in the unordered array $a_1, a_2, a_3, \ldots, a_n$. When the largest element is found, it is placed in the a_n-position; the previous value in the a_n-position is placed in the vacancy created elsewhere by the largest element. After this search and exchange have been made, the cycle is repeated, but now only the first $n - 1$ elements are examined, and the largest in this group is placed in a_{n-1}. Thus, as the cycles are repeated with fewer elements each time, the array is ordered. More specifically, the first cycle can be described as follows.

For $j = 1, 2, \ldots, n - 1$, whenever $a_n < a_j$, interchange the values of a_n and a_j.

Since the subsequent cycles will involve $a_{n-1}, a_{n-2}, \ldots, a_2$, this description can be expanded to:

For $i = n, n - 1, n - 2, \ldots, 2$ and for each value of $i, j = 1, 2, \ldots, i - 1$, whenever $a_i < a_j$, interchange the values of a_i and a_j.

These statements describe a nested iteration and are readily represented by a flow chart (Fig. 17–6). It is necessary to use a temporary variable t

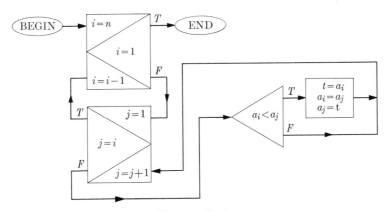

FIGURE 17–6

in the exchange of elements because the value of a_i must be preserved after the step $a_i = a_j$. If the condition were changed to $a_i > a_j$, the procedure would sort the array in descending order instead of ascending order as shown. In statement form, this simple sort is expressed as follows:

```
BEGIN     THROUGH S, FOR I = N, −1, I .E. 1
          THROUGH S, FOR J = 1, 1, J .E. I
          WHENEVER A(I) .L. A(J)
            T = A(I)
            A(I) = A(J)
            A(J) = T
 S        END OF CONDITIONAL
```

This simple sort is said to be of order n^2. There are $n - 1$ comparisons on the first cycle, $n - 2$ on the second, etc. In total there are $(n - 1) + (n - 2) + (n - 3) + \cdots + 1$ comparisons. Since the sum of this arithmetic progression is

$$\frac{n(n-1)}{2} = \frac{n^2}{2} - \frac{n}{2}$$

the method is said to be of order n^2.

There is another n^2-method for sorting which represents a slight refinement in that it permits early termination of the procedure if the elements happen to be in order before all $n(n - 1)/2$ comparisons have been made. This so-called "interchange" method searches the n elements for the largest, then $n - 1$ elements for the next largest, etc., but the method of finding the largest is different. All adjacent elements are compared for order and if they are not in ascending order, they are interchanged. If, in any cycle, no interchanges are made, then all the elements are in ascending order, and the sort is complete. On the first cycle:

For $j = 1, 2, \dots, n - 1$, whenever $a_j > a_{j+1}$, interchange a_j and a_{j+1}.

That is, the relations $a_1 > a_2$, $a_2 > a_3$, $a_3 > a_4$, $\dots$, $a_{n-1} > a_n$ are examined on the initial iteration. Note that once the largest value is encountered, it will be continually interchanged until it occupies the position a_n, since it will be greater than every element with which it is compared. If now a cycle index i is introduced, the statement of the algorithm becomes:

For $i = n, n - 1, \dots, 2$, and for each value of $i, j = 1, 2, \dots, i - 1$, whenever $a_j > a_{j+1}$, interchange a_j and a_{j+1}.

It is easier to describe in a flow chart (Fig. 17–7a) how the early termination can be recognized. An indicator variable, which is often called a

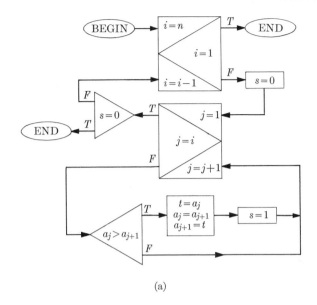

(a)

```
BEGIN    THROUGH L1, FOR I = N, −1, I .E. 1
         S = 0
         THROUGH L2, FOR J = 1, 1, J .E. I
         WHENEVER A(J) .G. A(J+1)
             T = A(J)
             A(J) = A(J+1)
             A(J+1) = T
             S = 1
L2       END OF CONDITIONAL
L1       WHENEVER S .E. 0, TRANSFER TO END
```

(b)

FIG. 17–7. (a) Flow chart. (b) Program.

"flag" or a "switch" by programmers, is set to zero before each cycle, i.e., whenever a new value of i is introduced. During a search cycle, if an interchange occurs, the indicator variable is given a nonzero value. Then at the end of a cycle, if the indicator value is zero, no interchanges occurred, and the sort is complete; otherwise more search cycles are necessary. The corresponding statements are presented in Fig. 17–7(b).

By the same justification as before, this method is of order n^2, but it seems reasonable to expect that the procedure would often terminate early. Not only does the interchange provide a way of observing whether the array is ordered, but the very process of finding the largest element on every cycle causes the elements to "move" in the right direction. One search cycle through the six-element array 2, 1, 4, 3, 6, 5 removes the local changes in order and, in addition, finds the largest element, 6. This example is somewhat contrived, and it is easy to think of other cases where only a minor change is needed and yet all search cycles must be completed. Such a case is the array 2, 3, 4, 5, 6, 1. Here all five search cycles would be carried out, and in each cycle there would be one interchange. If the interchange had started from the right and the smallest element had been found, ascending order would be achieved in one cycle. This observation suggests, in a very vague way, that an improvement might be achieved by making the interchanges from both ends of the set of elements about some central value, so that elements are more quickly "moved" close to their final positions in the ordered array.

Machines which are designed to sort punched cards by an electromechanical process (sorters) have a very efficient sorting scheme which is considerably better than the n^2 methods. However, it is difficult to implement this method, called a digit sort (or radix sort), on a digital computer. The method is, nonetheless, related to a very efficient sorting procedure which is used extensively in digital computing, and therefore a brief discussion of the digit sort is included here as an introduction to the computer method. The digit sort is perhaps best explained by an example. Suppose that 10 two-digit decimal numbers are given:

$$12, \quad 35, \quad 61, \quad 16, \quad 38, \quad 82, \quad 29, \quad 33, \quad 42, \quad 13$$

The first step is to rearrange the list by considering only the rightmost digits; i.e., grouping the 1's first, the 2's second, etc.

61,	12, 82, 42,	33, 13	35,	16,	38,	29
1's	2's	3's	5's	6's	8's	9's

Then, going from left to right in this new sequence, the numbers are rewritten in order by the tens' digits.

12, 13, 16	29	33, 35, 38	42	61	82
1's	2's	3's	4's	6's	8's

The task is now complete, but if there were more than two digits, the steps outlined above would be repeated each time, reordering the list by the next digit to the left. This sort was accomplished in $n \times$ (number of digits in largest number). Since the number of digits in an integer is proportional to the logarithm of the integer (e.g., $\log_{10} 100 = 2$, $\log_{10} 1000 = 3$, etc.), the method is of order $n \log (\max a_n)$. The sorting machine has ten pockets which correspond to the decimal digits and, depending upon the particular digit under consideration, the cards fall into the appropriate pocket. For the next cycle the cards are simply rerun through the machine, with the 1's preceding the 2's, etc. It is the open-ended pockets of the sorting machine which are difficult to simulate in the digital computer. Either a large amount of storage must be reserved for the various digit groups (as much as $10n$) or, before every cycle, a count of the occurrence of the various digits must be made so that the storage can be accurately allocated. Even with the latter approach, the sort requires $2n$ locations in storage. The sorting algorithms already discussed accomplished the ordering with only the original n storage elements. If, however, the digit sorts start with the leftmost digit, a method applicable for computers (but not for mechanical sorters) can be developed. When the original example array is grouped by the tens' digit, the result is:

$$12, \quad 16, \quad 13 \qquad 29 \qquad 35, \quad 38, \quad 33 \qquad 42 \qquad 61 \qquad 82$$

Now if each group is *separately* ordered on the units' digit and then combined, the sort is completed.

12	13	16
29		
33	35	38
42		
61		
82		

The problem arising in the mechanical implementation of this algorithm is that the number of groups (pockets) continues to increase, and the physical handling of cards therefore becomes impossible for many-digit numbers. But the presence of many groups does not present difficulties to a computer, provided that keeping track of the groups can be systematically carried out.

Grouping by decimal digits is of course the same as saying that multiples of ten are used as the dividing numbers for the groups. It is not necessary that multiples of ten be used. In fact, simple interchanges are possible (i.e., two pockets instead of ten) if binary separation is used. As one might expect, the binary separation takes more steps, but the example sequence can be sorted by this approach. The initial array is

$$12 \quad 35 \quad 61 \quad 82 \quad 16 \quad 38 \quad 13 \quad 29 \quad 33 \quad 42$$

The first step is to find the largest element. This is accomplished by going through one cycle of the interchange sort procedure. With the largest element in position a_n, the initial point of division is computed; it is the largest integral power of 2 less than a_n; for the example, it is 64. Any element greater than or equal to 64 which is encountered starting from the left is interchanged with the first element less than 64 that is found starting from the right. With the symbol 64 used to indicate the division point, the result of this first step is shown below. (The arrows indicate the next step.)

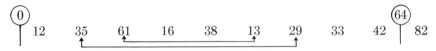

Now the two groups thus formed are divided in half, and the same sort of interchange is made. Since the one group contains only one element (82), no subdivision is possible for this group.

The new division points are simply midway between the existing division points.

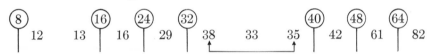

The next subdivision gives

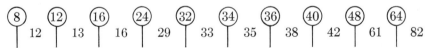

and the following one is

The next step completes the sort.

In practice, it is necessary to continue subdivision until there is a marker between each number; obviously, so long as there is more than one element in a group, they could be out of order.

Developing an algorithm of this process may seem like an ambitious project, but several of the constituent parts have already been discussed.

(1) The largest element determines the initial division point. The largest element can be found by one cycle of the interchange method.

(2) The initial increment of division (division point) is the largest integral power of two which is less than the largest element. Assume for the moment that all elements are positive.

(3) The increment of division is halved on every cycle. When the increment is one, or when there is no more than one element in every subdivision, the process is complete.

(4) The division points d can be computed by simply adding twice the division increment 2Δ. Interchanges cannot be made beyond the nth element.

(5) It is necessary to know where a subdivision begins and ends. Given the value of a point d being used to divide an interval, the interval starts with the first element greater than or equal to $d - \Delta$ and ends with the last one that is less than $d + \Delta$. Here Δ is the current increment of division.

(6) The process of interchange is to compare the elements from the left of a subdivision with the division point d until one is found for which $a_i \geq d$. Another index j is then used to select elements starting at the right end of the subdivision. When $a_j < d$, the elements a_i and a_j are interchanged. This interchange process continues until $i = j$.

Due to the complexity of this procedure, the flow chart is given in sections corresponding to the enumerated paragraphs above. Items (1), (2), and (3) have been described in more detail before.

(1) Finding the largest element and placing it in position a_n.

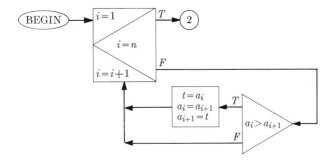

FIGURE 17–8

(2) Finding the integral power of two which is twice the initial increment of division.

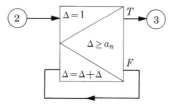

FIGURE 17–9

(3) The computed value of Δ above is halved on every cycle of the method.

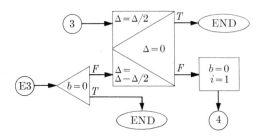

FIGURE 17–10

The variable b is a switch which is set to one if on a given cycle any subdivision contains two or more elements. The index i is the lower index of the subdivision being considered.

(4) The division points d are initially the value of Δ and are then increased by 2Δ for each new subdivision considered.

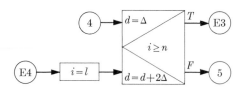

FIGURE 17–11

(5) The index l of the end of a subdivision is determined.

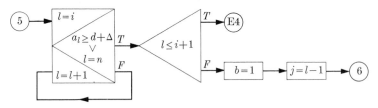

FIGURE 17–12

If there are no elements $< (d + \Delta)$, in which case $l = i$, or if there is only one element ($l = i + 1$), no interchanges are possible, and d is increased to the "mid-point" of the next subdivision.

(6) Interchange pairs where $a_i \geq d$ and $a_j < d$.

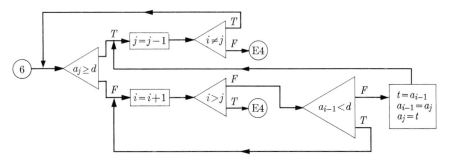

Figure 17–13

The program (Fig. 17–14) is written as an external function, SORT. (N, A), which sorts the N positive elements of the array A. There are as many complete cycles through the n elements being sorted as there are binary digits in the largest element. Thus the method is also of order $n \log_2 (\max a_n)$ or, since proportionality is all that is indicated, the designation can be $n \log (\max a_n)$. It was mentioned before that this process can terminate

```
        EXTERNAL FUNCTION (N, A)
        NORMAL MODE IS INTEGER
        ENTRY TO SORT.
        THROUGH L1, FOR I = 1, 1, I .E. N
        WHENEVER A(I) .G. A(I + 1)
            T = A(I)
            A(I) = A(I + 1)
            A(I + 1) = T
L1      END OF CONDITIONAL
L2      THROUGH L2, FOR DELTA = 1, DELTA, DELTA .GE. A(N)
        THROUGH E3, FOR DELTA = DELTA/2, DELTA/2 − DELTA, DELTA .E 0
        B = 0
        I = 1
        THROUGH E4, FOR D = DELTA, 2*DELTA D .GE. A(N)
L3      THROUGH L3, FOR L = I, 1, A(L) .GE. D + DELTA .OR. L .E. N
        WHENEVER L .LE. I + 1, TRANSFER TO E4
        B = 1
        J = L − 1
L4      WHENEVER A(J) .GE. D, TRANSFER TO L6
L5      I = I + 1
        WHENEVER I.G.J, TRANSFER TO E4
        WHENEVER A(I − 1) .L. D, TRANSFER TO L5
        T = A(I − 1)
        A(I − 1) = A(J)
        A(J) = T
L6      J = J − 1
        WHENEVER I .NE. J, TRANSFER TO L4
E4      I = L
E3      WHENEVER B .E. 0, FUNCTION RETURN
        FUNCTION RETURN
        END OF FUNCTION
```

Note: The increment is written as $\Delta/2 - \Delta$ so that the terminating relation can be met. Using integer division, when $\Delta = 1$, $\Delta/2 = 0$, and subtracting $\Delta/2$ as the flow chart indicates will not permit Δ to become equal to zero.

Fig. 17–14. Program for sorting algorithm.

early when all the subdivisions are groups of one. Clearly, when n is very large, this algorithm has a great advantage over the methods of order n^2. In a binary machine with a 36-bit word, $\log_2 (\max a_n) < 36$. One of several methods of improving this routine is to eliminate the computation of division points for empty subdivisions. If the next subdivision begins with a_i, the division to be used is

$$\left[\frac{a_i}{\Delta}\right] \cdot \Delta + \frac{\Delta}{2},$$

where the square brackets denote the integral part of the quotient indicated. This alteration can be accomplished by replacing two statements and replacing DELTA by DELTA/2 in the statement labeled L3.

THROUGH E3, FOR DELTA = DELTA, −DELTA/2,
DELTA .E. 1

THROUGH E4, FOR D = DELTA/2, (A(I)/DELTA)*DELTA
+ DELTA/2 − D, I.GE.N

This sort is often called an "$n \log n$" sort, and indeed, for average distributions it is of this order, since in $n \log n$ steps, enough divisions have been made to put every element into a separate subdivision. However, a badly skewed distribution such as the four numbers 2, 1, 10,621, 10,620 will require more than $n \log n$ steps.

Before leaving this programming example, it should be noted that the operations of finding integral powers of two, halving numbers, finding division points which are multiples of two, etc., can be accomplished very expeditiously with the built-in instructions of a binary machine. For this reason, such routines and, in fact, many nonnumerical algorithms, are written in assembly language. This does not mean that writing such algorithms in a statement language has no value. The statements can be regarded not only as a technique of carrying out a computation, but also as a tool permitting the unambiguous expression and communication of an algorithm. This latter use is perhaps the more important.

RECURSIVE ROUTINES

Functions whose definitions include direct or indirect references to the function being defined are called recursive functions. The subject of recursive functions (or routines) occurs with increasing frequency whenever programming systems or languages are discussed. For this reason, a brief explanation and some examples are included. The first two examples are drawn from numerical problems since they are the most familiar, but the topic is intentionally included in this section since the most useful applications of recursive functions are in the realm of nonnumerical problems.

The usual first example is the computation of n factorial ($n!$). This simple function of a single nonnegative integer can be defined in two ways.

$$(1) \qquad \begin{cases} f(n) = \prod_{i=1}^{n} i, & n > 0 \\ f(0) = 1 \end{cases}$$

In this form the external function is:

```
       EXTERNAL FUNCTION (N)
       NORMAL MODE IS INTEGER
       ENTRY TO NFACT.
       P = 1
       THROUGH S, FOR I = 2, 1, I .G. N
   S   P = P*I
       FUNCTION RETURN P
       END OF FUNCTION
```

The second definition is recursive.

$$(2) \qquad \begin{cases} f(n) = nf(n-1), & n > 0 \\ f(0) = 1 \end{cases}$$

For this form, it would be convenient to write the external function as

```
       EXTERNAL FUNCTION
       NORMAL MODE IS INTEGER
       ENTRY TO NFACT.
       WHENEVER N .E. 0, FUNCTION RETURN 1
       FUNCTION RETURN N*NFACT.(N − 1)
       END OF FUNCTION
```

However, there are some difficulties which should become more apparent if the computation is first examined in "tree" form, and then a specific case is represented by the appropriate flow chart. The computation (excluding $n = 0$) can be described by the tree in Fig. 17–15.

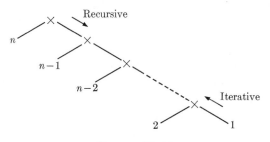

FIGURE 17–15

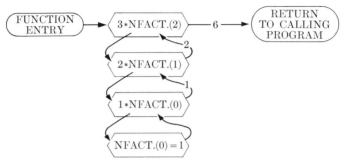

FIGURE 17–16

In the iterative approach (1), the computation begins at the branch ends terminated by 1 and 2. The variable of induction, $i = 1, 2, \ldots, n$, determines to what point along the tree the calculation is to be continued. In the recursive approach (2), the computation starts at the *principal connective*, the topmost multiplication operator in the tree. Since, in the first instance, this principal multiplication cannot be carried out, i.e., the lower branches of the tree have not been multiplied out yet, the multiplication by n must be *postponed*. Next, the multiplication by $(n - 1)$ must be postponed, then that by $n - 2$, etc., until a multiplication *can* be carried out. The first step that can be carried out is 1×2; next the postponed multiplication by 3, by 4, etc., are performed. The levels of postponement take the place of the variable of induction, and it is this process of "saving" operations and ultimately resuming them that is characteristic of recursive routines.

Some liberties must be taken with the flow-chart conventions previously used to illustrate this sequence of events for the specific case of $n = 3$ (Fig. 17–16). The initial entry was made with $n = 3$; 3 was, in effect, stored in the upper box and an entry made to the box below it with the argument 2. Here again, the 2 was stored in the box, and an entry made to NFACT. with the argument 1. With the 1 stored, the final entry with argument 0 is made, and the result $0! = 1$ is transmitted to the box above. The stored 1 is multiplied by this result, and the product (1×1) is transmitted upward. This product is in turn multiplied by the stored 2, and the product passed to the upper box where (3×2) gives the final result. The four hexagonal boxes above are really the same; there is only one NFACT. routine. It appears that storing the 2 would erase the previously stored 3; storing the 1 would erase the previously stored 2; etc. To make this procedure work, the temporary storage must be not a single element but a linear array, so that at one point (the bottom box), the integers 3, 2, 1 can be stored simultaneously. Actually, the linear array for storage need not be explicit if some array of the "last-on-first-off" type is provided. The term "last-on-first-off" refers to the fact that the numbers that are stored in the order 3, 2, 1 are recalled in reverse order (1, 2, 3) when they were used for multiplication. The addition of some statements to the programming language to provide for storage of this type should make this recursive operation workable. There is another similar, but less obvious, need for such storage. Note that all the returns (the outward-directed arrows) from the various entries return to the function itself, except for the upper box which returns to the calling program. The location of the return is stored internally in a function also, and so the same storage problem occurs here. It is necessary to enter in this *push-down* storage array, as it is often called, the return locations as well as the data numbers which are temporarily stored. With statements provided to fulfill this requirement, a workable recursive external function for the computation of $n!$ is

```
EXTERNAL FUNCTION (N)
NORMAL MODE IS INTEGER
ENTRY TO NFACT.
WHENEVER N .E. O, FUNCTION RETURN 1
SAVE RETURN
SAVE DATA N
T = NFACT. (N − 1)
RESTORE DATA N
RESTORE RETURN
FUNCTION RETURN T*N
END OF FUNCTION
```

In the light of the discussion above, the added statements are almost self-explanatory. The SAVE statements place the designated items on the push-down list. The RESTORE statements give the designated items the values of the next elements on the push-down array.

Another problem, which illustrates better the utility of the recursive statement of programs, is the computation of specific binomial coefficients. The binomial coefficients are the integer coefficients of the terms of $(a + x)^n$, i.e., a binomial raised to the nth power. The first few are

$$(a + x)^0 = 1 = c_{0,0}$$
$$(a + x)^1 = a + x = c_{1,0}a + c_{1,1}x$$
$$(a + x)^2 = a^2 + 2ax + x^2 = c_{2,0}a^2 + c_{2,1}ax + c_{2,2}x^2$$
$$(a + x)^3 = a^3 + 3a^2x + 3ax^2 + x^3$$
$$= c_{3,0}a^3 + c_{3,1}a^2x + c_{3,2}ax^2 + c_{3,3}x^3$$

The coefficients actually give the number of ways in which the term they multiply can be written. For instance, $c_{2,1} = 2$ multiplies ax, which may be written as ax or xa; $c_{3,1} = 3$ multiplies a^2x, which may be written aax, axa, or xaa. Actually $c_{3,1}$ could be obtained from $c_{2,1}$ and $c_{2,0}$; that is, $c_{3,1}a^2x = ac_{2,1}ax + xc_{2,0}a^2$, and so $c_{3,1} = c_{2,1} + c_{2,0}$. This is the basis for Pascal's triangle, in which the coefficients alone are written in pyramidal form, and each coefficient can be obtained by adding those diagonally above it.

n								
0				1				
1			1		1			
2		1		2		1		
3	1		3		3		1	
4	1	4		6		4		1

For the purpose at hand it is more convenient to arrange this table a little differently.

n \ k	0	1	2	3	4
0	1				
1	1	1			
2	1	2	1		
3	1	3	3	1	
4	1	4	6	4	1

The recursive definition for any entry in the table $c_{n,k}$ is

$$
\begin{cases}
c_{n,0} = 1 \\
c_{n,k} = 1 & \text{if } n = k \\
c_{n,k} = c_{n-1,k} + c_{n-1,k-1} & \text{if } n > k
\end{cases}
$$

The iterative definition of the same function, which is alternatively written as $C(n, k)$ or $\binom{n}{k}$, can be obtained by considering the combinations in detail. It is

$$ c_{n,k} = \frac{n!}{(n - k)!\,k!} $$

With just these two formulations, it is apparent that the recursive computation, which involves only additions, is superior to the direct iterative approach. Of course, there are some other possibilities. One is to iteratively compute the table until $c_{n,k}$ has been obtained. Written as an external function, the statements are

```
EXTERNAL FUNCTION (N, K)
NORMAL MODE IS INTEGER
DIMENSION C(40)
ENTRY TO BC.
C(0) = 1
THROUGH S1, FOR I = 1, 1, I .G. N
C(I) = 1
THROUGH S1, FOR J = I − 1, −1, J .E. 0
S1    C(J) = C(J) + C(J − 1)
FUNCTION RETURN C(K)
END OF FUNCTION
```

However, this program computes more table entries than are really necessary. Consider the calculation of $c_{4,2}$.

k \\ n	0	1	2	3	4
0	1				
1	1	1			
2	1	2	1		
3	1	3	3	1	
4	1	4	6	4	1

Only the diamond-shaped or "lozenge" part of the table is necessary to evaluate $c_{4,2}$. The recursive program written below evaluates only the entries inside the diamond.

```
EXTERNAL FUNCTION (N, K)
NORMAL MODE IS INTEGER
ENTRY TO BC.
WHENEVER K .E. 0, .OR. N .E. K, FUNCTION RETURN 1
SAVE RETURN
SAVE DATA N, K
C1 = BC.(N − 1, K)
RESTORE DATA K, N
SAVE DATA C1
C2 = BC. (N − 1, K − 1)
RESTORE DATA C1
RESTORE RETURN
FUNCTION RETURN C1 + C2
END OF FUNCTION
```

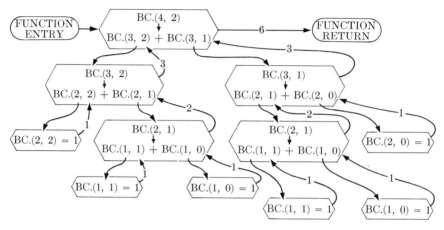

Fig. 17–17. Flow chart for the computation of $c_{4,2}$.

It is apparent from this example that the structure of the list statements is, in general,

$$\text{SAVE DATA } \mathcal{L}$$

$$\text{RESTORE DATA } \mathcal{L}$$

where the elements of $\mathcal{L}$ for the first statement may be expressions and in the second case the elements of $\mathcal{L}$ must be variables. Moreover, it is important to understand that the values are stored on the push-down list in the left-to-right order in which they appear in $\mathcal{L}$. Also the variable values are restored from the "top" of the list in the order of appearance, i.e., from left to right. The flow chart (Fig. 17–17) for the computation of $c_{4,2}$ can be expanded as in the factorial case. To clarify matters, the results of a particular entry into the routine is written in the line leading away from the box. In fact, the iterative program could be written so that only the necessary values are computed; however, the recursive statement of the procedure is often useful when one encounters difficulties in stating the "path" of the computation in an iterative form. Such problems occur in the realm of the more complex nonnumerical problems. The procedure for analytical differentiation (as opposed to numerical differentiation) is an illustration, but some recursive preliminaries need to be developed before this algorithm can be written.

FORMAL DIFFERENTIATION

In differentiating, one operates on expressions to produce other expressions. Expressions can be written in a variety of ways and can include a variety of operators. For simplicity only fully parenthesized expressions

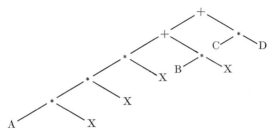

FIGURE 17–18

utilizing the four arithmetic operations and single-letter variables will be considered here. Thus, what might normally appear as $ax^3 + bx + cd$ would be written $(((((A*X)*X)*X) + (B*X)) + (C*D))$. The tree form of the latter term is given in Fig. 17–18. In Polish prefix form, the operator is to the left of the two operands on which it operates and is written without parentheses:

$$+ + * * * * \text{A X X X } * \text{ B X } * \text{ C D}$$

In array form, which will be useful in differentiation, the expression is

Line number	Operand	Operator	Operand
1	A	*	X
2	1	*	X
3	2	*	X
4	B	*	X
5	3	+	4
6	C	*	D
7	5	+	6

The integers in the operand columns refer to the previous line numbers.

It is very easy to convert any one of these forms into one of the others. The transition of particular interest is the algorithm that transforms the original fully parenthesized expression to array form. This procedure is recursive in the sense that action is postponed and characters are remembered until a certain condition is met. The original string of characters is entered, one character at a time, on a push-down list until a right parenthesis is encountered. At that point, the last three characters on the push-down list are removed to make one line of the array form. Consider that the example expression has been stored, one character at a time, up until the first right parenthesis. As each array line is formed, the line number replaces it in the list.

Original expression: $(((((A*X)*X)*X) + (B*X)) + (C*D))$

Push-down list	Array			
$(((((A*X)$				
$((((1*X)$	1	A	*	X
$(((2*X)$	2	1	*	X
$((3 + (B*X)$	3	2	*	X
$((3 + 4)$	4	B	*	X
$(5 + (C*D)$	5	3	+	4
$(5 + 6)$	6	C	*	D
	7	5	+	6

The program segment which produces the array form from the fully parenthesized expression is:

```
START       READ FORMAT F1, C(1) ... C(80)
            VECTOR VALUES F1 = $80C1*$
            I = 1
            THROUGH S1, FOR J = 1, 1, J .G. 80
            WHENEVER C(J) .E. $)$
                RESTORE DATA B(I), OP(I), A(I), LP
                SAVE DATA I
                I = I + 1
            OR WHENEVER C(J) .NE. $ $
                SAVE DATA C(J)
S1          END OF CONDITIONAL
```

Some comments on this program are: (1) The first statement causes 80 characters from a card (a blank is a character) to be read into the linear array $C(1) ... C(80)$. The reference to F1 is a format specification which specifies that up to 80 single character words (80C1) are to be formed from the contents of the card.

(2) The variable I is the line-number index and is initially set to one.

(3) The iteration statement increments through all 80 characters. There are three possible actions.

(a) If the character is a right parenthesis, $C(J)$ .E.$)$, the last four characters on the designated push-down list are removed, and the first three of these (not the last parenthesis LP) are inserted on the Ith row of the operand and operator arrays A, OP, B.

(b) The character under consideration is not a right parenthesis, and it is not a blank. In this case, the character is added to the push-down list.

(c) The character is a blank. The blank is skipped, and the next character is considered.

The reverse transformation is also simply accomplished. Starting with the principal connective (the last line in the array), the line numbers are replaced by the lines (enclosed in parentheses) which they represent. For the example, the reference to the principal connective is 7.

7   The 7 replaced by $(5 + 6)$

$(5 + 6)$ The 6 is replaced by $(C*D)$

$(5 + (C*D))$ The leftmost integer 5 is replaced by $(3 + 4)$

$((3 + 4) + (C*D))$ etc.

$((3 + (B*X)) + (C*D))$

$(((2*X) + (B*X)) + (C*D))$

$((((1*X)*X) + (B*X)) + (C*D))$

$(((((A*X)*X) + (B*X)) + (C*D))$

Since no more line references remain, the task is complete. The program segment which carries the array back to string form is

```
       THROUGH S3, FOR J = 1, 4, J .G. 300
       THROUGH S2, FOR K = J, −1, .ABS. C(K) .L. 1000 .OR.
         K .L. 1
S2     C(K + 4) = C(K)
       WHENEVER K .L. 1, TRANSFER TO S4
       SAVE DATA $)$, B(C(K)), OP(C(K)), A(C(K)), $($
S3     RESTORE DATA C(K) ... C(K + 4)
S4     PRINT FORMAT F1, C(5) ... C(J + 4)
```

Explanations: (1) J is the index of the rightmost character in the developing string. Initially, the line number of the principal connective occupies C(1). An arbitrary limit of 300 characters is set here.

(2) The next iteration starts from the right of the string and moves the characters four positions until an integer is encountered or until the entire string has been moved without encountering an integer. The characters, one per word, are left adjusted with the unused character positions filled in with blanks (for example, the character A is stored in a computer word as 216060606060). Then the test .ABS. C(K) .L. 1000 distinguishes a character from a line reference.

(3) In this case, the SAVE and RESTORE statements are just convenient ways of transferring the five elements into the "hole" created by the iteration.

(4) The final statement prints the reconstituted string. Since the string was displaced by 4 on the last search, C(5) ... C(J + 4) are printed. Again, the format is assumed to be specified as single-character words.

Differentiation is most easily accomplished by working on the array form. Writing first the usual formulas for differentiating arithmetic expressions illustrates that the recursive approach will be useful.

$$\frac{d}{dx}\,(\text{constant}) = 0$$

$$\frac{d}{dx}\,(x) = 1$$

$$\frac{d}{dx}\,(u \pm v) = \frac{du}{dx} \pm \frac{dv}{dx}$$

$$\frac{d}{dx}\,(uv) = u\frac{dv}{dx} + v\frac{du}{dx}$$

$$\frac{d}{dx}\left(\frac{u}{v}\right) = \frac{v(du/dx) - u(dv/dx)}{v^2} = \frac{1}{v}\left(\frac{du}{dx} - \frac{u}{v}\frac{dv}{dx}\right)$$

The last three are recursive in that d/dx appears on the right as well as on the left. The u and v refer to general expressions, and the presence of terms on the right such as du/dx and dv/dx implies that the formulas must again be applied. Indeed, all the operations must be postponed until a constant or the variable x is encountered. These same formulas can be expressed in array form. So that the definitions may be more readily related to the ultimate program, the symbol D. is used for differentiation with respect to x. The letter k is used to indicate the line number of the expression being differentiated, and the letter i indicates the line number of the principal connective of the resultant array form.

D.(constant) = 0

D.(X) = 1

D.$(A_k \pm B_k)$ =	i	D.(A_k)	$\pm$	D.(B_k)
	$i-2$	A_k	*	D.(B_k)
	$i-1$	B_k	*	D.(A_k)
D.$(A_k{*}B_k)$ =	i	$i-1$	+	$i-2$
	$i-3$	A_k	/	B_k
	$i-2$	$i-3$	*	D.(B_k)
	$i-1$	D.(A_k)	$-$	$i-2$
D.(A_k/B_k)	i	$i-1$	/	B_k

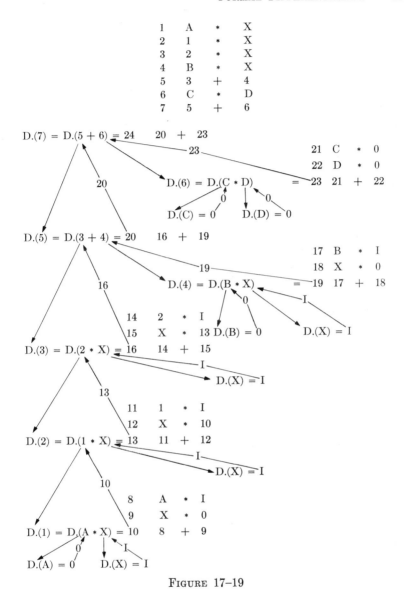

1	A	*	X
2	1	*	X
3	2	*	X
4	B	*	X
5	3	+	4
6	C	*	D
7	5	+	6

FIGURE 17–19

Note that the "differentiation routine" D. can be thought of as having but a single argument which can have three types of values. The argument may be (1) a line number k, in which case it is the expression appearing in the kth line which is to be differentiated, or (2) it may be the variable X and the derivative is one, or (3) it may be a letter (not an integer) which is not X and, as such, is a constant with derivative zero. The last case implies that there must be some way of distinguishing line references from integers which appear as constants in the expressions. This distinction is made by treating the former as binary integers and the latter as the BCD representation of integers, but this means of distinction will be clearer in the program. The example array can now be differentiated by starting with the principal connective. The diagram which describes this process is tantamount to writing a flow chart as was done for the earlier recursive examples. As in those cases, the value "returned" is inserted in the returning arrow. Here the nonzero integer values are simply the line numbers of the principal connective of the subexpression just produced, zero is the result obtained by differentiating a constant, and, for distinction, an I (identity) is returned from the differentiation of X (see Fig. 17–19).

An internal function which recursively differentiates the array form of an expression is given below. This is a function of a single variable (L) which operates on and adds to the array form of the expression. The array is composed of three linear arrays, A, OP, B, in which operands, operators, and operands are stored respectively. This function calls on another function (S.) of three arguments which simply stores one operation (i.e., two operands and an operator) in the array and increments the line number index (I). This "store" internal function directly returns the line number of the array entries that were made.

```
INTERNAL FUNCTION (L)
NORMAL MODE IS INTEGER
ENTRY TO D.
K = L
WHENEVER K .E. $X$, FUNCTION RETURN $1$
WHENEVER .ABS. K .G. 1000, FUNCTION RETURN $0$
SAVE RETURN
SAVE DATA K
DAK = D. (A(K))
RESTORE DATA K
SAVE DATA K, DAK
DBK = D.(B(K))
RESTORE DATA DAK, K
RESTORE RETURN
WHENEVER OP(K) .E. $ + $,
        FUNCTION RETURN S.(DAK, $ + $, DBK)
WHENEVER OP(K) .E. $ - $,
        FUNCTION RETURN S.(DAK, $ - $, DBK)
WHENEVER OP(K) .E. $*$, FUNCTION RETURN
        S.(S.(A(K), $*$, DBK), $ + $, S.(B(K), $*$, DAK))
WHENEVER OP(K) .E. $ - $, FUNCTION RETURN
    S.(S.(DAK, $ - $, S.(A(K), $*$, DBK), $/$, B(K)), $/$, B(K))
END OF FUNCTION
```

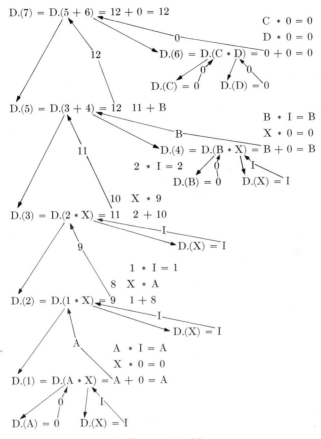

$$\text{Figure } 17\text{–}20$$

Since the store routine (S.) returns the line number of the expression stored, the three-line entry for the derivative of a product (and the four-line entry for the derivative of a quotient) can be written in nested form. For the product, the last line to be stored is

$$i \qquad i - 2 \qquad + \qquad i - 1$$

which, by reference to the internal function, is

$$\text{S.}(I - 2, \$ + \$, I - 1)$$

But when the other two lines are stored, the line numbers $I - 2$ and $I - 1$ are returned so that the entire production of three lines in the array can be written as

$$\text{S.(S.(A(K), \$*\$, DBK), \$ + \$, S.(B(K), \$*\$, DAK))}$$

The result of this entire operation is the line number of the addition, and this is what is returned by the differentiation array when a product is differentiated.

As has been indicated, it seems unnecessary to store all the expressions that can be readily simplified: multiplications with one of the operands unity or zero; additions with a zero operand; zero dividends; unity divisors—all these terms can be simplified to either zero or to one of the two operands. The store routine (S.) can be elaborated to recognize these cases and not provide a line in the array, but simply return the appropriate operand or zero directly. When this simplification is introduced in the example, considerably fewer lines are produced in the resultant array (Fig. 17–20). The entire derivative array is obtained by adding the additional lines obtained to the original.

1	A	*	X
2	1	*	X
3	2	*	X
4	B	*	X
5	3	+	4
6	C	*	D
7	5	+	6
8	X	*	A
9	1	+	8
10	X	*	9
11	2	+	10
12	11	+	B

When this array is transformed to the fully parenthesized string form by the technique of starting from the principal connective (12) that was described earlier, the result is

$$((((A*X)*X) + (X*((A*X) + (X*A)))) + B)$$

By collecting terms, using an exponent to indicate repeated multiplication, one identifies this result as the expected derivative (in lower-case letters):

$$3ax^2 + b$$

Figure 17–21 presents the entire program including the internal function which simplifies expressions and stores lines in the array. In a complete program which uses push-down storage, a linear array must be designated for this purpose. The executable statement of the form

$$\text{SET LIST TO } \upsilon$$

where υ indicates the array name, accomplishes this designation. The fact that this statement is executable, as opposed to a declaration, means that the designation may be changed during the computation; however, this facility is not used in the present case. The zeroth element of the array is the index of the list element most recently stored, and it is good practice to initially set this element to zero as is done here. Remarks, as opposed to statements, are designated by the letter R which precedes them.

Returning briefly to the original transformation from fully parenthesized expressions to array form, one finds that this process is readily generalized to include the implied parenthesizing that convention allows in expressions. In the procedure already discussed, the only task was to recognize a particular syntactical (i.e., structural) group, namely (operand-operator-operand). This group was recognized by the right parenthesis. The left parenthesis could have been used if the scan had been from right to left. In shorter terms, the program recognized

$$(A \text{ op } B)$$

as an expression and replaced it by an integer which was the line number of the expression in the array. To handle correctly such expressions as $(a \times b + c)$ and $(a + b + c + d)$ two other syntactical groups must also be recognized as expressions. The first is

$$\ldots \text{op}_1 \underline{A \text{ op}_2 B})$$

The underlined group followed by a right parenthesis and preceded by another operator (op_1) on the left is an expression and should be replaced by the integer line number. The second is

$$\underline{A \text{ op}_1 B} \text{ op}_2 \ldots$$

and is conditional. If, in an unparenthesized expression, the operation specified by op_1 is carried out in advance of the operation by op_2 (as in $\underline{a \times b} + c$), then $A \text{ op}_1 B$ is recognized as an expression and replaced by an integer. When this condition is met, op_1 "precedes" op_2. Obviously, the relative precedence of all operators that may appear in an unparenthesized expression must be established before the algorithm can be written. With these recognition rules, operations of equal precedence in an

```
R        DIFFERENTIATION ROUTINE
R
R
         NORMAL MODE IS INTEGER
         DIMENSION C(300), A(100), B(100), OP(100), V(1000)
         VECTOR VALUES F1 = $S1, 131C1*$
         SET LIST TO V
         V = 0
R        THIS SECTION READS A FULLY PARENTHESIZED EXPRESSION
R        AND CONVERTS IT TO ARRAY FORM.
R
START    READ FORMAT F1, C(1) ... C(80)
         PRINT FORMAT F1, C(1) ... C(80)
         I = 1
         THROUGH S1, FOR J = 1, 1, J .G. 80
         WHENEVER C(J) .E. $$
             RESTORE DATA B(I), OP(I), A(I), LP
             SAVE DATA I
             I = I + 1
         OR WHENEVER C(J) .NE. $ $
             SAVE DATA C(J)
S1       END OF CONDITIONAL
         C(1) = D, (I − 1)
R        THIS SECTION CONVERTS TO STRING FORM AND PRINTS
R        THE RESULTANT ARRAY FORM OF THE DIFFERENTIATED
R        EXPRESSION.
R
         THROUGH S3, FOR J = 1, 4, J .G. 300
         THROUGH S2, FOR K = J, −1, .ABS. C(K) .L. 1000 .OR. K .L. 1
S2       C(K + 4) = C(K)
         WHENEVER K .L. 1, TRANSFER TO S4
         SAVE DATA $)$. B(C(K)), OP(C(K)), A(C(K)), $,$
S3       RESTORE DATA C(K), C(... C(K + 4)
S4       PRINT FORMAT F1, C(5) ... C(J + 4)
         TRANSFER TO START
R        THIS RECURSIVE INTERNAL FUNCTION DIFFERENTIATES THE
R        ARRAY FORM OF AN EXPRESSION.
R
         INTERNAL FUNCTION (L)
         ENTRY TO D.
         K = L
         WHENEVER K .E. $X$ FUNCTION RETURN $1$
```

```
WHENEVER .ABS. K .G. 1000, FUNCTION RETURN $0$
SAVE RETURN
SAVE DATA K
DAK = D.(A(K))
RESTORE DATA K
SAVE DATA K, DAK
DBK = D.(B(K))
RESTORE DATA DAK, K
RESTORE RETURN
WHENEVER OP(K) .E. $ + $, FUNCTION RETURN S.(DAK, $ + $, DBK)
WHENEVER OP(K) .E. $ − $, FUNCTION RETURN S. (DAK, $ − $, DBK)
WHENEVER OP(K) .E. $*$, FUNCTION RETURN
1    S.(S.(A(K), $*$, DBK), $ + $, S. (B(K), $*$, DAK))
WHENEVER OP(K) .E. $/$, FUNCTION RETURN
1    S.(S.(DAK, $ − $, S.(S.(A(K), $*$, DBK), $/$, B(K))), $/$, B(K))
END OF FUNCTION

R         THIS INTERNAL FUNCTION STORES ONE LINE OF THE ARRAY
R         AND SIMPLIFIES THE EXPRESSION.
R
INTERNAL FUNCTION (U, V, W)
ENTRY TO S.
WHENEVER (W .E. $0$ .AND. (V .E. $ + $ .OR. V .E. $ − $))
1    .OR. (W .E. $1$ .AND. (V .E. $*$ .OR. V .E. $/$)), FUNCTION RETURN U
WHENEVER (U .E. $0$ .AND. V .E. $ + $
1    .OR. (U .E. $1$ .AND. V .E. $*$), FUNCTION RETURN W
WHENEVER (W .E. $0$ .AND. V .E. $*$)
1    .OR. (U .E. $0$ .AND. (V .E. $*$ .OR. V .E. $/$)), FUNCTION RETURN $0$
A(I) = U
OP(I) = V
B(I) = W
I = I + 1
FUNCTION RETURN I − 1
END OF FUNCTION
END OF PROGRAM


$ DATA

(((((A*X)*X) + (B*X)) − (C*D))
(((((A*X) + B)*X) − C)/(D*X))

RESULTS FOR THE TWO EXPRESSIONS ABOVE ARE

(((((A*X)*X) + (X*((A*X) + (X*A)))) + B)
(((((A*X) + B) + (X*A)) − (((((A*X) + B)*X) − C)*D)/(D*X)))/(D*X))
```

Fig. 17–21.   The entire program for a formal differentiation process.   The internal function which simplifies expressions and stores lines in the array is included.

unparenthesized expression will be executed in right-to-left order. It is more conventional to specify left-to-right order in such a case; this could be accomplished by scanning the characters of the expression starting from the right instead of the left. Such an algorithm is called a "jiggling scan"—jiggling because the push-down array jiggles back and forth as symbols are added and expressions are identified and removed. Unary operators are converted to binary operations with one zero operand as they are placed on the push-down list. This modification of the original program is included here. Again, only the arithmetic operations are included, and multiplication and division (*, /) precede addition and subtraction (+, −) in an unparenthesized expression. The unary minus (a dash) is given the same precedence as the binary minus; this is not completely consistent with practice. The program is given below.

```
           R
           R     AN EXAMPLE OF THE JIGGLING SCAN
           R
                 NORMAL MODE IS INTEGER
                 DIMENSION C(80), V(1000)
                 VECTOR VALUES F1 = $80C1*$
                 SET LIST TO V
START            READ FORMAT F1, C(1) ... C(79)
                 I = 0
                 V(1) = $($
                 V = 1
                 C(80) = $)$
                 THROUGH S1, FOR J = 1, 1, J .G. 80
S2               WHENEVER C(J) .E. $)$ .OR. (V(V − 1) .E. $*$ .OR.
                    V(V−1).E.$/$) .AND. (C(J).E.$+$ .OR. C(J).E.$−$)
                 I = I + 1
                 RESTORE DATA B(I), OP(I), A(I)
                 WHENEVER V(V) .E. $($ .AND. C(J) .E. $)$
                      V = V − 1
                      SAVE DATA I
                      TRANSFER TO S1
                 OTHERWISE
                      SAVE DATA I
                      TRANSFER TO S2
                 END OF CONDITIONAL
                 OR WHENEVER C(J) .NE. $ $
                 WHENEVER C(J) .E. $ − $, SAVE DATA $0$
                 SAVE DATA C(J)
S1               END OF CONDITIONAL
```

Comments: (1) Parentheses enclosing the expression are inserted by placing a left parenthesis in the first position on the push-down list (V(1)) and a right parenthesis in the 80th element of the symbol array C(80). This effectively limits the input expression to 79 characters.

(2) It is helpful to remember that $V \equiv V(0)$ contains the index of the "top" element on the list (i.e., the element most recently added); $V(V)$ is the top element, and $V(V - 1)$ is the one next to the top.

(3) When the isolated left parenthesis (i.e., no matching right) or the precedence situation is encountered, an expression is removed. The situation must then be reexamined before the next character is taken because additional expressions may be identified; hence there is a transfer back to S2.

(4) In the third from the last statement, the character enclosed in dollar signs is the unary minus, a dash. Unfortunately, the dash and minus sign are indistinguishable in printing, but they are represented by different BCD codes.

Corresponding alterations to the section of the differentiation program which forms the linear expression from the array form of the derivative would permit the elimination of redundant parentheses from the output. However, it is not necessary to include the details here.

If the given program were to operate on the expression

$$-((A + B*C) - D)/(B*C + D)$$

the three arrays would be given the values shown below.

I	A	OP	B
1	B	*	C
2	A	+	1
3	2	−	D
4	B	*	C
5	4	+	D
6	3	/	5
7	0	−	6

As a last remark on a program of this type, we wish to note that it is possible to make the recognition and replacement of syntactical groups much more general. In fact, a general translation scheme can be programmed in about 60 statements, recognizes arbitrary syntactical groups by means of comparison with a given syntax table, and replaces these groups, not only with integers, but with arbitrary output forms. Such programs are the basis of the statement-recognition sections of many translators. The decomposition of expressions is accomplished by an elaboration of the jiggling scan that has been described.

A PERMUTATION PROGRAM

Both the binomial-coefficient and the differentiation recursive programs refer to themselves twice in the scope of the definition. These references are diagrammatically represented in Fig. 17–22. It is interesting to think of a recursive routine with a variable number of references to itself contained in the definition. This is the sort of problem that confronts one when the recursive evaluation of a determinant by minors is attempted. In fact, this problem, as well as others, may be abstracted to the problem of producing all the permutations of n things, where n is variable. When n is fixed, the obvious approach is to write a nested iteration of depth n. The value of each iteration variable may not be the same as any of the "enclosing" iteration variables. For example, with $n = 3$, the following program segment would print all the permutations (i.e., the possible orderings) of the integers 1, 2, 3. There are 3!, or 6, in all.

```
      THROUGH S, FOR I = 1, 1, I .G. 3
      THROUGH S, FOR J = 1, 1, J .G. 3
      THROUGH S, FOR K = 1, 1, K .G. 3
S     WHENEVER I .NE. J .AND. I .NE. K .AND. J .NE. K, PRINT
      RESULTS I, J, K
```

Of the $3^3 = 27$ digit combinations produced by the triple iteration, only $3! = 6$ are used. This inefficiency coupled with the fact that n cannot be a variable in this program (since n iteration statements are required) suggests that there is a better approach. For example, one could actually systematically interchange the digits to form the permutations; this guarantees that no identical digits will be produced. One method of proceeding is to start with the natural order (1, 2, 3) and interchange each of the numbers in turn with the rightmost one, so that three sequences having 1, 2, 3 in the rightmost position are produced.

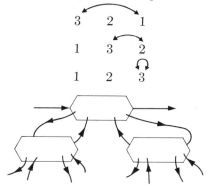

FIGURE 17–22

The last is, of course, an interchange with itself, but it produces one of the three possibilities. Now, when one of these has been produced, the next step is to start with that particular order and repeat the interchanges with the first two digits.

$$3 \quad 2 \quad 1$$

$$2 \quad 3 \quad 1$$
$$3 \quad 2 \quad 1$$

$$1 \quad 3 \quad 2$$

$$3 \quad 1 \quad 2$$
$$1 \quad 3 \quad 2$$

$$1 \quad 2 \quad 3$$

$$2 \quad 1 \quad 3$$
$$1 \quad 2 \quad 3$$

The column of triples on the right are the six permutations. A program capable of carrying out these steps must save the original order $(1, 2, 3)$ so that the three triples on the left can be produced. Also, each of these three must be saved so that the permutations of the first two numbers can be produced from them. The SAVE and RESTORE statements work well in this situation, and this scheme is encoded in the following program segment.

```
          SET LIST TO V
          V = 0
          VECTOR VALUES A(1) = 1, 2, 3
          THROUGH S1, FOR I = 1, 1, I .G. 3
          SAVE DATA A(3) ... A(1)
          A(3) = V(V − I + 1)
          A(I) = V(V − 2)
          THROUGH S2, FOR J = 1, 1, J .G. 2
          SAVE DATA A(3) ... A(1)
          A(2) = V(V − J + 1)
          A(J) = V(V − 1)
          PRINT A(1) ... A(3)
   S2     RESTORE DATA A(1) ... A(3)
   S1     RESTORE DATA A(1) ... A(3)
```

The interchanges are made by the appropriate transfers from the push-down list V to the array A. The program is still specific for $n = 3$, but it is now apparent how this restriction can be removed. The two loops

ECONOMICS LIBRARY AND STATISTICS

have identical structures except that the terminal value of the iteration is reduced by one in the second case and the A-array is printed when no more interchanges are possible. The problem is solved by making the iteration statement itself recursive, that is, by saving and restoring the value of the iteration variable and its terminal value, and by permuting the A-array. When the terminal value has been reduced to unity, the current permutation is printed. A complete program to produce the permutations of 1, 2, ..., N is given below.

```
                NORMAL MODE IS INTEGER
                DIMENSION V(1000), A(10)
                SET LIST TO V
                V = 0
START           READ DATA
                THROUGH S1, FOR M = 0, 1, M .E. N
S1              A(M + 1) = M + 1
S3              THROUGH S2, FOR I = 1, 1, I .G. M
                SAVE DATA M, A(N) ... A(1), I
                A(M) = V(V − I)
                A(I) = V(V − M)
                M = M − 1
                WHENEVER M .G. 1, TRANSFER TO S3
                PRINT RESULTS A(1) ... A(N)
S4              WHENEVER V .E. 0, TRANSFER TO START
S2              RESTORE DATA I, A(1) ... A(N), M
                TRANSFER TO S4
                END OF PROGRAM
Data
         N = 4 *
         N = 3 *
         N = 2 *
         N = 1 *
```

Comments: (1) The iteration terminating with S1 sets $A(1)$, $A(2)$, ..., $A(N)$ initially to the values 1, 2, ..., N and also leaves $M = N$.

(2) The condition for termination is that the push-down list V be empty, that is, $V(0) = 0$. Although the permutations of a particular digit, and therefore the iteration terminating with S2, are completed, there may be more "saved" permutations to be altered.

This routine is recursive and yet it is not expressed as a function. The earlier examples could have been programmed in a similar way without the definition of functions. It appears that the essential aspect of a recursive routine is the postponement of action and the necessary saving of

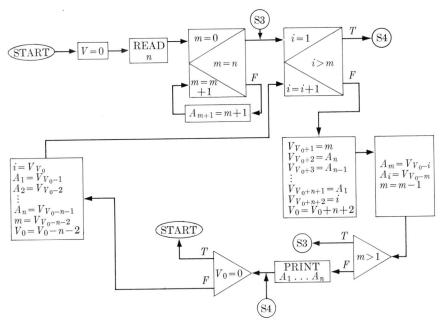

FIGURE 17–23

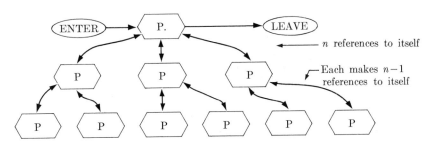

FIGURE 17–24

information until the information is restored to resume the action. The information is usually, but not always, used, saved, and restored in a "last-saved-first-restored" fashion (a push-down list). In more elaborate problems, this order is not preserved, and access to everything on the push-down list, not only the last entry, is required. Such access is possible in the programming language used here, but other operations and, in fact, entire artificial languages have been devised which simplify the expression of such algorithms. The permutation program can be represented by a flow chart in a completely conventional way, as shown in Fig. 17–23. In so doing, one somewhat obscures the recursive origin of the algorithm, and the argument can be raised that the statement description is more informative than the flow chart. The recursive formulation of the problem is given first.

EXAMPLES. Print all the permutations of $1, 2, \ldots, n$. Let the $n!$ sets of n elements $a_1, a_2, \ldots, a_n$ be represented by $P[a_1, a_2, \ldots, a_n]$. Then

$$P[a_1, a_2, \ldots, a_n] = \begin{cases} P[a_2, a_3, \ldots, a_n], a_1 \\ P[a_1, \ldots, a_{k-1}, a_{k+1}, \ldots, a_n], a_k \\ \qquad k = 2, 3, \ldots, n-1 \\ P[a_1, a_2, \ldots, a_{n-1}], a_n \end{cases}$$

$$P[a_k] = a_k, \qquad k = 1, 2, \ldots, n$$

An element appearing after the right bracket implies that it is appended to each of the sets of integers. Initially, $a_1, a_2, \ldots, a_n$ have the values $1, 2, \ldots, n$, but on each recursive application of the formulas above, the $a_1, a_2, \ldots, a_m$ $(1 \leq m \leq n)$ are identified with a different subgroup of the integers $1, 2, \ldots, n$. If the problem were written as a function and the flow-charting scheme previously used were again employed for $n = 3$, the block structure shown in Fig. 17–24 would result. Certainly the previous diagram is more explicit, but it is debatable whether it conveys the simple recursive structure of the algorithm as well as the block diagram, or for that matter, the original statement of the problem.

This final section is included to illustrate that digital computers can, and are, being used for nonnumerical problems. Moreover, the programming language, which was motivated primarily by the notation of algorithms for the solution of numerical problems, is useful for such diverse problems as sorting and formal differentiation. Recursive routines do not seem to have a large application in numerical problems since such algorithms can always be more effectively written as iterations. This fact seems to argue against the language designers who ask that *all* functions automatically have the capability (and complexity) of being recursive. In some nonnumerical problems, recursive definition gives a much needed property, namely, simplification of statement. In these cases, where recursive definition is well suited, it becomes apparent that different kinds of storage schemes are useful. To describe such algorithms succinctly, perhaps operations involving variable arrays and lists should be included in the programming language.

A Simple Compiler

CHAPTER EIGHTEEN

A nonnumerical problem of great interest to people concerned with digital computing is the translation of one artificial language into another. The specific problem of translating from a statement-type programming language to machine instructions, called *compiling*, is the primary source of this interest. In truth, the details of even a simple compiling program (i.e., a compiler) are probably beyond the introductory level, and the reader may wish to skip the development of the short example program that is presented at the end of this chapter. However, the preliminaries to writing such a program are very instructive since they bring together some apparently diverse topics that have already been introduced. In particular, the types and definitions of languages, the form of machine languages, and the recursive processing of strings of characters are all considered in the construction of a compiler.

LANGUAGES AND THEIR DEFINITIONS

Artificial languages can be categorized by the form of the rules or *grammar* which govern the *production* of sentences in the languages. In English, for instance, sentences may be produced by a sufficient elaboration of the following diagram.

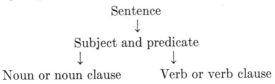

This type of construction can be described in terms of the metalinguistic symbols that were used before. Enclosing the descriptive terms in pointed brackets introduces a set concept. For example, ⟨sentence⟩ means the set of entities called sentences. One could equally well use S, for instance, to designate the set of sentences, but, since these sets tend to proliferate in language, the bracketed notation (due to Backus) is useful in that it indicates the content of the set. The word "and" above indicates concatenation; the subject is followed by the predicate as shown:

$$\langle \text{Sentence} \rangle \; : := \; \langle \text{Subject} \rangle \; \langle \text{Predicate} \rangle$$

Correspondingly, the set designations are simply written adjacent to each other. The symbol : := may be read "is defined by."

SOME SAMPLE DEFINITIONS

The word "or" above is the exclusive or (either but not both) and is designated by the symbol |. With this notation, the portion of a production grammar above can be written as

$$\langle \text{Subject} \rangle \; : := \; \langle \text{Noun} \rangle \mid \langle \text{Noun clause} \rangle$$
$$\langle \text{Predicate} \rangle \; : := \; \langle \text{Verb} \rangle \mid \langle \text{Verb clause} \rangle$$
$$\langle \text{Sentence} \rangle \; : := \; \langle \text{Subject} \rangle \; \langle \text{Predicate} \rangle$$

The symbols which are at the ends of the branching diagram above, such as those represented by ⟨noun⟩, are called terminal symbols.

When the major concern is translating, the rules for the production of sentences are not as important as the rules for the *recognition* of sentences and parts of sentences. Such a recognition grammar permits one to identify the structural constituents (i.e., syntax groups) of a sentence given as a string of characters. Once this identification has been accomplished, the syntax groups can be replaced by the equivalent structures in the target language of the translation. Often the production grammar can also serve as a recognition grammar, but this is not always possible. The existence of a recognition grammar is one of the discriminating features in the development of a language hierarchy.

In what follows, some simple languages are defined. Each succeeding example is a little more general than its predecessor. In fact, the first examples do not produce a language in the sense of a useful tool for description and communication, but the rules nonetheless produce sentences, albeit extremely simple ones.

(1) $\langle \text{alpha char} \rangle \; : := \; A \mid B \mid C \mid D \mid \ldots \mid Z$

$\langle \text{var name} \rangle \; : := \; \langle \text{alpha char} \rangle \mid \langle \text{alpha char} \rangle \; \langle \text{alpha char} \rangle$

The set designations suggest that the possible sentences produced by these definitions could be variable names. This language has a finite set of sentences, $26*27 = 702$ in all, namely, $A, B, \ldots, Z, AA, AB, \ldots, AZ,$ $BA, BB, \ldots, ZZ$. As such it is called a *finite-state* language.

(2) $\langle \text{digit} \rangle \; : := \; 0 \mid 1 \mid 2 \mid 3 \mid 4 \mid 5 \mid 6 \mid 7 \mid 8 \mid 9$

$\langle \text{nonneg integer} \rangle \; : := \; \langle \text{digit} \rangle \mid \langle \text{digit} \rangle \; \langle \text{nonneg integer} \rangle$

The permissible sentences are all the nonnegative integers, an infinite set. Note that the second definition is recursive. This language is no longer finite, but it does share a property with (1), namely, that each definition depends only on itself (i.e., it may be recursive) or on the lines that precede it. Both languages are *sequentially* definable. The integer constants in practical translators are finite state since there must be some upper limit to the number of digits that may be written as integers.

(3) $\langle$var$\rangle$: := $A \mid B \mid C \mid D \mid \langle$var$\rangle$ $(\langle$exp$\rangle)$

   $\langle$exp$\rangle$: := $\langle$var$\rangle$ $\mid$ $\langle$exp$\rangle$ + $\langle$exp$\rangle$

The parentheses, for example the left, are not placed in brackets, $\langle($\rangle$, since this symbol represents a set of entities which has one element, (. As with a constant in function notation, the element itself is used to designate a single-element set. The variables (var) defined here may be $A, B, C, D,$ $A(B), A(A + B + D)$, etc., and the expressions (exp) are of the form $A, B, A + B, A + B(A + D)$, etc. The set $\langle$var$\rangle$ is *not sequentially definable* since it depends on the line that follows it. Reversing the lines simply makes $\langle$exp$\rangle$ vary from sequential definition. Such languages, in which components of phrases are themselves phrases, are called *phrase-structure* languages. A great deal of mathematical notation falls in this category.

(4) $\langle$var$\rangle$: := $A \mid B \mid C \mid D$

   $\langle$add op$\rangle$: := + $\mid$ −

   $\langle$exp$\rangle$: := $\langle$var$\rangle$ $\mid$ $(\langle$exp$\rangle)$

   $(\langle$exp$\rangle$: := $(\langle$exp$\rangle$ $\langle$add op$\rangle$ $\langle$exp$\rangle$ $\mid$ $(\langle$exp$\rangle$*$\langle$exp$\rangle$ $\mid$ $(\langle$exp$\rangle$/$\langle$exp$\rangle$

   $\langle$add op$\rangle$ $\langle$exp$\rangle$: := $\langle$add op$\rangle$ $\langle$exp$\rangle$*$\langle$exp$\rangle$ $\mid$ $\langle$add op$\rangle$ $\langle$exp$\rangle$/$\langle$exp$\rangle$

Here again expressions (exp) are defined, but in the last two lines the definitions hold only in certain contexts. When the language being defined has a phrase structure and, in addition, certain syntactical groups are identified only in particular contexts, it is said to be a *general-phrase structure* language. This definition takes care of the precedence problem in unparenthesized expressions. In the preceding examples, the definitions are reversible in the sense that, given a string of symbols, it is possible to compare the symbols with the right-hand sides of the definitions, progressively identify larger syntactical units, and by so doing, determine unambiguously that the symbols represent a unique sentence. Perhaps the truth of these remarks is not obvious, but they will be more convincing when the mechanics of the comparison are discussed. The following definitions produce sentences but a given string of symbols cannot be uniquely recognized.

(5) $\langle char \rangle ::= A \mid B \mid C \mid \ldots \mid Z$

   $\langle var \rangle ::= \langle char \rangle \mid \langle char \rangle \langle var \rangle$

   $\langle product \rangle ::= \langle var \rangle \langle var \rangle$

If the product operator is explicit, say $\times$, instead of indicated by juxtaposition as the definition states, the difficulty is apparent. The string ABC may mean $A \times B \times C$ or ABC or $A \times BC$ or $AB \times C$. When no recognition grammar exists, the language is *undecidable*. Although this example does not indicate it, very general languages, such as certain Turing machines, are in this category. It is also possible that a language is *decidable* but that the recognition grammar cannot be written in the tabular form used thus far. This is the case when the rules for recognition vary depending upon the string of characters being examined. For example, if the leading character in a variable name were a digit from 1 to 9 followed by that many characters, multiplication indicated by juxtaposition could be deciphered. Thus 2A14ZY3Q1F obtained by placing together the variable names 2A1, 4ZY3Q, and 1F can easily be recognized as 2A1 $\times$ 4ZY3Q $\times$ 1F.

Language elements at the statement level can also be defined by such disjunctions of concatenated syntax groups. As an example, which will be used later, the following statements define a language whose four single-letter variables can be combined into expressions by means of the four binary arithmetic operators. In unparenthesized expressions, the normal rules of precedence apply, and from expressions, variables, and the substitution operator $=$, a substitution statement is defined:

   $\langle var \rangle ::= A \mid B \mid C \mid D$

   $\langle add\ op \rangle ::= \ + \mid -$

   $\langle sub\ statement \rangle ::= \langle var \rangle = \langle exp \rangle$

   $\langle exp \rangle ::= \langle var \rangle \mid (\langle exp \rangle)$

   $(\langle exp \rangle ::= (\langle exp \rangle \langle add\ op \rangle \langle exp \rangle \mid (\langle exp \rangle)*\langle exp \rangle \mid (\langle exp \rangle/\langle exp \rangle$

   $\langle add\ op \rangle \langle exp \rangle ::= \langle add\ op \rangle \langle exp \rangle*\langle exp \rangle \mid \langle add\ op \rangle \langle exp \rangle/\langle exp \rangle$

A difficulty arises here unless an order of production (or recognition) is assumed. Since a variable is an expression, an attempt should be made to produce (or recognize) the statement syntax group (which involves the variable) before the variable is identified as an expression. In short, the definitions should be considered in top-to-bottom order. A permissible sentence in this language is

$$A = (((B*C + D)*(A - C/D))/(B*B))$$

MACHINE LANGUAGE

The sentences in machine language are programs which are directly executable by a machine, and the terminal symbols are the basic instructions which can be decoded by the circuitry. Machine language is not a phrase-structure language and hence cannot be defined by the techniques described. Actually, for the problem at hand, namely translation from a phrase-structure source language *to* machine language, one is not interested in what are the possible sentences but rather what are the sentences (perhaps clauses) which are equivalent to the syntactical groups identified in the source language. Before we consider this equivalence for the last language described, it is worthwhile to review briefly the format of the machine language that was introduced earlier. A simplified schematic (Fig. 18–1) is again useful.

The letters AC and MQ are abbreviations for accumulator and multiplier quotient unit, respectively. The instruction which would go to CONTROL to transfer the number in location 4096 to the accumulator is

$$(\underbrace{000101000000000000}\quad \underbrace{000001000000000000})_2$$

Operation: clear accumulator and add to it the contents of address indicated   Address $= (4096)_{10}$

In octal form, this is

$$(050000010000)_8$$

Although this instruction is not directly acceptable to a machine, it is most often written

CLA   LOC

Here CLA is a mnemonic code for the operation (clear and add) and LOC is the symbol used to represent the specific location. The symbol LOC may

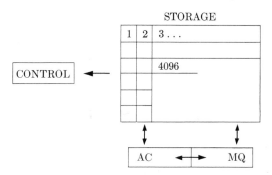

STORAGE

FIGURE 18–1

be thought of as a variable whose value in this example is $(4096)_{10} = (10000)_8$. This symbolic form of writing the machine instructions is called the *assembly-language* form and, since the subsequent translation to the numerical version is a straightforward matter, assembly language is a suitable output language for a compiler. With the notation C(A) defined to mean "Contents of address A," the following assembly instructions cause the arithmetic operations and the transfers to and from the arithmetic unit to be carried out.

Instruction	Meaning
CLA A	$C(A) \rightarrow C(AC)$
LDQ A	$C(A) \rightarrow C(MQ)$
STO A	$C(AC) \rightarrow C(A)$
STQ A	$C(MQ) \rightarrow C(A)$
ADD A	$C(A) + C(AC) \rightarrow C(AC)$
SUB A	$C(AC) - C(A) \rightarrow C(AC)$
MPY A	$C(A) \times C(MQ) \rightarrow C(AC) + C(MQ)$ (i.e., the product occupies both the AC and MQ registers)
DIV A	$(C(AC) + C(MQ)) \div C(A) \rightarrow C(MQ)$

If a variable can be designated by a single letter in some statement-type source language, the equivalent entity in machine language is a location which, in assembly language form, may be indicated by means of the same symbol. This equivalent production can be written under the source-language form to illustrate the relation between the syntax elements in the source language and the object assembly language:

$$\langle \text{var} \rangle ::= A \mid B \mid C \mid D$$
$$\langle \text{var} \rangle ::= A \mid B \mid C \mid D \leftarrow \text{equivalent assembly form}$$

In this case, the definitions look identical. Consider now the simple expression $(A + B)$:

$$\text{CLA} \quad A$$
$$\text{ADD} \quad B$$

In the original, this expression has no name; it is simply indicated by parentheses. One must adopt some convention for the machine form such as, for example, that the value of an expression is left in the accumulator. The two-instruction sequence above is consistent with this rule, and the formal definition pair is

$$\langle \text{exp} \rangle ::= (\langle \text{var} \rangle + \langle \text{var} \rangle)$$
$$\langle \text{exp} \rangle ::= \text{CLA} \ \langle \text{var} \rangle$$
$$\text{ADD} \ \langle \text{var} \rangle$$

According to the usual practice, the machine instructions are written in a vertical column. If a variable is considered to be an elementary form of an expression, the accumulator convention requires the following definitions:

$$\langle\text{exp}\rangle ::= \langle\text{var}\rangle$$

$$\langle\text{exp}\rangle ::= \text{CLA } \langle\text{var}\rangle$$

The sequential nature of machine instructions requires that new symbols which do not appear in the statement form be introduced when the expressions become more complicated. When an expression is written in array form, the line numbers that are used to designate expressions are these new symbols. Thus the expression $((A + B) + (C + D))$ becomes in machine language:

$$
\begin{array}{ll}
\text{CLA} & \text{A} \\
\text{ADD} & \text{B} \\
\text{STO} & \text{TEMP} \\
\text{CLA} & \text{C} \\
\text{ADD} & \text{D} \\
\text{ADD} & \text{TEMP}
\end{array}
$$

The symbol TEMP (for temporary storage location) is needed because the value of the two parenthesized subexpressions were required simultaneously and the convention of using the accumulator as the repository of an expression value is not adequate. The generated symbol TEMP can be regarded as a name for the $(A + B)$ subexpression.

When the simultaneous identification of several expressions is required, it is easier to use the more systematic symbols E_1, E_2, E_3, E_4, ... From the foregoing it is seen that an expression formed from the sum of two expressions is defined as

$$\langle\text{exp}\rangle ::= (\langle\text{exp}\rangle + \langle\text{exp}\rangle)$$

$$
\begin{array}{l}
\langle\text{exp}\rangle ::= \langle\text{exp}\rangle \\
\qquad \text{STO } E_1 \\
\qquad \langle\text{exp}\rangle \\
\qquad \text{ADD } E_1
\end{array}
$$

The symbol $\langle\text{exp}\rangle$ refers to a set of items called expressions. When specific expressions are considered, it is generally necessary to identify the expressions in the output form. The sequence which computes a particular expression can be thought of as the *meaning* of the original syntactical group. In linguistics the meaning attached to a syntactical group is called the *semantics*.

$$\text{exp} \; ::= \; (\text{exp}_1 + \text{exp}_2)$$
$$\text{exp} \; ::= \quad \text{exp}_1$$
$$\text{STO } E_1$$
$$\text{exp}_2$$
$$\text{ADD } E_1$$

Since in the definition of a language, forms other than expressions are identified and named, a more general notation, say $\mathfrak{F}$ for form, is suggested.

$$\langle \text{exp} \rangle \; ::= \; (\langle \text{exp} \rangle + \langle \text{exp} \rangle)$$
$$\mathfrak{F}_2$$
$$\text{STO } E_1$$
$$\mathfrak{F}_4$$
$$\text{ADD } E_1$$

The syntactical group on the right of the definition has five parts: (, $\langle \text{exp} \rangle$, +, $\langle \text{exp} \rangle$, and). Each of these parts can be regarded as a reference to a set, although three of them, (, + ,), are sets with single members. The machine-language equivalent is interpreted as an element from the second (from left to right) set above, $\mathfrak{F}_2$, followed by the constant STO, and then the generated symbol E_1. Then an element from the fourth set, $\mathfrak{F}_4$, is followed by ADD and a second reference to E_1. Note that there are three types of elements in the machine-language equivalent: (1) references to elements of the equivalent syntactical form, $\mathfrak{F}_k$, (2) constants such as STO, and (3) a unique symbol generation (E_1). One other element is needed to implement the translation of a general phrase-structure language, but first the syntax table and the machine equivalents are written for the first four rows of the last example in the preceding section:

$$\langle \text{var} \rangle \; ::= \quad A \mid B \mid C \mid D$$
$$\qquad\qquad\qquad A \quad B \quad C \quad D$$
$$\langle \text{add op} \rangle \; ::= \qquad + \quad \mid \; -$$
$$\qquad\qquad\qquad \text{ADD} \quad \text{SUB}$$
$$\langle \text{sub statement} \rangle \; ::= \; \langle \text{var} \rangle = \langle \text{exp} \rangle$$
$$\mathfrak{F}_3$$
$$\text{STO } \mathfrak{F}_1$$
$$\langle \text{exp} \rangle \; ::= \; \langle \text{var} \rangle \mid (\langle \text{exp} \rangle)$$
$$\text{CLA } \mathfrak{F}_1 \qquad \mathfrak{F}_2$$

When the recognition of a syntactical group depends upon the context, the equivalent output form is in the same context; that is, the entire syntactical group, not just the equivalent output form, must be a part of the output. Using a subscripted S to indicate a syntactical element, one can write the remaining lines as follows:

$$(\langle\exp\rangle) ::= (\langle\exp\rangle \langle\text{add op}\rangle \langle\exp\rangle) \mid (\langle\exp\rangle*\langle\exp\rangle) \mid (\langle\exp\rangle / \langle\exp\rangle)$$

$\mathcal{F}_4$	$\mathcal{F}_2$	$\mathcal{F}_4$
STO E_1	STO E_1	STO E_1
$\mathcal{F}_2$	$\mathcal{F}_4$	$\mathcal{F}_2$
$\mathcal{F}_3$ E_1	STO E_2	DIV E_1
S_1	LDQ E_1	STQ E_1
	MPY E_2	CLA E_1
	S_1	S_1

$$\langle\text{add op}\rangle \langle\exp\rangle ::= \langle\text{add op}\rangle \langle\exp\rangle*\langle\exp\rangle \mid \langle\text{add op}\rangle \langle\exp\rangle / \langle\exp\rangle$$

$\mathcal{F}_2$	$\mathcal{F}_4$
STO E_1	STO E_1
$\mathcal{F}_4$	$\mathcal{F}_2$
STO E_2	DN E_1
LDQ E_1	STQ E_1
MPY E_2	CLA E_1
S_1	S_1

The symbol S_1 designates the first syntactical element (S_2 the second, S_3 the third, etc.) which, for these two definitions, is the left parenthesis and an element of the set $\langle\text{add op}\rangle$, respectively. The inclusion of S_1 with the output form shows that this first syntactical element must appear before the output form, as indicated to the left of the definition symbol. It may appear that S_1 should head the list of equivalent instructions, but the next section demonstrates that the choice of position shown is correct.

The equivalents are not unique. Many other choices of machine-language sequences could be chosen. The sequence chosen for multiplication here is somewhat specialized; only for restricted values of the operands could the product be assumed to be in the accumulator as shown. In general, if efficient machine-language output is desired, the number of syntactical elements to be recognized in the source language must be expanded. For instance, if it were desired to have variables appear in the machine language simply as a variable, say A, instead of as an expression CLA A, it would be necessary to define expressions in terms of variables as well as other expressions. For example,

$$\langle \text{var} \rangle ::= A \mid B \mid C \mid D$$

$$\langle \text{exp} \rangle ::= \langle \text{var} \rangle \mid \langle \text{var} \rangle + \langle \text{var} \rangle \mid \langle \text{var} \rangle + \langle \text{exp} \rangle \mid \langle \text{exp} \rangle$$

$$+ \langle \text{var} \rangle \mid \langle \text{exp} \rangle + \langle \text{exp} \rangle \mid \quad \text{etc.}$$

THE TRANSLATION PROCEDURE

The process of translation can be described as the repeated searching of a syntax table of the type just illustrated and the replacement of every recognized group with the equivalent machine-language sequence, as well as the new syntax category. This process is recursive in the sense that not every character under examination is part of a syntax group, and hence the character must be stored until the addition of subsequent characters creates a recognizable group. As in the earlier recursive examples, this necessary postponement of recognition is facilitated by the push-down storage. However, in this production of longer and longer sequences of machine language, the storage is not always of the last on-first off type. This recursive operation can be illustrated by translating the source statement

$$A = (B + C)$$

Starting from the right, the characters are added to a list. The list is written horizontally, with the new elements added to the left. The structure of the list is such that the set designation (for example, $\langle \text{exp} \rangle$) precedes the specific member of the set. Single characters which are not in the syntax table are assumed to be single-member sets which stand for themselves. For clarity in this example, such entries will be bracketed. To illustrate,) appears as $\langle) \rangle$, * as $\langle * \rangle$, etc. Accordingly, the first list entry would be $\langle) \rangle$, followed by C. Checking the syntax reveals that C is a variable and the equivalent output form is C. With this replacement made, the list now stands at

$$\langle \text{var} \rangle, \quad C, \quad \langle) \rangle$$

The search of the syntax table is continued; $\langle \text{var} \rangle$ is recognized as being included in $\langle \text{exp} \rangle$, and the list is further altered. The constant CLA is written below the specific form of $\langle \text{var} \rangle$:

$$\langle \text{exp} \rangle, \quad C, \quad \langle) \rangle.$$
$$\text{CLA}$$

Next, $+$ is identified as a member of $\langle$add op$\rangle$ with output form ADD; by the two-step process above, B is identified as an expression, and the $\langle()$ is added to the list:

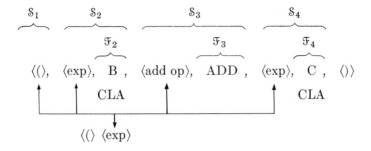

At this point the syntax group indicated by arrows is recognized, and replacement by the equivalent sequence gives

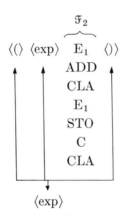

The subsequent recognition of $\langle() \langle$exp$\rangle \langle\rangle\rangle$ simply eliminates the parentheses:

$$\langle\text{exp}\rangle \; E_1$$
$$\text{ADD}$$
$$\text{B}$$
$$\text{CLA}$$
$$E_1$$
$$\text{STO}$$
$$\text{C}$$
$$\text{CLA}$$

With the remaining two characters added, the list is

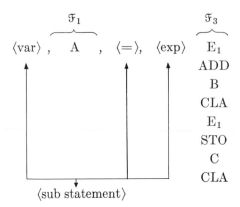

The final list is

⟨sub statement⟩	A
	STO
	E_1
	ADD
	B
	CLA
	E_1
	STO
	C
	CLA

When the output form is written with two elements to a line from the bottom up, the translation is seen to be complete:

$$
\begin{array}{ll}
\text{CLA} & \text{C} \\
\text{STO} & E_1 \\
\text{CLA} & \text{B} \\
\text{ADD} & E_1 \\
\text{STO} & \text{A}
\end{array}
$$

The translation algorithm begins to take shape. However, there are some practical matters that need to be considered before a program can be written. For computer processing it is more convenient to use simple integers to indicate the set names rather than the bracketed form:

$$\langle \text{var} \rangle \equiv 1$$
$$\langle \text{add op} \rangle \equiv 2$$
$$\langle \text{exp} \rangle \equiv 3$$
$$\langle \text{sub statement} \rangle \equiv 4$$

The output forms vary in length; in fact, they grow larger as the more macroscopic syntax groups are recognized. Since these forms are interspersed with the set names on the push-down list, it is necessary to indicate on the list itself how many elements are in a specific output form. This indication is simply included as a count of the elements immediately preceding the output form. With these alterations the next to last list of the preceding example is

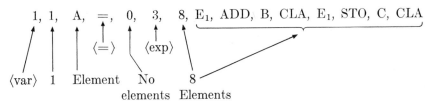

It is perhaps helpful to think of the list as being composed of syntax elements of the form

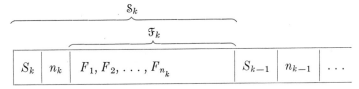

This is the structure of the elements that are put on the list. When a syntax group is recognized, a number of these syntax elements are removed, and a replacement(s) created from them which is then put back on the push-down list. The counts are, of course, essential for making comparisons with the syntax table since it is the set names S_k, S_{k-1}, S_{k-2}, ... which are compared, and these can be picked from the list only if n_k, n_{k-1}, n_{k-2}, ... are known.

A SIMPLE COMPILER

A program to carry out the procedure outlined above can be divided into four parts:

(1) A section which reads the syntax table and a statement to be translated.

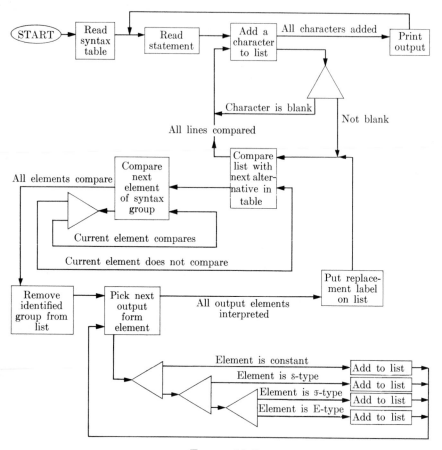

FIGURE 18–2

(2) An iterative section which adds non-blank characters from the source statement to a push-down list for subsequent identification in a syntax group.

(3) As each character is added by (2) or a replacement is made by (4), all the alternatives on the right of the syntax table are compared with the most recent additions on the list. If the entire table is searched and no match is found, another character is added by (1) and the process repeated.

(4) If a syntax group is recognized, the elements of the equivalent output form are interpreted and the recognized group is replaced. After replacement the table search is restarted (3).

A block schematic is presented in Fig. 18–2 to illustrate this organization; the four sections are subsequently flow-charted in more detail.

THE READ SECTION

The syntax table can be encoded by writing the information relevant to each alternative recognition group as a row of a matrix S. To clarify this encoding scheme, the entire syntax table with the equivalent output forms are reproduced in Table 18–1. The integer set names are written under the bracketed form.

TABLE 18–1

```
⟨var⟩ ::=  A | B | C | D
  1        A   B   C   D
           A   B   C   D
⟨add op⟩ ::= + | −
  2          +   −
           ADD SUB
⟨sub statement⟩ ::= ⟨var⟩ = ⟨exp⟩
  4                   1    =   3
⟨exp⟩ ::= ⟨var⟩ | (⟨exp⟩)
  3         1        3
          CLA  𝔉₁   𝔉₂
```

(⟨exp⟩ ::= (⟨exp⟩ ⟨add op⟩ ⟨exp⟩ | (⟨exp⟩ * ⟨exp⟩ | (⟨exp⟩/⟨exp⟩										
(3		(3	2	3	(3	*	3	(3	/	3
		$\mathfrak{F}_4$			$\mathfrak{F}_2$			$\mathfrak{F}_4$		
		STO E_1			STO E_1			STO E_1		
		$\mathfrak{F}_2$			$\mathfrak{F}_4$			$\mathfrak{F}_2$		
		$\mathfrak{F}_3$ E_1			STO E_2			DIV E_1		
		S_1			LDQ E_1			STQ E_1		
					MPY E_2			CLA E_1		
					S_1			S_1		

⟨add op⟩ ⟨exp⟩ ::= ⟨add op⟩ ⟨exp⟩ * ⟨exp⟩ | ⟨add op⟩ ⟨exp⟩/⟨exp⟩								
2	3	2	3	*	3	2	3	/	3
			$\mathfrak{F}_2$				$\mathfrak{F}_4$		
			STO E_1				STO E_1		
			$\mathfrak{F}_4$				$\mathfrak{F}_2$		
			STO E_2				DIV E_1		
			LDQ E_1				STQ E_1		
			MPY E_2				CLA E_1		
			S_1				S_1		

The first element in a particular row, say the hth, is the set name for the syntax group (for example, 1 for ⟨var⟩), the second element is a count of the number of elements in the syntax group, and this is followed by the syntax group itself. The equivalent output form follows the syntax group; again it is preceded by a count of the number of elements in the output form. The four alternatives for ⟨var⟩ require four rows of the matrix; in input card form they are:

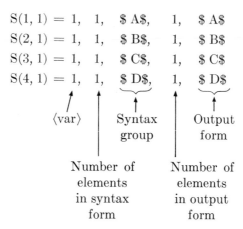

$$S(1, 1) = 1, \quad 1, \quad \$ A\$, \quad 1, \quad \$ A\$$$
$$S(2, 1) = 1, \quad 1, \quad \$ B\$, \quad 1, \quad \$ B\$$$
$$S(3, 1) = 1, \quad 1, \quad \$ C\$, \quad 1, \quad \$ C\$$$
$$S(4, 1) = 1, \quad 1, \quad \$ D\$, \quad 1, \quad \$ D\$$$

⟨var⟩   Syntax group   Output form

Number of elements in syntax form   Number of elements in output form

As before, when the binary-coded decimal (BCD) representation of a character is required instead of a value which the symbol represents, the enclosing dollar signs must be added. In more complicated cases the output form may contain up to four different types of elements, and a code is needed to make it possible for the program to distinguish between them. A wide variety of coding choices can be made; however, some of these are found to be clumsy in practical applications unless some symbol-manipulation operations are introduced which have not been discussed. A choice in which the distinction is to be made by considering the characters as integers consists of the following steps.

(1) Write constants with a preceding blank, for example,

$$\$ A\$, \$ CLA\$, \$ STO\$, \text{etc.}$$

(2) Write references to specific forms, $\mathfrak{F}_k$, by using the positive integer k.

(3) Write references to specific syntax groups S_k by using the negative of k, for example, $-k$.

(4) Write a symbol to be generated as $\$E0000k\$$. Here k may be more than the one digit shown.

If an example of each of these is written in octal form, the rules for distinction become apparent.

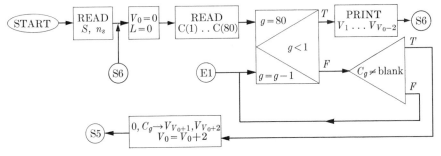

FIGURE 18–3

$$\begin{array}{cccccc} & \text{b} & \text{C} & \text{L} & \text{A} & \text{b} & \text{b} \end{array}$$

(1) $ CLA$ = $(60\ 23\ 43\ 21\ 60\ 60)_8$ = $(-202343216060)_8$

(2)   6   = $(000000000006)_8$

(3) -5 = $(-000000000005)_8$

$$\begin{array}{cccccc} \text{E} & 0 & 0 & 0 & 0 & 2 \end{array}$$

(4) $E00002$ = $(25\ 00\ 00\ 00\ 00\ 02)_3$ = 250000000002

Six BCD characters can be stored in an IBM 7090 computer word (6×6 bits = 36 bits). If fewer than six are written between dollar signs, then blanks (b = (60_8)) are added on the right to fill out the word. Viewed strictly as integers now, the four cases are a large negative integer, a small positive integer, a small negative integer, and a large positive integer, respectively. "Small" is assumed to be defined as <100. With these conventions the line representing the last alternative is represented in input-card form as the 14th row of the S-matrix.

$$S(14, 1) = 3,\ 4,\ 2,\ 3,\ \$/\$,\ 3,\ 11,\ 4,\ \$ \text{ STO}\$,\ \$E00001\$,\ 2,\ \$ \text{ DIV}\$,\ \$E00001\$$$

$$\$ \text{ STQ}\$,\ \$E00001\$,\ \$ \text{ CLA}\$,\ \$E00001\$,\ -1$$

⟨exp⟩

4 elements in syntax group

11 elements in output form

The ⟨add op⟩ does not appear explicitly since the final -1 (the coded form of s_1) restores the first syntactical group, whatever it is, to the list.

To achieve consistency of Fig. 18–3 with the program that follows, V is the name of the array used as a push-down list and V_0 the index of the most recently added element. Thus V_{V_0} is the "top" element. For additions to the list, list operations are indicated by

$$A_1 \ldots A_n \rightarrow V_{V_0+1} \ldots V_{V_0+n}$$
$$V_0 = V_0 + n$$

and for deletions, the arrow is reversed and V_0 is decreased.

$$A_1 \ldots A_n \leftarrow V_{V_0} \ldots V_{V_0-n+1}$$
$$V_0 = V_0 - n$$

THE SYNTAX-TABLE SEARCH

The alternative in the h-row of S has $S_{h,2}$ elements in its identifying syntactical group, starting with $S_{h,3}$. These elements must be compared with the first $S_{h,2}$ set names on the list. Whenever an element fails to compare, the next line is tried. If no matching groups are found, another character is read. The set names in the V-list are not consecutive, and the selecting index P must be decreased by the count of the interspersed output forms plus two (Fig. 18–4).

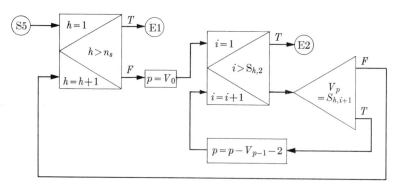

FIGURE 18–4

GENERATING OUTPUT FORMS

The syntax groups which were identified are transferred to an auxiliary array A. The appropriate parts of this array, along with constants and symbols, are transferred back to the list V to form the new syntactical group. A variable called L in the program is incremented by the necessary amount (TL) so that adding it to the symbols that are read from the table always produces a unique symbol. Moreover, the generated syntactical group must be preceded by a count when it is written on the list V. This count, C, is incremented as necessary. When an S-type code is encountered, the count C and the set name $S_{h,1}$ are immediately placed on V and the designated syntactical element is then rewritten on the list. The distinction

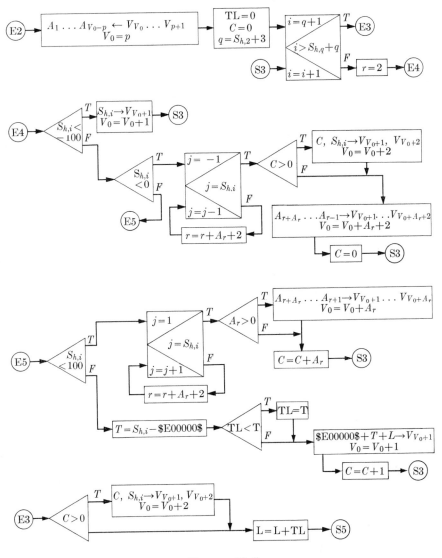

FIGURE 18–5

between the types of output elements is accomplished by positive and negative integer separation as indicated earlier. The flow chart in Fig. 18–5 illustrates the entire procedure. Writing the "save" and "restore" operations explicitly, as was done in this flow chart, obscures in a certain sense the algorithm. This type of program may be more understandable in the statement form (Fig. 18–6) than in the flow-chart version. The output

```
        R
        R              AN EXAMPLE OF A RECURSIVE, SYNTAX-FREE,
        R              GENERAL OUTPUT SCAN
        R
        NORMAL MODE IS INTEGER
        DIMENSION C(80), V(1000), A(1000), S(400,SDIM)
        VECTOR VALUES SDIM = 2, 1, 20
        VECTOR VALUES F1 = $80C1*$
        VECTOR VALUES F2 = $2(S2, C6)*$
        SET LIST TO V
        READ DATA
   S6   V = 0
        L = 0
        READ FORMAT F1, C(1) ... C(80)
        THROUGH S1, FOR G = 80, −1, G.L.1
        WHENEVER C(G).NE.$ $
        SAVE DATA 0, C(G)
   S5   THROUGH S1, FOR H = 1, 1, H.G.NS
        P = V
        THROUGH S2, FOR I = 1, 1, I.G.S(H, 2)
        WHENEVER V(P).NE.S(H, I + 2), TRANSFER TO S1
   S2   P = P − V(P − 1) − 2
        RESTORE DATA A(1) ... A(V − P)
        TL = 0
        COUNT = 0
        Q = S(H, 2) + 3
        THROUGH S3, FOR I = Q + 1, 1, I.G.S(H, Q) + Q
        R = 2
        WHENEVER S (H, I).L. −100
                SAVE DATA S(H, I)
                COUNT = COUNT + 1
        OR WHENEVER S(H, I).L.0
                THROUGH S4, FOR J = −1, −1, J.E.S(H, I)
   S4           R = R + A(R) + 2
                WHENEVER COUNT .G. 0, SAVE DATA COUNT, S(H, 1)
                SAVE DATA A(R + A(R)) ... A(R − 1)
                COUNT = 0
        OR WHENEVER S(H, I).LE.100
                THROUGH S7, FOR J = 1, 1, J.E.S(H, I)
   S7           R = R + A(R) + 2
                WHENEVER A(R).G.0, SAVE DATA A(R + A(R)) ... A(R + 1)
                COUNT = COUNT + A(R)
        OTHERWISE
                T = BCDBN.(S(H, I) − $E00000$)
                WHENEVER TL.L.T, TL = T
                SAVE DATA $E00000$ + BNBCD.(T + L)
                COUNT = COUNT + 1
   S3   END OF CONDITIONAL
        WHENEVER COUNT.G.0, SAVE DATA COUNT, S(H, 1)
        L = L + TL
        TRANSFER TO S5
   S1   END OF CONDITIONAL
        PRINT FORMAT F2, V(1) ... V(V − 2)
        TRANSFER TO S6
        END OF PROGRAM


   $ DATA
   S(1, 1) = 1, 1, $A$, 1, $ A$
   S(2, 1) = 1, 1, $B$, 1, $ B$
   S(3, 1) = 1, 1, $C$, 1, $ C$
   S(4, 1) = 1, 1, $D$, 1, $ D$
   S(5, 1) = 2, 1, $ + $, 1, $ ADD$
   S(6, 1) = 2, 1, $ − $, 1, $ SUB$
   S(7, 1) = 4, 3, 1, $ = $, 3, 3, 3, $ STO$, 1
   S(8, 1) = 3, 1, 1, 2, $ CLA$, 1
   S(9, 1) = 3, 3, $($, 3, $)$, 1, 2
   S(10, 1) = 3, 4, $($, 3, 2, 3, 7, 4, $ STO$, $E00000$, 2, 3, $E00001$, −1
   S(11, 1) = 3, 4, $($, 3, $*$, 3, 11, 2, $ STO$, $E00001$, 4, $ STO$, $E00002$, $ LDQ$,
        $E00001$, $ MPY$, $E00002$, −1
   S(12, 1) = 3, 4, $($, 3, $/$, 3, 11, 4, $ STO$, $E00001$, 2, $ DIV$, $E00001$, $ STQ$,
        $E00001$, $ CLA$, $E00001$, −1
   S(13, 1) = 3, 4, 2, 3, $*$, 3, 11, 2, $ STO$, $E00001$, 4, $ STO$, $E00002$, $ LDQ$,
        $E00001$, $ MPY$, $E00002$, −1
   S(14, 1) = 3, 4, 2, 3, $/$, 3, 11, 4, $ STO$, $E00001$, 2, $ DIV$, $E00001$, $ STQ$,
        $E00001$, $ CLA$, $E00001$, −1
   NS = 14*
           A = (((B*C + D)*(A − C/D))/(B*B))
```

FIGURE 18–6

for the source statement shown is

CLA	B	STO	E00008
STO	E00001	CLA	D
CLA	B	STO	E00003
STO	E00002	CLA	C
LDQ	E00001	DIV	E00003
MPY	E00002	STQ	E00003
STO	E00010	CLA	E00003
CLA	D	STO	E00004
STO	E00007	CLA	A
CLA	B	SUB	E00004
STO	E00005	STO	E00009
CLA	C	LDQ	E00008
STO	E00006	MPY	E00009
LDQ	E00005	DIV	E00010
MPY	E00006	STQ	E00010
ADD	E00007	CLA	E00010
		STO	A

Two functions, BCDBN. and BNBCD., are referred to in the program and require some explanation. When integers are printed, they must be in BCD form, e.g., 31 appears as two BCD characters, 0301. However, for computation the integer must be in the usual binary form $(011111)_2 = (37)_8$. The two functions convert the integer argument from one form to the other—BCDBN. from BCD to binary and BNBCD. from binary to BCD.

CONCLUDING REMARKS

The compiling program illustrated here is a generalization of the statement decomposition into array form that was described in connection with the differentiation program. In that case the rules for recognizing the syntactical groups were built into the program in the sense that the logic of the decomposition was embedded in the statements. The more general approach is syntax-free in that the syntax is contained in a table which is treated as data by the program. Built into the program is the procedure for comparing a list against the table and, when similar groups are found, substituting output forms also obtained from the table. To be sure, the two-column printing format was specified with assembly language in mind, but the output forms are not limited to this specific structure.

As is often the case with general procedures, they become very inefficient when used in a specific, fairly narrow application. Practical translation to machine language is really not feasible by the straightforward application of the technique described. The recognition of constants, variable names, and the components of ordinary arithmetic expressions are much more effectively carried out by programs with built-in syntax recognition. However, at the level of statements, the tabular-search recognition procedure can be used to great advantage. Even at the statement level, though, some modifications in language structure are useful to eliminate the possibility that entire programs, containing perhaps many hundreds of statements, will have to be stored on a list before being recognized as a single syntactical unit. In spite of these qualifications, the procedure described is basic. Cognizance of the general approach leads to much more rational and consistent specializations of the algorithms than are generally produced from a completely empirical approach to a specific translation problem.

BIBLIOGRAPHY

ARDEN, B. W., B. A. GALLER, and R. M. GRAHAM. *The MAD Manual.* The University of Michigan Computing Center, 1961.

BACKUS, J. W., ACM-GAMM Conference. International Conference on Information Processing, June 1959.

DWYER, PAUL S. *Linear Computations.* John Wiley and Sons, 1951.

GINSBURG, S., *Introduction to Mathematical Machine Theory*, Addison-Wesley Publishing Co., Inc., 1962.

HAMMING, RICHARD W. *Numerical Methods for Scientists and Engineers.* McGraw-Hill Book Co., 1962.

HASTINGS, CECIL, JR. *Approximations for Digital Computers.* Princeton University Press, 1955.

HILDEBRAND, F. B. *Introduction to Numerical Analysis.* McGraw-Hill Book Co., 1956.

HOUSEHOLDER, ALSTON S. *Principles of Numerical Analysis.* McGraw-Hill Book Co., 1953.

I.B.M. Reference Manual. 709/7090 *Data Processing System.* International Business Machines Corporation, 1960.

IRONS, E. T. "A Syntax Directed Compiler for ALGOL 60," *Communications of the Association for Computing Machinery,* Vol. 4, No. 1, January 1961.

KUNZ, KAISER S. *Numerical Analysis.* McGraw-Hill Book Co., 1957.

ROGERS, HARTLEY, JR. "The Present Theory of Turing Machine Computability," *Journal of the Society of Industrial and Applied Mathematics,* March 1959.

STANTON, RALPH G. *Numerical Methods for Science and Engineering.* Prentice-Hall, 1961.

WANG, HAO. "A Variant to Turing's Theory of Computing Machines," *Journal of the Association of Computing Machinery,* **4,** pp. 63–92 (1957).

A Summary
of the MAD
Programming Language

APPENDIX A

The purpose of this section is to provide the novice with a working summary of the MAD language. To this end, the exposition is informal and brief, with a heavy reliance on examples; some pitfalls are also indicated. Many interesting features of the language are not mentioned, and some are oversimplified, but, for those interested, the *MAD Manual* describes these omissions and corrects these sins.

TABLE A–1

THE STATEMENT CARD FORMAT

Columns 1–10	Statement labels may be punched anywhere in these columns.
Column 11	If the statement portion of the card is a remark, this fact is designated by punching the letter R in this column. Column 11 is also used to designate the continuation of a statement. Any of the digits (0, 1, 2, . . . , 9), in any order, may be punched for this purpose. Only the continuation cards, not the first, are punched in this column. There may be at most 10 cards in a statement.
Columns 12–72	The statement may start anywhere in these columns. The readability of complex programs is improved if indenting is used to emphasize scopes of conditions and iterations.
Columns 73–80	A personal identification and/or a sequence number can be punched in these columns. *The statement cannot continue into these columns.*

Table A–1 specifies the statement card format, and Fig. A–1 shows punched cards illustrating a continued statement followed by a remark.

349

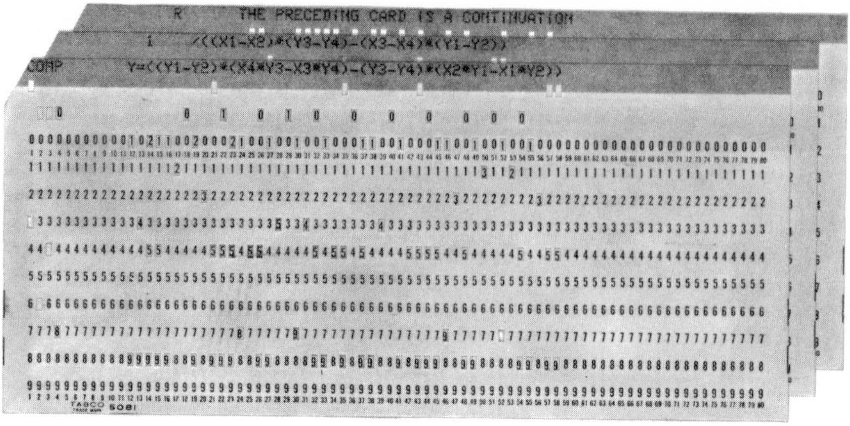

FIGURE A-1

The language.   The permissible characters are:

(1) A B C D E F G H I J K L M N O P Q R S T U V W
     X Y Z

(2) 0 1 2 3 4 5 6 7 8 9

(3) + − * / ( ) . , = $

Alphabetic characters are listed as item (1), *numerical* characters as item
(2), and the *special characters* as item (3).   The alphabetic and numerical
characters combined are called *alphanumeric*.   Except in comments to be
printed, blank spaces, if any appear, are simply ignored.

The basic elements of the language are constants, variables, operators,
relations, and grouping marks.   These elements are combined to form
expressions, and the expressions, in turn, are combined with more encom-
passing operators (often designated by English words) to form statements.

In the usual numerical problem, two kinds (or *modes*) of numbers are
useful: integer and floating-point.   Integers are used for counting and subscripts, and floating-point numbers are used to represent fractions and, in
general, real numbers.   When constants are written, the form of the constant must indicate what mode was intended.   For variables, the mode
must be declared, either implicitly or explicitly.   Declaration statements
are needed for this purpose and for the purpose of allocating contiguous
storage locations to arrays.

Constants.   All numerical constants may be preceded by a + or − sign,
but in the absence of a sign, the number is assumed to be positive.

Integer constants are written without a decimal point.   The magnitude
of an integer constant I is restricted to $|I| \leq 268435455$.

EXAMPLES.   12, −8, +16400, −61, 0

The binary-coded decimal (BCD) representation of a string of six characters or less also is an integer constant and is indicated by enclosing the characters in dollar signs. (See Chapter 17, on nonnumerical problems, for the character equivalence.) If fewer than six characters are specified, they are left justified in the 36-bit word and blanks are inserted for the unspecified characters on the right.

EXAMPLES. ABC, $($, $+$, $E00001$

Floating-point constants must have a decimal point. No more than eight digits (excluding sign and decimal point) should be written.

EXAMPLES. 0., 6.3189314, $-$.000642, $+$12966.12, 2.0

Floating-point constants in exponential form. When the magnitude of a constant is such that it is not readily expressed in the above form, it may be written in exponential form, i.e., as a number times an integral power of ten. Just the number and the integral exponent are written. The exponent is at the right of the number following the letter E (for exponent). Thus 10.2×10^{-18} is written 10.2E $-$ 18. The decimal point does not have to appear in the number part, e.g., 5×10^{24} is written 5E24.

EXAMPLES. .0072E $-$10, $+$1.86E$+$12, 21.432983E1, $-$312.6E $-$3, 1E $-$5

No more than eight digits can be written in the number part, and the magnitude of a floating-point number F is restricted to $.11540473 \times 10^{-38} \leq |F| \leq .53183945 \times 10^{38}$ and $F = 0$.

Variables. *Variable names* are written as groups of six or less alphanumeric characters, where the leading character is alphabetic.

EXAMPLES. ALPHA, X, A, B, EPSILON, X1, S4, Y123, BETA, CONST, MOVE

Subscripted variables are written by appending integer subscripts enclosed in parentheses to the right of a variable name. The subscript may be an integer expression as well as a constant.

EXAMPLES. ALPHA(I), B(2), X1(4), Y12(I + J), A(I, J),
MATRX(J, K), BETA(I + 1, K)

Statement labels are formed by the same rule that applies to variables: six or less alphanumeric characters, with the initial character alphabetic. The labels may have a constant integer subscript.

EXAMPLES. LABEL, S1, L4, START, S(1), L3(4), BETA(3)

Operators. Where no distinct symbols are available, operators are written as a letter(s) with a period on either side.

Arithmetic operators of addition, subtraction, multiplication, division, and exponentiation are represented by $+$, $-$, $*$, $/$, and .P., respectively. The multiplication operator *must always be written*. The form of variable names and subscription makes it impossible for juxtaposition to mean multiplication.

Unary operators, minus and absolute value, are represented by $-$ and .ABS., respectively. The use of a unary $+$ is permissible, but never needed.

Boolean operators "and," "or," and "not" ($\wedge$, $\vee$, $\frown$) are written .AND., .OR., and .NOT.

Relations. The relations $<$, $\leq$, $>$, $\geq$, $=$, $\neq$, are written .L., .LE., .G., .GE., .E., .NE., respectively. There is an equals symbol "$=$," but it is reserved for use as a substitution symbol. Therefore Boolean expressions, such as $i + 1 = k$, *must* be expressed by means of the symbol .E., for example, I $+$ 1 .E. K.

Grouping marks. The two parentheses, ( ), as well as the comma, are used for grouping. Parentheses are used to enclose subscript expressions and arithmetic expressions. An arithmetic expression is any meaningful combination of constants, variables, and operators. Commas are used to separate elements of a list, such as a list of arguments, a list of variables to be printed, a list of values to be printed, etc. A comma should *never* be used after the last element in such a list. *Precedence* of operations is governed by the usual conventions. For instance, A*X $+$ B is usually understood to mean (A*X) $+$ B. The execution of the multiply operation *precedes* addition in an unparenthesized expression. Knowledge of the precedence of operators permits a simpler statement of many expressions, but the desired order of computation can always be attained by inserting the appropriate parentheses. The relative precedence of operators in an unparenthesized expression is given by the table below. An operator precedes every operator listed below it. Operators of equal precedence are on the same line and are executed in left-to-right order in an unparenthesized expression.

> .ABS.
> .P.
> Unary $-$
> *, /
> $+$, $-$
> .E., .NE., .G., .GE., .L., .LE.
> .NOT.
> .AND.
> .OR.
> $=$ (substitution operator)

Expressions. Although variables and constants are expressions *per se*, they may be combined with operators, relations, and grouping marks to form other expressions.

Function references are also expressions. Frequently executed computations, such as computations of the sine, cosine, square root, solution of linear equations, etc., are either automatically available or they may be defined. (See function definitions.) The function name, assigned to such a computation, is written according to the same rules that govern variable names, i.e., six alphanumeric characters or less, with a leading alphabetic character. This name *must* be followed by a period, and then the arguments are enclosed in parentheses to the right of the period. The arguments, if there are more than one, are separated by commas. This name, with the arguments, represents a single value that a function computes.

EXAMPLES. SIN.(X), COS.(Z + 3.1416), DETERM.(N, A),
SQRT.(X + 2.*Y), ARCTAN.(X, Y)

Arithmetic expressions are formed by using arithmetic operators.

EXAMPLES. X + Y, (X + Y), (X1 + X2)/(Y1 − Y2), ((ALPHA(I) +
SIN.(Z1))/(3.*X) + 10.62), (A(I, J) + D)*K

Boolean expressions are formed from relations and Boolean operators.

.ABS. X .L. EPSLON, I .G. N, I. .G. K .AND. Z
.LE. 100, ALPHA + 1 .E. 32 .OR. ROOT .L. 0, I .L.
1 .AND. J .E. 4

To simplify the description of statements that follows, the symbol υ is used to designate any variable, including those with complicated subscript expressions; $\mathcal{E}$ is used to designate any arithmetic expression, and if more than one expression is involved, $\mathcal{E}_1$, $\mathcal{E}_2$, . . . are used; $\mathfrak{R}$ is used to designate a Boolean expression and, where needed, $\mathfrak{R}_1$, $\mathfrak{R}_2$, . . . are used; $\mathcal{S}$ is used to indicate a statement label, including those with a subscript.

Executable statements. *The substitution statement* is of the form:

$$\upsilon = \mathcal{E}$$

Substitution is the step for which the symbol "$=$" is reserved. Note that in this context a statement such as J + 4 = X + Y does *not* make sense, since the left-hand side is an expression, not a variable. Statements such as I = I + 1 are acceptable substitution statements and are quite common. They simply mean that the current value of I plus 1 becomes the new value of I.

EXAMPLES

X = Z*(4.0−ETA),   A(I, J + 6) = 1.0/A(I, I),   COSX = COS.(X)

The transfer statement is of the form:

TRANSFER TO $\mathcal{S}$

Examples. TRANSFER TO L4
     TRANSFER TO S(I)

The conditional prefix is not a complete statement but a prefix to other executable statements and is of the form:

WHENEVER ℜ,

Examples. WHENEVER I .E. J, X = 8*Z4
     WHENEVER ALPHA .L. 10, TRANSFER TO LABEL

The terminal comma is important; it distinguishes this prefix from another statement.

The end statement must be physically the last statement of a program, but it is also executable in the sense that it causes the program to terminate. It is simply

END OF PROGRAM

The iteration statement is of the form:

THROUGH S, FOR $v = \varepsilon_1, \varepsilon_2, ℜ$

The statements immediately following this statement, up through and including the statement labeled S, are repeated until the Boolean expression ℜ is true. When ℜ is true, the first statement after the statement labeled S is executed (unless S is also the terminus of other iterations). On each repetition the variable v, which was initially given the value of ε_1, is increased by the value of ε_2. The statement S may be the label of the iteration statement itself, in which case the repetitions do not reset v to the value of ε_1, but the indicated incrementing by ε_2 is carried out. The statements that follow, including the one labeled S, are called the *scope* of the iteration. The scope may contain other iteration statements.

Examples. THROUGH S, FOR I = 1, 1, I .G. N
     THROUGH S, FOR X = XZERO, −DELTAX, .ABS.
     F .L. 1E−5

The fixed-list iteration statement is useful when the incrementing is not systematic enough to be described by an expression. It is of the form:

THROUGH S, FOR VALUES OF $v = \varepsilon_1, \varepsilon_2, \varepsilon_3, \ldots, \varepsilon_n$

As before, the statements through S are repeated, but on each repetition the variable v is given the value of the next expression in the list.

Examples. THROUGH L, FOR VALUES OF BETA = 1, 7, 9, 17, 61
     THROUGH L, FOR VALUES OF BETA = X + 4., Y,
     Z − 8., 12.0

The compound conditional statement group is, as the name implies, not a single statement but a group. The form of the group is:

WHENEVER $\mathcal{R}_1$

———
———

———

OR WHENEVER $\mathcal{R}_2$

———

———

———

OR WHENEVER $\mathcal{R}_3$

———

———

———

END OF CONDITIONAL

The horizontal lines indicate the locations of other statements. The statements immediately following a Boolean expression are executed only if the expression is true, and after the execution of such a group of statements, the next statement executed is the one following the terminating statement, END OF CONDITIONAL, unless this statement is also the end of an iteration scope. Only the group following the *first* true condition is executed. There may be an arbitrary number of relations, although only three are shown here. It is often convenient to write as the last Boolean expression one that is always true, such as

OR WHENEVER 2 .E. 2

The single word OTHERWISE can be used in place of such an "always-true" condition. Note that there are no commas after the Boolean expressions, and that the OR does not appear in the first relation. The END OF CONDITIONAL may be labeled and serve as the terminus of the scope of an iteration.

EXAMPLES.   WHENEVER A(I) .L. X

        I = I − K

OR WHENEVER A(I) .G. X

        I = I + K

OTHERWISE

    TRANSFER TO OUT

END OF CONDITIONAL

The label-bearing statement composed of the single word

CONTINUE

is occasionally useful. When the entire scope, or the last statements in the scope, of an iteration is conditional, it is useful to have this statement, which causes no computation, serve as the terminal statement in the iteration.

An input statement is:

READ DATA

Only these two words are necessary. Additional information may appear to the right of the word DATA, but it does not affect the computation and acts only as a comment. The values read are identified on the data cards by using the same variable names that were used in the program. This statement causes the designated variables to be given the values punched on the data cards. Cards are read until a terminating asterisk (*) is encountered. Then the next statement is executed.

An output statement is of the form:

$$\text{PRINT RESULTS } \mathcal{V}_1, \mathcal{V}_2, \ldots, \mathcal{V}_n$$

The list of variables which are to be printed may include single variables (subscripted or not) or blocks of variables. A block is indicated by writing the first variable in the block and then three periods followed by the last variable in the block. More than one block may be designated in an output list. Generally, the variable name prints with the value, but if the variable is a dummy variable (see "Function definition"), then the substituted variable name will not print; the correct value will be obtained, however.

EXAMPLES

PRINT RESULTS X, Y, BETA(0) ... BETA(N)

PRINT RESULTS I, A(1) ... A(12), Q, R, M(L, N) ... M(P, Q)

An input-output statement is:

READ AND PRINT DATA

The execution of this statement is the same as that described for READ DATA except that the information read, both variable names and values, is printed also.

The comment statement is written in the form:

$$\text{PRINT COMMENT } \$\alpha_0\alpha_1\alpha_2 \ldots \alpha_n\$$$

The string of characters $\alpha_1\alpha_2 \ldots \alpha_n$ $(n < 132)$ is the actual comment to be printed at the point in the program where the statement is inserted. The statement may include any of the permissible characters (including blank spaces) except the character $. The dollar signs are used to delimit the comment to be printed. The leading character, α_0, which is not printed, is a code to control the vertical spacing of the line to be printed. The code is:

$\alpha_0 = 1$ The comment will print at the top of a page.

$\alpha_0 = $ blank   The comment will be single spaced.

$\alpha_0 = 0$ The comment will be double spaced.

$\alpha_0 = 2$ The comment will print at the beginning of the next half page.

EXAMPLES

PRINT COMMENT $1 JOHN DOE PROBLEM 1$

PRINT COMMENT $0 THE ROOTS OF THE EQUATION ARE $

The execute statement is used to refer to functions which do not produce a direct result. This statment is of the form:

$$\text{EXECUTE } \mathcal{F}. \ (\mathcal{V}_1, \mathcal{V}_2, \ldots)$$

Here $\mathcal{F}$ is a function name and $\mathcal{V}_1, \mathcal{V}_2, \ldots$ are variable names or, if they are not output variables or arrays, they may be expressions.

EXAMPLES.   EXECUTE LINEQ.(N, A)

EXECUTE MATMPY.(M, N, P, M1, M2)

Declaration Statements. *Vector initialization* can be accomplished with a statement of the form:

$$\text{VECTOR VALUES } \mathcal{V} = C_1, C_2, C_3, \ldots, C_n$$

where $\mathcal{V}$ is the name of an element of a linear array (or the equivalent linear element for a higher-dimensional array), and, *before* the program is executed, $\mathcal{V}$ is given the value of the constant C_1, $\mathcal{V}_{+1}$ (the next contiguous element of the array) is given the value C_2, $\mathcal{V}_{+2}$ the value of C_3, etc. This statement has a wide variety of uses; one of the most common is to specify the dimension information required for a two-dimensional array. In sequence, the three dimension numbers required are: (1) the number of subscripts or "dimension" of the array, (2) the linear subscript that corresponds to the (1, 1) subscript of the array, and (3) the number of elements in a row of the array. As an example, the following statement for the dimension vector DIM causes

$$\text{DIM}(0) = 2, \ \text{DIM}(1) = 1, \ \text{DIM}(2) = 10.$$
$$\text{VECTOR VALUES DIM} = 2, 1, 10$$

We wish to emphasize that the list must be composed of constants, not expressions or variables, and that a final comma should *not* be written.

EXAMPLES.   VECTOR VALUES A(12) = 2.4, −6.8, 3.215

VECTOR VALUES GAMMA = 1, 9, −11, 6, 2

The dimension statement is a declaration and does not result in any computation, but serves to allocate computer storage to the designated arrays. The statement is of the form

$$\text{DIMENSION } \mathcal{V}_1(n_1, \mathcal{V}_{d1}), \mathcal{V}_2(n_2, \mathcal{V}_{d2}), \ldots$$

where $\mathcal{V}_1, \mathcal{V}_2, \ldots$ are array names and n_1, n_2 are *constants* which give the largest linear subscript that would ever be encountered for the corresponding array. In other words, the total number of storage elements reserved for $\mathcal{V}_1$ will be $n_1 + 1$. (The $+1$ is due to the zeroth subscript.) *If the array has dimension two or greater*, it is necessary to specify, in addition, the first element of the appropriate dimension vector, which, for $\mathcal{V}_1$ for instance, is $\mathcal{V}_{d1}$.

EXAMPLES.   DIMENSION A(100), B(10), GAM(100, DIM)

DIMENSION A1(20), M(4000, Q(12))

Arrays which have been assigned initial values by a vector initialization statement need not appear in a dimension statement unless space for more than the designated number of constants is to be reserved.

A mode declaration statement which declares variables to have an integer range is:

$$\text{INTEGER } \mathcal{V}_1, \mathcal{V}_2, \mathcal{V}_3, \ldots$$

Normally it is assumed that, unless declared otherwise, all variables are floating point. This statement causes the variables listed to be treated as integers. At times this list must also include function names. The direct result of a function must be identified as to mode. In such cases, the function name (with period but without arguments) is included in the list.

EXAMPLES.   INTEGER I, J, M, N, TRIANG., INTER.

It is possible to make the implicit case other than floating point by including a statement such as:

NORMAL MODE IS INTEGER

If floating-point variables occurred in such a problem, they would have to be declared, i.e.,

$$\text{FLOATING POINT } \mathcal{V}_1, \mathcal{V}_2, \ldots$$

Function definitions.   Function definitions are accomplished by means of the statements already described, but one must also specify:

(1) What set of statements constitute the definition.

(2) The variables upon which the function value depends (i.e., the dummy variables).

(3) The name(s) that are assigned to the function.

(4) The points of return to the calling program.

(5) The value to be returned to the calling program (i.e., the direct result).

The definition limits and dummy variables [items (1) and (2)] are given by the pair of statements

EXTERNAL FUNCTION $(\mathcal{v}_1, \mathcal{v}_2, \ldots)$

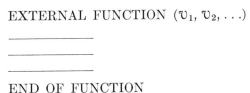

END OF FUNCTION

The intervening statements define the function. $\mathcal{v}_1, \mathcal{v}_2, \ldots$ are not actual variables in the sense that they are never given values. Their meaning is restricted (or bound) to the set of statements in the definition. This list of dummy variables may include dummy function names (the period must be written) or dummy statement labels (these must be declared to be in statement-label mode). The modes of the dummy variables must be specified either implicitly or explicitly. However, *dummy* variables that are regarded as arrays must not appear in a dimension statement. The first few statements of a definition could be:

EXTERNAL FUNCTION (X, Y, I, K, F., L)

INTEGER I, K

STATEMENT LABEL L

$\vdots$

For an external function, the END OF FUNCTION fulfills the same role as the END OF PROGRAM statement, and the latter is not needed.

The assigned names of functions [item (3)] are given at the point at which the statement sequence corresponding to that name begins. The statement is:

ENTRY TO $\mathcal{F}$.

where $\mathcal{F}$ is the assigned function name. The period is necessary.

EXAMPLES.   ENTRY TO COS.

ENTRY TO SIN.

The point of return and value to be returned [items (4) and (5)] are given in one statement.

FUNCTION RETURN ε

where ε is the expression whose value is directly returned. There may be several such statements in a definition and, since this is an executable statement type, they may have a conditional prefix. It is possible to construct functions which do not have a direct return, and in these cases FUNCTION RETURN is used without an expression. Such functions generally return more than one value to the calling program. The mechanism is simply that one or more of the dummy variables are "output variables"; a call for such a function changes the value of designated variables, and this is the way in which results are returned to the calling program. When values of arrays are generated or altered by a function, the output array(s) must be dummy variables.

EXAMPLES.   FUNCTION RETURN 2

FUNCTION RETURN 4 *(DET — ETA)

The internal function is defined in the same manner as the external function. Unlike the external function, it is not an independent program, but is embedded in some larger program (which may be an external function). As before, the dummy variables have meaning only between the statements:

INTERNAL FUNCTION $\mathfrak{F}.(\mathcal{V}_1, \mathcal{V}_2, \ldots)$

———————

———————

———————

END OF FUNCTION

The difference lies in the other variables (actual variables) which appear in the range of the definition. These variables have the same meaning that they have elsewhere in the larger program. In an implicit way, an internal function may depend upon other variables not specifically designated as dummy variables. The mode declarations in this case do not have to be in the scope of the definition. The dummy variables may appear in mode declaration statements elsewhere in the program.

The short internal function definition defines, in one statement, functions which have only one name and one direct result. The form of the defining statement is:

INTERNAL FUNCTION $\mathfrak{F}.(\mathcal{V}_1, \mathcal{V}_2, \ldots) = \varepsilon$

where $\mathfrak{F}$ is the name of the function being defined, $\mathcal{V}_1, \mathcal{V}_2, \ldots$ are the dummy variables, and $\mathcal{E}$ is the expression whose value is returned to the calling program.

EXAMPLES

INTERNAL FUNCTION TAN.(A) = SIN.(A)/COS.(A)

INTERNAL FUNCTION D.(X, Y) = SQRT.(X*X + Y*Y − R*R)

In the last example, R is an actual variable, and its current value, however it is determined by the program including this definition, would be used in every reference to the defined function D.

Push-down storage statements.   It is often useful, particularly in recursive problems, to use a linear array for temporary storage where the last number stored in this array is usually the first to be recalled.

The array designation statement of the form

SET LIST TO υ

is an executable statement which specifies the array υ to be used for push-down storage until another designation statement is encountered.   The value of the zeroth element of the array $\upsilon(0) = \upsilon$ serves as an index of the next available location in the array.   Accordingly, the first use of a designation statement is generally followed by a substitution of the form $\upsilon = 0$.

EXAMPLES.   SET LIST TO ARRAY
                   SET LIST TO PD

The save statement is of the form

SAVE DATA $\mathcal{L}$

where $\mathcal{L}$ is a list of constants, variables, or expressions.   Array segments indicated by the block notation may be list elements also.   The values that correspond to the names in the list are stored in the next available push-down elements in left-to-right order.

EXAMPLES.   SAVE DATA 1, X + Y, Z, A(M) ... A(N)
             SAVE DATA I, A(1) ... A(N), M

The restore statement is of the form

RESTORE DATA $\mathcal{L}$

where $\mathcal{L}$ is a list of variable names.   The block notation may be used when some of the variable names designate contiguous array elements.   The leftmost variable in the list is given the value of the top (i.e., most recently added) element in the push-down array.

EXAMPLES.   RESTORE DATA ALPHA, BETA, D(M) ... D(1)
RESTORE DATA M, A(N) ... A(1), I

In *recursive functions* the return location of the function must be entered on the push-down list and must ultimately be restored for return to the calling program. The statements are:

SAVE RETURN

RESTORE RETURN

The Operating
System

For a high-speed digital computer, such as those of the IBM 709/7090 type, to be used efficiently for the solution of a large number of problems, a computer program is needed to control the flow of problems to and from the computer. Such a program is variously called a monitor, an operating system, an executive routine, or simply "the system." A problem may consist of several distinct program sections, which may even be written in different programming languages, as well as a section of data. It is the task of the system to correctly handle every section, i.e., to use the appropriate translator to produce the equivalent machine code, and then to combine the machine instructions from the several sections for execution. This process of combining includes the making of connections between the program segments; the determination of what subroutines are required by the combined program; the search of the magnetic-tape subroutine library for the subroutines called; the inclusion of these subroutines with the submitted program; the loading of the entire program into storage; and finally, the transfer of control to the program to be executed. In addition, the system monitors the time of execution of the program, the number of output pages printed, and if applicable, the number of punched cards produced by the program. This monitoring operation is desirable since it is quite possible to write, by mistake, a program which goes through the same set of instructions indefinitely. Since the output (printing and punched cards) are written on magnetic tape and subsequently converted to paper and cards by other machines, a repeating cycle which includes an output step can produce great quantities of output in a short time unless the amount of output and time of computation are monitored.

For the system to accomplish this combined supervisory task, the programmer must include some information about the program that is submitted. This information can be grouped in four categories.

(1) Identification, i.e., the programmer's name and assigned job number.

(2) Estimates of the execution time and the number of printed pages and punched cards to be produced by the *submitted* program. These are required by the monitoring procedure described above.

(3) Processing instructions which apply to the entire program.

(4) Processing instructions which just apply to a particular segment.

A problem, including the information above, is submitted on punched cards. Just as there was a specific format for statement cards, this control information must be punched on cards in a certain manner. Items (1) and (2) are punched on a yellow identification card.

	Columns on card
Name	2–24
Assigned computing center number	32–36
Student problem number	39
Execution time estimate, in minutes	52–54
(all three columns must be punched)	
Page output estimate	58–60
(all three columns must be punched)	
Output card estimate	64–66
(these columns may be blank but, if punched, all three columns must be punched)	

Two identical copies of this card must precede a problem deck. An estimate of 001 minute and 005 pages can be used for most student problems.

The processing instructions, items (3) and (4), are punched on solid blue cards. These cards *must have* the character $ punched in column 1. The processing instructions are words or groups of words and may be punched in columns 2 through 64 without regard for spaces. Separate instructions must be separated by commas. Each section of the problem must be preceded by at least one of these blue processing instruction cards. Those instructions which pertain to the entire program, item (3), must be punched in the *first* set of processing instruction cards in the problem deck. Two processing instructions in this category are:

EXECUTE—This is an instruction to the system to execute the program after the indicated translations have been successfully completed.

DUMP—This instruction causes the relevant locations in core storage to be printed as octal numbers *if*, for some reason, the program fails to run to completion.

The remaining processing functions, item (4), apply to sections of the problem only and are punched on processing instruction cards immediately preceding the section. These instructions may be on the same cards as the instructions just described (separated by commas), but the order on the cards is immaterial.

COMPILE MAD—The following cards are MAD statements (either a main program or an external function) and must be translated to machine instructions.

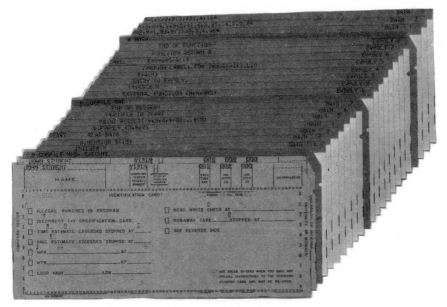

FIGURE B-1

PRINT OBJECT—A listing of the machine instructions for this section is to be produced with the printing of output.

DATA—The following cards are data. The data section, if there is one, must be the last group of cards in the problem deck.

It is good practice, but not always necessary, to make the main program the first section of a problem deck.

Columns 73 through 80 of all cards (identification, statement, processing instruction, data) are reserved for personal identification. These columns may be left blank, but it is good practice to punch some problem identification and sequence number.

To illustrate these points, a problem deck whose make-up is typical of student problems is reproduced in Fig. B-1. The first section is a main program which reads a data set, the degree, the argument, and the coefficients of a polynomial, and then evaluates the polynomial by means of an external function which is defined in the second section. The main program indicates that this process is repeated until all data sets have been used. Three data sets are shown. It should be understood that the description of the system given here is not complete. There are many other processing instructions, which are described in the system manual, but the set given here is adequate for beginning programmers.

Exercises

EXERCISES FOR CHAPTER 1

1. Write a program, using the Turing machine operations, which finds the first occurrence of the letter z to the right of the current symbol.

2. Suppose that a message (i.e., a string of symbols) is encoded on a storage tape by means of the following simple code:

c is written for a

d is written for b

e is written for c

$\vdots$

z is written for a

a is written for x

b is written for y

c is written for z

and

$\#$ is written for blank

Using the Turing machine operations, write a program to replace the message by the decoded version.

3. Using two symbols, $*$ and 0 for the absence of $*$, use the Wang machine operations, $\rightarrow \leftarrow *$ and n, to write the equivalent of the Turing operations given below. Write the new symbols to the right of the given symbols on the storage tape.

1	If 0,	1	5
2	If 1,	2	5
3	If 2,	3	5
4	If 3,	0	5
5			

Consider the code for 0, 1, 2, 3 to be 00, 0$*$, $*$0, and $**$, and assume that at the beginning, the current symbol is the left one of the given pair of symbols.

4. Insert the understood parentheses in the following expressions.

(a) $a \times b - c/d$

(b) $-a + b/c \times d$

(c) $-a^b$

Is the term "well-understood conventions" justified?

5. Express the following more concisely, using $\sum$- and $\prod$-operators.

(a) $y_0 + (x - x_0)y_1 + (x - x_0)(x - x_1)y_2$
$\quad + (x - x_0)(x - x_1)(x - x_2)y_3$

(b) $(x_0 - x_1)(x_0 - x_2)(x_0 - x_3) + (x_1 - x_0)(x_1 - x_2)(x_1 - x_3)$
$+ (x_2 - x_0)(x_2 - x_1)(x_2 - x_3) + (x_3 - x_0)(x_3 - x_1)(x_3 - x_2)$

(c) $a_1b_1 + a_1b_2 + a_1b_3 + a_2b_2 + a_2b_3 + a_3b_3$

6. Write the expression in 5(a) in nested form. Does a similar parenthesizing seem useful for 5(b)?

EXERCISES FOR CHAPTER 2

1. Using the restricted alphabet of this chapter and the rules for writing constants, define a variable name convention which would permit adjacent variables or constants to indicate multiplication. Remember that 1E2 or even 1E are legitimate constants.

2. Would the two-character combinations, digit followed by a letter, be identifiable from variables, constants, and operators? For example, excluding 1E, 2E, etc., could the following relations be conceivably encoded?

$$\neq \quad \sim \quad 1U$$
$$> \quad \sim \quad 1V$$
$$\geq \quad \sim \quad 1W$$
$$< \quad \sim \quad 1L$$
$$\leq \quad \sim \quad 1N$$
$$= \quad \sim \quad 1Z$$

3. Find at least one *syntactical* error in each of the following statements. Statement labels, if any, appear at the left.

(a)		TRANSFER TO 1ST
(b)		Z = ((XBAR + Q(I))/2.56318
(c)	ST(6)	WHEN .ABS. Y.L.EPS, TRANSFER TOO
(d)		F.(I, J) = Z4 − 138.1*(A + D/Y)
(e)		WHENEVER X.L.XO .AND J.G.K, I = I + 1
(f)	ST(M)	A(4, 3) = A(1, 2)*2.0 E .5
(g)		P = (XA − XO)(XA − X1)
(h)		WHENEVER M.E.M., TRANSFER TO S(Q + 8)
(i)	END	X + 4 = −G.(98.2, F.(R, S + 25.0))*((A − B)/Y)

4. Given that numbers representing the symbols of an alphabet having L members are stored as elements of the linear array ALPHA(1) ... ALPHA(L), write the basic Turing operations in terms of the two basic statements and the conditional prefix.

5. With the statements defined thus far, is it reasonable to require that a statement following an unconditional transfer statement must be labeled? Explain.

EXERCISES FOR CHAPTER 3

1. Illustrate with flow charts the following situations: (a) the scope of an iteration statement terminates with a transfer statement, and (b) the scope is terminated with a transfer statement with a conditional prefix. Are both these cases reasonable constructions?

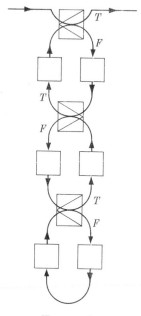

FIGURE 1

2. The permissible nesting of iteration "loops" is described graphically by Fig. 1. The rectangular boxes on the sides of the loops may be empty, contain substitution statements, or other loops similar in structure. The statements

$$K = 0$$
$$\text{THROUGH SA, FOR } I = 1, 1, \text{I.E.10}$$
$$\text{THROUGH SB, FOR } J = 1, 1, \text{J.E.20}$$
$$\text{SA} \quad K = K + 1$$
$$\text{SB} \quad K = K + 2$$

cannot be so described. Verify that this is an invalid construction by drawing a flow chart.

3. The statement

$$\text{TRANSFER TO S(K)}$$

can be described as a "variable remote transfer." Show how this fact can be described by a flow chart.

4. The following statements represent a valid and useful construction. Draw the corresponding flow chart.

$$P = 0$$
THROUGH STM, FOR I = 1, 1, I.G.K
WHENEVER I.L.5
$$P = P + X(I)$$
OR WHENEVER I.L.10
$$P = P + 1$$
OTHERWISE
$$P = P - 2$$
STM   END OF CONDITIONAL

5. The input data can be regarded as a "waiting list of simple substitution statements." By pursuing this analogy, explain why the output list may contain expressions and the input data list may not.

6. Array names must appear in a DIMENSION statement. With this in mind, comment on the convention used to distinguish function references from array elements. For example, F.(I) and F(I) are a function reference and an array element, respectively.

7. Since subscripts must have an integer range, is there redundant information contained in the statements below?

INTEGER I, J
DIMENSION A(10), B(20)
ZBAR = A(I + 4) + B(J)

Would it be difficult to find statement-formation errors in a language which had no redundancy? Explain.

EXERCISES FOR CHAPTER 4

1. Draw a flow chart and write the corresponding statements which define the computation of the scalar product of two 3-element vectors as an external function. For two vectors, $[x_0, x_1, x_2]$ and $[y_0, y_1, y_2]$, the single direct result is

$$p = x_0 y_0 + x_1 y_1 + x_2 y_2$$

Could this function be defined as a one-line internal function?

2. The vector product of two 3-element vectors has three results which are the elements of the resultant product vector $[z_0, z_1, z_2]$. These elements are defined as

$$z_0 = x_1 y_2 - x_2 y_1, \quad z_1 = x_2 y_0 - x_0 y_2, \quad z_2 = x_0 y_1 - x_1 y_0$$

Write an external function which defines this computation. Could this function be defined as a one-line internal function?

3. The flow-chart convention for functions (Fig. 1) that has been used permits any number of entries and exits. The exits are indicated by the statement

$$\text{FUNCTION RETURN } \varepsilon$$

where ε is the direct result. An alternative frequently proposed is to express an exit by $\mathfrak{F}. = \varepsilon$, where $\mathfrak{F}.$ is a function name. For example, F. $= X$ or G. $= Z4 - 6$. Comment on the relative merits of these two conventions.

4. Assuming that you have available a function EXP.(X) which computes e^x, write an internal function with two entries SINH. and COSH. which computes

$$\sinh x = \tfrac{1}{2}(e^x - e^{-x})$$
$$\cosh x = \tfrac{1}{2}(e^x + e^{-x})$$

and returns the appropriate value as a direct result.

5. As a practical matter it is sometimes valuable to reduce the number of references to dummy variables in the defining statements. When the dummy variable represents a single variable, can you suggest a method of reducing the number of references to one, regardless of the number in the original formulation? Can your method be used when the dummy variable represents an array?

6. If the values zero and one produced by the INTER. function are considered to be the Boolean values rather than integer values, how would this affect the conditional prefix in the statement labeled ST in the final example of this chapter?

7. Write an external function DIST.(X, Y, A, B) which computes, as a direct result, the distance of a point (X, Y) to a straight line whose slope is A and whose y-intercept is B. The distance is measured along a perpendicular from the line passing through the point (X, Y).

8. Using the function given in Exercise 7, write a main program which reads a set of points and then computes the sum of the squares of the distances of these points from a given straight line. Do you know of any algorithm which would adjust the values of A and B so that the sum of squares would be decreased?

9. Given the vertices of a triangle $(X1, Y1)$, $(X2, Y2)$, $(X3, Y3)$, the area may be found by evaluating the determinant:

$$\frac{1}{2} \begin{vmatrix} X1 & Y1 & 1 \\ X2 & Y2 & 1 \\ X3 & Y3 & 1 \end{vmatrix}$$

Write an external function which determines the triangle area. A reference to this function could be

$$TA = \text{AREA.}(X1, Y1, X2, Y2, X3, Y3)$$

EXERCISES FOR CHAPTER 5

1. The principal classifying adjectives for the machine described are: binary, fixed-word length, single address, sequential. Find brochures for two other commercially available machines and categorize them, using the appropriately modified adjectives. Be sure that one of the machines is a "data processor," i.e., a machine designed to handle administrative tasks, such as payroll, inventory, sales accounting, etc.

2. Write a program for the Wang machine which transfers a two-bit number two spaces to the right on the storage tape, then makes a mark to the right of the transferred number, and transfers to the nth instruction; assume initially that the current symbol is the leftmost of the two bits.

3. Machines which store the numbers that are arithmetically processed and the instructions controlling this processing in the same storage used to be called "ambiguous-word" machines. Now virtually all machines are of this type. Give some reasons for this common storage and name at least one advantage resulting from the separation of these two types of words.

EXERCISES FOR CHAPTER 6

1. Write two versions of a symbolic machine-language program which computes

$$S = \sum_{i=1}^{6} a_i$$

by using index register 1 for the necessary subscripting and testing operations. For the first version, decrease the index register value in steps of -1 and for the second, increase the value in steps of $+1$. Remember that the index register is always *subtracted* from the address it modifies. Assume that the values of the array elements a_1, a_2, a_3, ..., a_6 are stored in $(1001)_8$, $(1002)_8$, $(1003)_8$, ..., $(1006)_8$, respectively. The first instruction of the program should be located in $(2000)_8$ and the sum stored in $(1100)_8$.

2. A combined operation which is very useful in cycles such as the addition cycle of Problem 1 is: (TIX) Transfer with Index.

If $C(IRk) > D$ 2   D   k

$C(IRk) - D \rightarrow C(IRk)$

and

$A \rightarrow C(ILC)$

otherwise

$C(ILC) + 1 \rightarrow C(ILC)$

If the contents of the index register designated (k) are greater than the constant D, D is subtracted from the index register and the address gives the next instruction. If the contents of the index register are less than or equal to D the next instruction in sequence is executed. Write the program of Problem 1, using this operation to replace the incrementing and testing steps. Note that since the increment (D) is the final value, the index must also "count down," i.e., decrease from its largest value to 1.

3. Subroutines often require the input of more than one number. One method of transmitting more numbers is to store these numbers immediately after the TSX operation which causes a transfer to the subroutine and then use the following sequence of instructions in the main program and the subroutine.

3000	TSX 4000, 4	Subroutine starting at location $(4000)_8$
3001	(value 1 stored here)	4000 CLA 1, 4
3002	(value 2 stored here)	4001 LDQ 2, 4
3003	$\vdots$	4002 $\vdots$
		TRA 3, 4

Using the numerical locations and the knowledge of what the TSX operation does, explain the purpose of the three instructions shown in the subroutine.

4. In the 709 and 7090 series of machines one can use a variant of many of the instructions when the address in the instruction does not designate the location of the value to be used in the operation, but rather the *location of the address* of the value to be used. Such an *indirectly addressed* instruction is often indicated by appending an asterisk to the operation, that is, CLA* A, where A is the address of the address of the desired number. Define this operation by using the "contents-of" notation used to describe operations symbolically. How could indirect addressing be used to transmit values to a subroutine? (See Problem 3.)

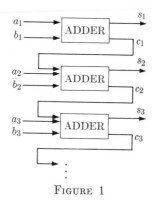

FIGURE 1

5. The addition of two multidigit binary numbers can be described by the diagram presented in Fig. 1. The a's and b's are the bits of the two numbers to be added, the c's are the carry bits, and the s's are the bits of the sum. List the possible values of the operands a, b, c for one adder and the corresponding results s and c in tabular form. These results could be expressed as a Boolean function of the operands and such a device implemented by simple "and," "or," and "not" circuits.

EXERCISES FOR CHAPTER 7

1. Do the following simple addition problems by using the appropriate addition table.

(a) $(3176)_8$
     $+ \quad (227)_8$

(b) $(7658)_8$
     $+ \quad (3417)_8$

(c) $(110111)_2$
     $+ (100110)_2$

(d) $(101111)_2$
     $+ (110111)_2$

2. Convert to decimal form:
   (a) $(674)_8$
   (b) $(.172)_8$
   (c) $(101101)_2$
   (d) $(.0111)_2$
   (e) $(734.262)_8$
   (f) $(1011.11)_2$

3. Convert to octal form:
   (a) $(75)_{10}$
   (b) $(0.375)_{10}$
   (c) $(121.875)_{10}$
   (d) $(1011100.01110)_2$

4. Convert to binary form:
   (a) $(83)_{10}$
   (b) $(.725)_{10}$
   (c) $(100.3)_{10}$
   (d) $(321.422)_8$

5. Perform the following multiplications by using the appropriate multiplication table.

(a) $(532.61)_8$
     $\times \quad (315)_8$

(b) $(10111.11)_2$
     $\times \quad (1001)_2$

6. Convert the following floating-point numbers (i.e., octal form of a fraction times a power of 2) to decimal exponential form.
   (a) -206610000000
   (b) 225132000000
   (c) 176400000000

7. Given that the scale factors of three fractional operands a, b, c (each with magnitude > 0.1) are 10^4, 10^6, and 10^{-2}, respectively, what is the scale factor of the following expressions?

   (a) $a \times b \times c$ Is the value of this expression necessarily a fraction?
   (b) $a + b + c$ Is the result of this expression necessarily a fraction?
   (c) $(a + c)/b$ What approximate limits must be imposed on the magnitude of b to guarantee that the result will be a fraction?

8. In the early days of computing, the hexadecimal (base 16) representation of binary numbers was often used. Given that the sixteen symbols are

$$
\begin{array}{llll}
0 = 0 & 4 = 4 & 8 = 8 & 12 = c \\
1 = 1 & 5 = 5 & 9 = 9 & 13 = d \\
2 = 2 & 6 = 6 & 10 = a & 14 = e \\
3 = 3 & 7 = 7 & 11 = b & 15 = f
\end{array}
$$

verify this addition:

$$
\begin{array}{r}
3a9b \\
+\quad e52f \\
\hline
11fca
\end{array} \; .
$$

EXERCISES FOR CHAPTER 8

1. In range-number calculations, divisors of the form

$$
\begin{bmatrix} 0.1 \\ -0.1 \end{bmatrix}
$$

are not permitted. Explain.

2. Programs (even machines) have been proposed which carry out all arithmetic operations using some number-with-error form. Evaluate the quadratic expression

$$
3.25x^2 - 7.32x + 1.50
$$

using range-number arithmetic. Assume that the coefficients are significant numbers and that the value of $x = 1.5$ is exact.

3. Evaluate the expression of Problem 2 by means of arithmetic operations using approximation-error numbers.

4. It is tempting to say that the average of the upper and lower bounds could be used to represent the range number. Show that this approach leads to a contradiction, i.e., the "average" result does not correspond to the range-number result. Consider, for example, the square of the range number

$$
\begin{bmatrix} x_H \\ x_L \end{bmatrix}
$$

5. When round-off error is the factor limiting accuracy in a computing process, carrying more digits in the numbers will alleviate the problem. In a fixed-word length machine, one must, in such instances, represent one number by more than one word. The rules for arithmetic operations using *double-precision* numbers can be obtained in a manner similar to the approximation-error operations. Thus, if the fraction a has two ten-digit parts, $a = a_1 + a_2 \cdot 10^{-10}$, then both a_1 and a_2 are fractions. Adding a similar double-precision number b gives

$$
\begin{aligned}
a + b &= (a_1 + a_2 \cdot 10^{-10}) + (b_1 + b_2 \cdot 10^{-10}) \\
&= (a_1 + b_1) + (a_2 + b_2) \cdot 10^{-10}
\end{aligned}
$$

What would the two parts of the product of the double-precision number a and b be?

EXERCISES FOR CHAPTER 9

1. Approximate $f(x) = x^2 + 4x + 2$ by a straight line in $(1, 2)$. For this approximation, choose the Taylor series that makes the maximum error in the interval as small as possible.

2. In a certain computation it is desired to approximate $f(x) = 2^x$ in $(0, 1)$. How many terms of the Taylor series approximation are needed to ensure that the maximum error is less than 0.001. It is useful here to remember that

$$(d/dx)a^x = \log_e a \cdot a^x$$

and that

$$\log_e 2 \approx 0.7.$$

3. The truncated Taylor series approximation $\sin x = x$ is often used for small angles. As a function of x, what is the maximum error in this approximation? When some terms of a series are zero, it is best, in terms of the error estimate, to truncate the series after a zero term. Why?

4. In some small computers there is no built-in division. However, one method of effectively dividing is to multiply the dividend by the reciprocal of the divisor and to write the reciprocal as a series involving only multiplication and addition, i.e.,

$$\frac{y}{x} = y\left(\frac{1}{x}\right).$$

Obtain such a reciprocal expression by finding the Taylor series expansion of

$$\frac{1}{x} = \frac{1}{1 - (1 - x)}, \qquad 0 < x < 2$$

In these cases, the accuracy of the quotient is determined by analysis of the error term.

5. What conclusion may be drawn when the kth divided differences are constant? Can any conclusive statement be made about the "true" function from which the points were taken? Explain your answer in terms of the divided-difference error term.

6. In calibrating a thermometer, the following points were obtained:

Reading	Temperature
0	2
10	14
40	38

In a data-processing program, readings are to be converted to temperature. Hence a function must be generated which represents temperature as a function of reading. Find a function which when evaluated at readings of 0, 10, 40 gives the tabulated temperatures.

7. Construct a second-degree divided-difference polynomial, using the last three points from the following set.

x	$f(x)$
-1	4
0	2
2	4
3	20

Evaluate the polynomial at $x = 1$. What is the approximate error?

EXERCISES FOR CHAPTER 10

1. Using Newton's method, write a program to solve $a^x + x = 0$ for values of $a > 1$.

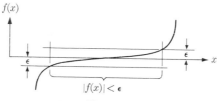

FIGURE 1

2. In some equations, $f(x) = 0$, the value of the function f may be very small in the neighborhood of a root, e.g., roots of high multiplicity (Fig. 1). The relation $|f(x)| < \epsilon$ permits a large range of x-values. This problem may be eliminated by requiring that the difference between successive trial roots, as well as the value of the function, be small. Alter the statements in Problem 1 to include this additional criterion for convergence.

3. Draw the flow chart of an algorithm which employs Newton's method to solve an equation $f(x) = 0$, but in addition, uses the information that there is a sign change in an interval (a, b). One approach is never to permit a trial value outside of the interval and to keep reducing the interval size as function evaluations are made.

4. Write a program which computes the roots of a polynomial by removing quadratic factors from the original polynomial. This program is similar in overall structure to the given program except that the synthetic division is more complex. Also, the roots of the quadratic factors, as well as the root of a linear factor, must be computed if the degree of the original polynomial is odd.

EXERCISES FOR CHAPTER 11

1. In a certain algorithm, it is convenient to make the elements of a 12×14 matrix (i.e., 12 rows and 14 columns) correspond to the elements of a linear array A starting with A(1). Write the dimension statement and dimension vector initialization statement which set up this correspondence. Assume that the first matrix element is designated A(1, 1).

2. A vector whose values are initially set by a VECTOR VALUES statement need not appear in a dimension statement or a mode declaration, since the minimum number of array elements and the mode are apparent from the initial values. When the dimension information is read as data, however, such declarations about the dimension vector must be made. Assuming the correspondence indicated in Problem 1, write the statements which dimension the array A and read the dimension vector values as data. Show also the format of the data card containing these values.

3. Write the statements requested in Problem 1, but assume that the first matrix elements are designated $A(0, 0)$.

4. A common programming error which often does not cause any difficulty is to use the same name to designate an array and a single variable. For example, B and B(I, J) appear in the same program. Under what circumstances will this cause difficulties?

5. It is sometimes convenient, particularly when an array is used as a function argument, to designate a subarray with the starting subscripts $(1, 1)$. For example,

$$
\begin{array}{cccc}
d_{11} & d_{12} & d_{13} & d_{14} \\
d_{21} & d_{22} & d_{23} & d_{24} \\
d_{31} & d_{32} & d_{33} & d_{34} \\
d_{41} & d_{42} & d_{43} & d_{44}
\end{array}
\quad \Rightarrow \quad
\begin{array}{cc}
d_{11} & d_{12} \\
d_{21} & d_{22}
\end{array}
$$

When this notation is used, what change in the dimension vector would permit reference to the subarray?

6. Write the statements to compute

$$
\sum_{\substack{i,j \\ i \ne j}}^{10} x_i y_j = x_1 x_2 + x_1 x_3 + \cdots + x_1 x_{10} + x_2 x_1 + x_2 x_3 + \cdots + x_2 x_{10}
$$
$$
+ \cdots + x_{10} x_9
$$

using the relation I.NE.J in the scope of the double iteration.

7. The x's in the following line represent decimal digits and the squares blank spaces.

$$\underbrace{\Box XXX \Box\Box \pm XX.XXX \Box\Box \pm XX.XXX \Box\Box\Box \pm XX.XE \pm XX \Box\Box \pm XXX}$$

| Integer | Floating-point numbers | Understood decimal point |

Initial blanks have the same effect as initial zeros.

(a) Write a read statement and the associated format description which causes the variables N, W, X, Y and Z to be given values which have been punched in a card in this form.

(b) Write a print statement and the associated format description which cause the current values of $I + 4$, P, $P + Q$, R, S, to be printed in the form described. Arrange for this line of print to be the first on a page. In this case, the understood decimal point should be printed.

8. It is possible to store six of the 6-bit BCD characters in one word of storage, and therefore, when characters are being read, the number of characters to be stored in one word (m in the general description) must be specified. This specification is made by following the code letter C with the number of characters per word. Write the read statement and format specification to read the first ten characters from a card and then store one character per word in the array C(1) ... C(10).

9. A transfer vector is a list of subroutine (or function) names which are generally the first words in a program. In describing a relocatable program, one must give the *number* of such names, as well as the list itself. Explain why this number, the transfer vector size, is also required.

EXERCISES FOR CHAPTER 12

1. The divided-difference interpolation program does not use the nested evaluation technique because the error-term computation is most easily carried out if each term is computed separately. Alter this program to delete the error-term computation and evaluate the divided-difference polynomial by the more efficient nested method.

2. If only the "upper diagonal" of a difference table is to be used, all differences can be computed without the use of auxiliary storage and stored in the linear array which originally held the ordinate values. For example,

$$
\left.\begin{matrix} f(x_0) \\ f(x_1) \\ f(x_2) \\ f(x_3) \end{matrix}\right\} \quad \text{is replaced by} \quad \left\{\begin{matrix} f[x_0] \\ f[x_0, x_1] \\ f[x_0, x_1, x_2] \\ f[x_0, x_1, x_2, x_3] \end{matrix}\right.
$$

Write a program which reads n points and then computes the divided differences in this manner.

3. Lagrangian interpolation can also be computationally simplified when the abscissas are equally spaced. When the substitution $x = x_0 + hs$ is made in the Lagrangian coefficients,

$$
c_i = \prod_{i \neq j} \frac{(x - x_j)}{(x_i - x_j)}
$$

the interval size, h, cancels out of the numerator and denominator, and the coefficients are functions of the variable s. Obtain the equal-interval Lagrangian formula for the second degree (i.e., three-point) case and flow chart an external function which would carry out second-degree interpolation, given as arguments an interpolant x_a and the necessary arrays of ordinates and abscissas.

4. Starting with the assumption that the five "lower diagonal" elements of an equal-interval backward-difference table are stored in a linear array (similar to Problem 1), write a program that computes $f(x_k + h)$ and then replaces the

current differences with the new values. Diagrammatically,

$$
\left.\begin{array}{l}
f(x_k) \\
\nabla f(x_k) \\
\nabla^2 f(x_k) \\
\nabla^3 f(x_k) \\
\nabla^4 f(x_k)
\end{array}\right\}
\begin{array}{c}
\text{Compute} \\
\rightarrow f(x_k + h) \rightarrow
\end{array}
\left\{\begin{array}{l}
f(x_k + h) \\
\nabla f(x_k + h) \\
\nabla^2 f(x_k + h) \\
\nabla^3 f(x_k + h) \\
\nabla^4 f(x_k + h)
\end{array}\right.
$$

5. The function $s(s-1)(s-2)\ldots(s-n+1) = s^{(n)}$, called a *factorial*, appears in the equal-interval forward-difference interpolating polynomial. Using the notation defined on the right above and the forward-difference operator Δ, write this polynomial in concise operational form.

EXERCISES FOR CHAPTER 13

1. Write a program which reads a set of values tabulated at equal intervals of the argument and the number of entries in the table. Using Simpson's rule, find the definite integral of this tabular function. If there is an odd number of intervals, use one application of the trapezoidal rule to complete the numerical integration.

2. If the tabular values are not given at equal intervals, the Newton-Cotes formulas do not directly apply. Integrate the second-degree Lagrangian interpolating polynomial over two intervals to obtain a formula which could be used for this unequal-interval case.

3. Write a program which integrates a function F. over the interval (A, B) by applying the three-point Gaussian formula N times. Read the values of A, B, and N. What changes and additions must be made to turn this program into an external function which directly returns the definite integral value?

4. It is useful if the "degree of orthogonality" of two vectors is scaled to vary from 0 to 1; that is, the degree is 0 if the vectors are orthogonal, and 1 if they are collinear. If each element of a vector x_1, x_2, x_3 is divided by the length of the vector $\sqrt{x_1^2 + x_2^2 + x_3^2}$, the new vector is of length 1.

$$
\left\{\left(\frac{x_1}{\sqrt{x_1^2 + x_2^2 + x_3^2}}\right)^2 + \left(\frac{x_2}{\sqrt{x_1^2 + x_2^2 + x_3^2}}\right)^2 + \left(\frac{x_3}{\sqrt{x_1^2 + x_2^2 + x_3^2}}\right)^2\right\}^{1/2} = 1
$$

Flow chart the algorithm for computing this normalized measure of orthogonality between two vectors x_1, x_2, $\ldots$, x_n and y_1, y_2, $\ldots$, y_n.

EXERCISES FOR CHAPTER 14

1. Rewrite SLEQ. so that the computation of new elements within a row proceeds from right to left and reduces all the elements, even those resulting in zeros. This version requires three statements less than SLEQ. does.

2. The "back solution" is the solution of a specialized system of equations such as

$$x_1 + a_{12}x_2 + a_{13}x_3 = a_{14} \tag{1}$$

$$x_2 + a_{23}x_3 = a_{24} \tag{2}$$

$$x_3 = a_{34} \tag{3}$$

Write the algorithm, using the "indented" form described in this chapter, by substituting x_3 in equation (2) to determine x_2, and then x_2 and x_3 in equation (1) to determine x_1. Extend the algorithm to n equations instead of three.

3. The basic operation of the forward solution, with division, is

$$a'_{ij} = a_{ij} - a_{ik}a_{kj}$$

with appropriate ranges for i, j, and k. There is a variant of this basic elimination scheme, called the Crout method, which carries out these basic steps in a different order. The algorithm for a single column of right-hand sides is:

$$k = 1, 2, \ldots, n - 1$$
$$j = k + 1, \ldots, n + 1$$
$$a_{kj} = a_{kj}/a_{kk}$$
$$i = k + 1$$
$$j = k + 1, \ldots, n + 1$$
$$l = 1, 2, \ldots, k$$
$$a_{ij} = a_{ij} - a_{il}a_{lj}$$

Write a program which carries out the forward solution by means of this algorithm.

4. The advantage of the Crout method (Problem 3) is that an individual element is computed from

$$a_{ij} = a_{ij} - \sum_{l=1}^{k} a_{il}a_{lj}$$

Some machines have a built-in operation of "multiply" and "accumulate" which could be used with this algorithm but not with the Gauss-Jordan algorithm. Why? Can the maximal-element reduction be employed with the Crout method?

5. Show that interchanging two rows (or columns) of a square matrix changes the sign of the determinant.

6. The function MAXINV. interchanges rows and columns of the final matrix. Add some statements to this part of the program to count the number of interchanges, thus permitting the sign of the determinant to be determined.

7. Write a program which solves a system of linear equations by the Gauss-Jordan method but which uses as a pivot element the largest (in magnitude) of the reduced elements in the *pivot column*. Interchange rows to put the selected row in the pivot position. Does this approach involving a limited maximal

element solve the zero divisor problem? Will this method require the rearrangement of the solution vector at the end of the procedure?

8. Modify the Gauss-Seidel iterative program to make a total-step algorithm; that is, the current trial solution vector is used for the evaluation of the entire set of equations before the values are improved.

EXERCISES FOR CHAPTER 15

1. If a "least-absolute-value" criterion were used, would you expect the resulting approximation to be the same as that produced by the least-squares criterion? Explain your answer in terms of the relative weights of the deviations.

2. The computation of the coefficients of the normal equations can be described in five statements. Although the program is not so efficient as the one illustrated, the statements do provide a concise description of the algorithm. Write these five executable statements. Assume, if necessary, that $0^0 \equiv 1$.

3. Verify the transformation of the example

$$e^x \approx 1 + x + \frac{x^2}{2} + \frac{x^3}{6} + \frac{x^4}{24} + \frac{x^5}{120}$$

to Chebyshev form by writing the Taylor series coefficients in array form and then using the recursion formula to produce the corresponding array of Chebyshev coefficients.

4. It is desired to approximate a function F. in an interval (A, B) by using the first three Chebyshev coordinate functions. Assuming that a numerical integration routine, INTEG.(A, B, N), is available, write a program to compute

$$a_0 = \frac{1}{\pi} \int_{-1}^{1} \frac{g(x)}{\sqrt{1 - x^2}}\, dx$$

$$a_1 = \frac{2}{\pi} \int_{-1}^{1} \frac{x g(x)}{\sqrt{1 - x^2}}\, dx$$

$$a_2 = \frac{2}{\pi} \int_{-1}^{1} \frac{(2x^2 - 1)g(x)}{\sqrt{1 - x^2}}\, dx$$

Here

$$\text{F.}(Z) = f(z) = f\left(\frac{(b - a)x + b + a}{2}\right) = g(x)$$

and N is the number of applications of the integrating procedure.

5. To extend the previous problem to compute $a_0, a_1, \ldots, a_n$, one must systematically produce the Chebyshev polynomials. From the definition of these polynomials, suggest a method of systematically evaluating the higher-order polynomials without having to write each one explicitly.

6. If the function to be approximated is tabulated at 0, π/N, $2\pi/N$, ..., $(2N - 1)\pi/N$, one can determine the coefficients of the approximation

$$f(\theta) = a_0 + a_1 \cos \theta + a_2 \cos 2\theta + \cdots + b_1 \sin \theta + b_2 \sin 2\theta + \cdots$$

without resorting to numerical integration. Flow chart a procedure to compute a specified number of these coefficients.

EXERCISES FOR CHAPTER 16

1. Write a program to numerically solve $y' = x^2 - y$ in the interval $(0, 1)$. The initial conditions are at $x = 0$, $y = 1$. Use the two functions that have been defined in this chapter.

2. Numerically solve $y' = y$ in the interval $(0, 1)$, where $y = 1$ at $x = 0$. Find the first values by using Taylor's series and then continue with the three-point open integration formula. Check the resulting values of the function y with the true solution.

3. Alter the Milne predictor-corrector function to iterate on the closed integration; that is, repeat the computation of the new point, y_{n+1}, using the corrector formula until there is no change in successive values.

4. Draw a flow chart of the Runge-Kutta-Gill algorithm.

5. Numerically solve $y'' = -y$ in $(0, 4)$ given that $y = 0$ and $y' = 1$ at $x = 0$. Print the values of both y and y' and check these with the true solution.

EXERCISES FOR CHAPTER 17

1. Describe the values that the variable X would assume as a result of these two substitution statements:

$$X = AB$$
$$X = \$AB\$$$

2. In programs dealing with symbol manipulation, the arithmetic operations are not so frequently employed. Usually, it is not meaningful to evaluate expressions such as $\$ABC\$*\$X + Y\$$. Addition can be used in a limited way to combine symbols, e.g.,

$$\$A*B\$ = \$A00\$ + \$0*0\$ + \$00B\$$$

There are two shifting operators in MAD, .LS. and .RS., which are also useful in these contexts. Thus

$$C = A \;.RS.\; B$$

means that C is given the value of A but with the bits in variable A shifted to the right in the word as many places as there are binary positions designated by the current value of B. Write the expression on the right, using the right-shift operator and the operands $\$A00\$$, $\$*00\$$, and $\$B00\$$. Characters are always adjusted to the left of the 36-bit word; the unspecified bits are zero.

3. The *and* ($\wedge$) and *or* ($\vee$) operators that have been previously defined dealt with two operands which were single bits. In symbol manipulation it is con-

venient to have these operators applied to the corresponding bits of entire words. If these full-word operators are designated .A. and .V., then

(a) AB = $A0$ .V. $0B$

(b) C = B .V. 1

(c) $0B0$ = ABC .A. $0B0$

Verify these relations by writing out the six-bit BCD representations of the characters and applying the *and* and *or* operations to the corresponding bits.

4. Write a "double-ended" interchange sort program; that is, the interchange cycle starts alternately from the beginning and the end of the list of elements to be stored. What are the advantages, if any, of this approach over the simple interchange procedure?

5. Devise a binary search algorithm which does not require that the initial point of comparison be an integral power of two. It is necessary to remember that only the integral portion of an integer quotient is retained. Be sure to test the algorithm by using as arguments the extreme values in the table.

6. Modify the program which converts the array form of an expression to the fully parenthesized string form so that redundant parentheses are eliminated in the final string form. What change must be made in the original program to produce the Polish prefix (i.e., parenthesis-free) string form of the expression?

7. The factorial function which appears in equal-interval interpolating polynomials can be written in conventional polynomial form:

$$s^{(n)} = s(s-1)(s-2)\cdots(s-n+1) = \sum_{k=0}^{n} S(n,k)s^k$$

The coefficients $S(n, k)$ can be written in pyramidal form similar to Pascal's triangle.

n \ k	0	1	2	3	4
0	1				
1	0	1			
2	0	−1	1		
3	0	2	−3	1	
4	0	−6	11	−6	1

It is apparent that

$$S(n, k) = 1 \quad \text{for} \quad n = k$$
$$S(n, 0) = 0 \quad \text{for} \quad n > 0$$

and it can be deduced that

$$S(n+1, k) = S(n, k-1) - n\,S(n, k) \quad \text{for} \quad 0 < n < k$$

Write a recursive program which will compute an arbitrary $S(n, k)$, or *Stirling number* as these coefficients are called.

8. In the example permutation program no function is defined. Rewrite the program defining the production of permutations as a function.

9. Determinant evaluation by minors is a variant of the permutation program. As an exercise (it is not an effective method of computing determinants), write a recursive routine which evaluates a determinant of arbitrary order by minors.

EXERCISES FOR CHAPTER 18

1. What is the difficulty in translating the statement

$$D = A + B * C$$

to assembly language using the last syntax table developed for syntax recognition? What additions to the syntax table will correct this difficulty?

2. Manually simulate the translation process using as a source statement

$$D = (A * (B + C)).$$

3. Define a syntax table which will produce a more efficient sequence of machine instructions by using variables as operands. For example, the translation of $A = B + C$ results in

$$
\begin{array}{ll}
\text{CLA} & \text{C} \\
\text{STO} & E_1 \\
\text{CLA} & \text{B} \\
\text{ADD} & E_1 \\
\text{STO} & \text{A}
\end{array}
$$

although the same computation can be done by

$$
\begin{array}{ll}
\text{CLA} & \text{C} \\
\text{ADD} & \text{B} \\
\text{STO} & \text{C}
\end{array}
$$

4. Some machines have two-address instructions; that is, two operands may be specified in a single instruction. Consider a hypothetical machine which has a single accumulator (AC) and the following arithmetic operations. The "contents of" notation is used on the right to give the meaning of the operations.

$$
\begin{array}{llll}
\text{ADD} & \text{A} & \text{B} & \quad C(A) + C(B) \rightarrow C(AC) \\
\text{SUB} & \text{A} & \text{B} & \quad C(A) - C(B) \rightarrow C(AC) \\
\text{MPY} & \text{A} & \text{B} & \quad C(A) \times C(B) \rightarrow C(AC) \\
\text{DIV} & \text{A} & \text{B} & \quad C(A) \div C(B) \rightarrow C(AC) \\
\text{STO} & \text{A} & - & \quad C(AC) \rightarrow C(A)
\end{array}
$$

Rewrite the syntax table of the example program so that the translated results will be expressed in terms of these operations.

Index

ABCDE698765432